ST. PETER'S SECONDARY SCHOOL

BOOK _____ **96-21**

This book is the property of St. Peter's Secondary School, Barrie, Ontario. It is loaned for the semester to the students whose signature appears below. At the close of the semester, it is expected that the book will be returned in good condition, free from misuse.

YEAR	NAME	ROOM
98	David Miller	207
98	GILLIAN MACLEAN	P. 3
99	Everett Ryke	P. 3
99-00	Cory Poulton	206
Y2K	Sean Burke	206
00/01	Adriana Wilson	246

CALCULUS

Series General Editor
Ronald G. Dunkley

Text General Editor
Ronald G. Scoins

Authors
Ian J. McGee   Gordon T. Nicholls   Peter J. Ponzo   John A. Savage   John Wainwright

Holt, Rinehart and Winston of Canada, Limited

Series General Editor
Ronald G. Dunkley
University of Waterloo
Waterloo, Ontario

Text General Editor
Ronald G. Scoins
University of Waterloo
Waterloo, Ontario

Authors
Ian J. McGee
University of Waterloo
Waterloo, Ontario

Gordon T. Nicholls
Preston High School
Waterloo County Board of Education
Cambridge, Ontario

Peter J. Ponzo
University of Waterloo
Waterloo, Ontario

John A. Savage
Lasalle Secondary School
Sudbury Board of Education
Sudbury, Ontario

John Wainwright
University of Waterloo
Waterloo, Ontario

Reviewing Consultants
Ron Crawford
Bayview Secondary School
York Region Board of Education
Richmond Hill, Ontario

Neil MacEwan
Vincent Massey Secondary School
Windsor Board of Education
Windsor, Ontario

John McGrath
Crestwood Secondary School
Peterborough County Board of Education
Peterborough, Ontario

Joseph B. Tonin
A.N. Myer Secondary School
Niagara South Board of Education
Niagara Falls, Ontario

Rod Yeager
North Park Secondary School
Peel Board of Education
Brampton, Ontario

Production Coordinator
Francine Geraci

Graphic Design, Art and Assembly
Blue Line Productions Inc.

Cover Photo by
Tony Stone—Worldwide/Masterfile

Executive Editor
Ken Leland

Content Editor
Santo d'Agostino

Copy Editor
Freya Godard

Canadian Cataloguing in Publication Data

Main entry under title:

Calculus

Includes index.
ISBN 0-03-922049-4

1. Calculus.   I. McGee, Ian J.   II. Scoins, Ronald G.

QA303.C34 1988   515   C88-093061-6

The metric usage in this text conforms to the standards established by the Canadian General Standards Board.

Printed in Canada
4 5 6 7 8 97 96 95 94 93

Table of Contents

Preface

This text introduces the basic concepts of Calculus and some of their applications. In the accompanying flowchart, the content is divided into "basic core," "extended core," and "enrichment," as a guide for the instructor.

The emphasis in the book is on understanding and applying the ideas rather than just developing the rules of Calculus. The approach taken strikes a balance between formal proofs and geometric arguments.

The authors thank Mrs. Kay Harrison for her excellent preparation of the manuscript, Giuseppe Russo for keeping us honest by checking all the answers, and the staff at Holt, Rinehart and Winston, especially Mr. Ken Leland, for their professional assistance and attention to detail in the preparation of this text for publication.

Principal Features

- Care has been taken to motivate new concepts.

- The interpretation of the derivative as the slope of a tangent line or as a rate of change is introduced early and is used in examples and exercises thereafter.

- Applications are integrated into the development.

- The value of curve sketching is stressed throughout the text. Both non-Calculus and Calculus techniques are used. The aim is to be able to sketch graphs that include all the essential features, without making an exact plot.

- The exercises are designed to meet the needs of a wide variety of students. As well as providing drill in the basic techniques, some questions provide a deeper understanding of the topics. In most exercises instructors will find more questions than are necessary to master the concepts.

- A set of problems is included in each section. These will provide students with an opportunity to enhance their problem-solving skills. Students intending to pursue university studies in Engineering, Mathematics, or Science are encouraged to try them.

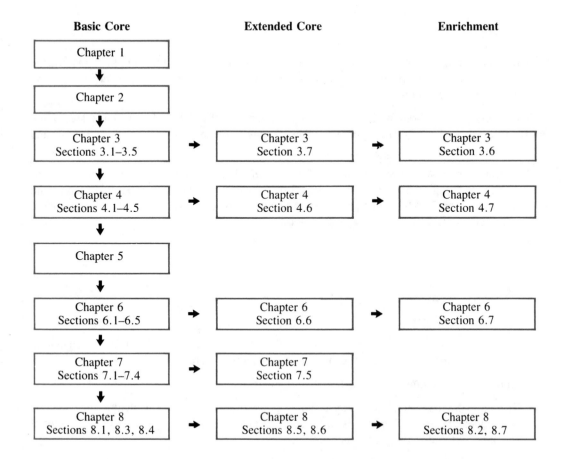

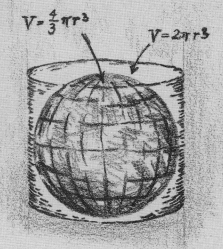

$V = \frac{4}{3}\pi r^3$

$V = 2\pi r^3$

Archimedes *(287 B.C. – 212 B.C.) was born in Syracuse, Sicily and ranks with Newton and Gauss as one of the three greatest mathematicians who ever lived. Without a knowledge of algebra (which came much later) and without even a convenient number system (our decimal number system also come later), he invented a general method for finding areas and volumes. For example, he proved that the volume of a sphere was two-thirds the volume of the smallest cylinder which contained it. (The sphere and cylinder are engraved on his tombstone.) He gave a procedure for approximating π (showing it was between $\frac{22}{7}$ and $\frac{223}{71}$), for finding square roots and for representing large numbers (remember that the decimal number system was not available to him). In addition to mathematics, he discovered "Archimedes' Principle" (which states that a floating object displaces its weight of liquid) and the laws of the lever (which he put to great use in inventing weapons — super catapults — used against the Romans). The force that one can achieve with the aid of a lever led him to say, "Give me a lever and a place to stand and I can move the earth."*

Introduction to Calculus

**CHAPTER** **1**

1.1 What is Calculus?

Two simple geometric problems originally led to the development of what is now called Calculus. Both problems can be stated in terms of the graph of a function $y = f(x)$.

- **The problem of tangents:** Calculate the slope of the tangent line to the graph of a function at a given point P.

- **The problem of areas:** Calculate the area under the graph of a function between $x = a$ and $x = b$.

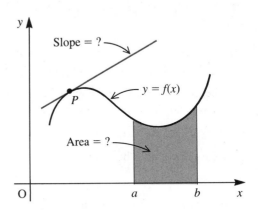

One's initial reaction might be that these problems are rather limited in scope. What makes them of great significance and interest, however, is that they have far-reaching applications in many areas of science and technology. In this book we shall concentrate on these two problems, on the ideas and techniques that have been developed for solving them, and on the applications that arise from them.

Interest in the problem of tangents and the problem of areas dates back to classical Greece, when scientists such as Archimedes of Syracuse (287 B.C.–212 B.C.) used great ingenuity to solve special cases of these problems. Further progress was made in Europe in the seventeenth century, most notably by Pierre de Fermat (1601–1665) and by Isaac Barrow (1630–1677), Newton's professor at Cambridge University, who recognized that there is a close connection between the problem of tangents and the problem of areas. But it took the genius of Isaac Newton (1642–1727) and Gottfried Wilhelm Leibniz (1649–1716) to crystallize these ideas and to understand their full significance. Using the analytic geometry of René Descartes (1596–1650), they showed independently how these two problems could be solved by means of new operations on functions, called differentiation and integration. The connection between the two problems was formalized in the so-called Fundamental Theorem of Calculus, which was also discovered independently by both men. Over the centuries, further research by mathematicians from many different countries has created a problem-solving tool of immense power and versatility, which is known today as Calculus.

Newton and Leibniz achieved their success without clearly understanding the concept of the limit of a function, which is now recognized as being fundamental to Calculus. It remained for Augustin-Louis Cauchy (1789–1857), Karl Weierstrass (1815–1897), and others to clarify this concept, thereby providing a firm foundation for the subject.

We begin our study of Calculus by discussing the problem of tangents and the related idea of rate of change. This leads us to the study of limits and, at the end of this chapter, to the concept of the derivative of a function.

1.2 The Slope of the Tangent Line

In this section we shall discuss the "problem of tangents" and explain how to calculate the slope of the tangent line to the graph of a function such as $f(x) = x^2$.

We begin with a brief review of how to find the slope of the line joining two points. Let $P_1(x_1, y_1)$ and $P_2(x_2, y_2)$ be any two points in the plane. The change in x between P_1 and P_2 is

$$\Delta x = x_2 - x_1$$

and the change in y between P_1 and P_2 is

$$\Delta y = y_2 - y_1$$

The slope m of the line joining P_1 and P_2 is defined as

$$m = \frac{\Delta y}{\Delta x} = \frac{y_2 - y_1}{x_2 - x_1}$$

Recall also that the slopes m_1 and m_2 of two perpendicular lines satisfy the relation

$$m_1 m_2 = -1$$

provided that neither slope is zero.

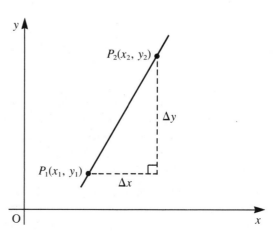

Let O be the centre of a circle and let P be a point on the circle. We can find the slope of the tangent line to the circle at P by using the fact that it is perpendicular to the radius OP.

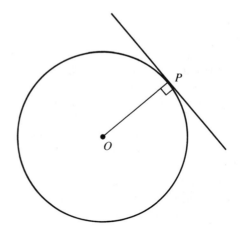

Example 1. Find the equation of the tangent line to the circle $x^2 + y^2 = 25$ at the point $P(3, 4)$.

Solution. The slope m_1 of the radius OP is

$$m_1 = \frac{4 - 0}{3 - 0}$$
$$= \frac{4}{3}$$

Let m_2 be the slope of the tangent line at P. Since the tangent line at P is perpendicular to OP, then

$$m_2 = -\frac{1}{m_1}$$
$$= -\frac{3}{4}$$

Thus the equation of the tangent line to the circle at $P(3, 4)$ is

$$\frac{y - 4}{x - 3} = -\frac{3}{4}$$

or

$$y - 4 = -\frac{3}{4}(x - 3) \qquad \square$$

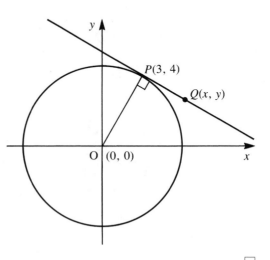

Unlike the circle, most curves do not have simple geometrical properties that are useful for calculating slopes of tangent lines, so a more general approach is required.

Consider a curve $y = f(x)$ and a point P that lies on the curve. In order to describe the tangent line at P geometrically, consider another point Q on the curve. The line joining P and Q is called a **secant line** for the curve. Think of Q as a moving point that slides along the curve towards P, so that the secant line PQ moves successively closer to the tangent line at P. Therefore, the slope of the secant line PQ becomes a progressively better estimate of the slope of the tangent line at P. This suggests the following definition of the slope of the tangent line.

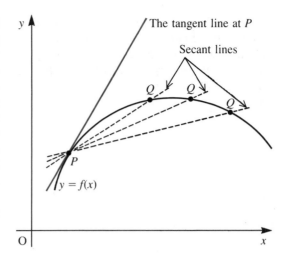

The **slope of the tangent line** to a curve at a point P is the limiting slope of the secant line PQ as the point Q slides along the curve towards P.

We now illustrate this idea by finding the slope of the tangent line to the parabola $y = x^2$ at the point (2, 4).

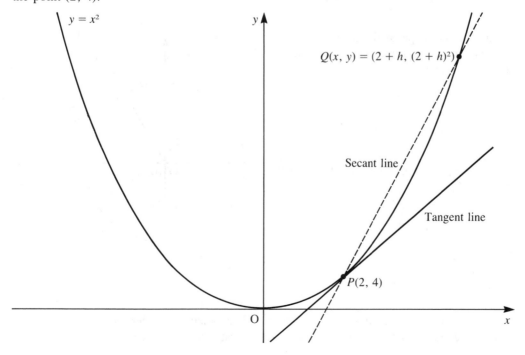

Let P be the point $(2, 4)$ on the parabola. Choose a nearby point Q on the parabola and calculate the slope of the secant line PQ. Since we are interested in points Q that are close to $P(2, 4)$, it is convenient to write the x coordinate of Q as

$$x = 2 + h$$

where h is a non-zero number. Since Q lies on the parabola $y = x^2$, the y coordinate of Q is

$$y = (2 + h)^2$$

The variable h determines the position of Q on the parabola. As Q slides along the parabola towards P, h **will take on values successively closer to 0**. We say that "h approaches 0" and use the standard notation "$h \to 0$".

The changes in x and y between P and Q are

$$\Delta x = (2 + h) - 2$$
$$= h$$

and

$$\Delta y = (2 + h)^2 - 4$$
$$= 4h + h^2$$

Thus, the slope of the secant line PQ is

$$\frac{\Delta y}{\Delta x} = \frac{4h + h^2}{h}$$
$$= 4 + h$$

where $h \neq 0$. The slope m of the tangent line at P is defined to be the limiting value of the slope of the secant line PQ as Q slides along the parabola towards P, that is, as $h \to 0$. We write "$\lim_{h \to 0}$" as the abbreviation for "limiting value as h approaches 0." Therefore, the slope of the tangent line is

$$m = \lim_{h \to 0} \frac{\Delta y}{\Delta x}$$
$$= \lim_{h \to 0} (4 + h)$$

As $h \to 0$, the value of $4 + h$ approaches 4 and hence

$$\lim_{h \to 0} (4 + h) = 4$$

Thus, the slope m of the tangent line is

$$m = 4$$

Example 2. Find the slope of the tangent line to the curve $y = 4 - x^2$ at the point $(-1, 3)$.

Solution. Find the slope of the secant line PQ, where Q is a point on the curve close to P. Write the x coordinate of Q as

$$x = -1 + h$$

Then the y coordinate of Q is

$$y = 4 - (-1 + h)^2$$

The changes in x and y between P and Q are

$$\Delta x = (-1 + h) - (-1)$$
$$= h$$

and

$$\Delta y = [4 - (-1 + h)^2] - 3$$
$$= 2h - h^2$$

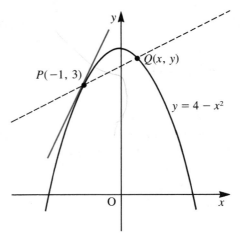

Thus, the slope of the secant line PQ is

$$\frac{\Delta y}{\Delta x} = \frac{2h - h^2}{h}$$
$$= 2 - h$$

where $h \neq 0$. The slope of the tangent line is

$$m = \lim_{h \to 0} \frac{\Delta y}{\Delta x}$$
$$= \lim_{h \to 0} (2 - h)$$

As $h \to 0$, the value of $(2 - h)$ approaches 2. Thus,

$$\lim_{h \to 0} (2 - h) = 2$$

and the slope of the tangent line is $m = 2$. Note that the slope of the tangent line at $(-1, 3)$ is **positive**. This means that as one moves to the right at $x = 1$, the graph moves **upwards**. $\square$

We now generalize the method used above to derive a convenient formula for the slope of the tangent line to the graph of any function. Consider any function

$$y = f(x)$$

and a fixed point $P(a, f(a))$ on the graph of $f(x)$.

Let $Q(x, y)$ be another point on the graph. The calculation is simplified if the x coordinate of Q is written as

$$x = a + h$$

where $h \neq 0$. Then the y coordinate of Q is

$$y = f(a + h)$$

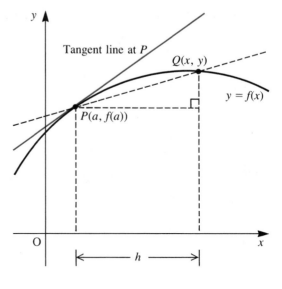

The changes in x and y between P and Q are

$$\Delta x = (a + h) - a$$
$$= h$$

and

$$\Delta y = f(a + h) - f(a)$$

Thus, the slope of the secant line PQ is

$$\frac{\Delta y}{\Delta x} = \frac{f(a + h) - f(a)}{h}$$

This quotient has a fundamental place in Calculus and is referred to as **the difference quotient**. The slope m of the tangent line at P is the limiting value of the difference quotient $\dfrac{\Delta y}{\Delta x}$ as $Q \to P$ or, equivalently, the limiting value of $\dfrac{f(a + h) - f(a)}{h}$ as $h \to 0$.

The slope of the tangent line to the graph of $y = f(x)$ at the point $P(a, f(a))$ is

$$m = \lim_{h \to 0} \frac{\Delta y}{\Delta x} = \lim_{h \to 0} \frac{f(a + h) - f(a)}{h}$$

This result can help to streamline the calculation of the slope of a tangent line, as is shown in Example 3.

Example 3. Find the slope of the tangent line to the rectangular hyperbola

$$y = \frac{1}{x}$$

at the point $\left(\frac{1}{2}, 2\right)$.

Solution. The slope of the tangent line can be found by using the limit of the difference quotient. The slope of the tangent line at $\left(\frac{1}{2}, f\left(\frac{1}{2}\right)\right)$ is

$$m = \lim_{h \to 0} \frac{\Delta y}{\Delta x}$$

$$= \lim_{h \to 0} \frac{f\left(\frac{1}{2} + h\right) - f\left(\frac{1}{2}\right)}{h}$$

$$= \lim_{h \to 0} \frac{\dfrac{1}{\frac{1}{2} + h} - 2}{h}$$

$$= \lim_{h \to 0} \frac{\dfrac{1 - 2\left(\frac{1}{2} + h\right)}{\frac{1}{2} + h}}{h}$$

$$= \lim_{h \to 0} \frac{1 - 1 - 2h}{h\left(\frac{1}{2} + h\right)} \quad = \lim_{h \to 0} \frac{-2h}{x\left(\frac{1}{2} + h\right)}$$

$$= \lim_{h \to 0} \frac{-2}{\frac{1}{2} + h}$$

$$= -4$$

At the point $\left(\frac{1}{2}, 2\right)$ the slope of the tangent line is -4. Note that the slope of the tangent line at $\left(\frac{1}{2}, 2\right)$ is **negative**. This means that as one moves to the right at $x = \frac{1}{2}$, the graph moves **downwards**.   □

To conclude this section, we discuss the tangent line in a real-life situation. Imagine a car travelling at night along a winding road, which we represent as the graph of a function. The car's headlights will project a beam of light in the direction of the tangent line at each instant. An observer in a helicopter could visualize the shape of the road by noting the change in direction of the headlight beam. This suggests that we can use our knowledge of the slopes of tangent lines to a curve to deduce information about the shape of that curve. This idea will be developed and applied throughout this book.

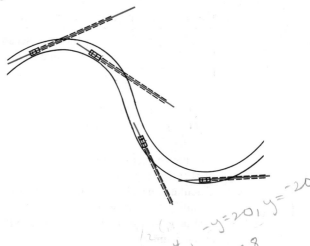

Exercises 1.2

1. Determine the slope of each straight line.

a. $\dfrac{x}{2} - \dfrac{y}{5} = 4$
b. $4x + 5y - 16 = 0$

c. $\dfrac{x}{a} + \dfrac{y}{b} = 1$

2. Find the equation of the straight line that passes

a. through $(-1, 2)$ and has a slope of $-\dfrac{1}{2}$.
b. through the points $(3, 1)$ and $(-2, -5)$.
c. through $(2, -1)$ and is perpendicular to $3x - 2y = 6$.

3. Find the equation of the tangent line to each circle at the given point. Sketch the circle and the tangent line.

a. $x^2 + y^2 = 169$; $(5, 12)$
b. $(x - 1)^2 + (y + 2)^2 = 25$; $(5, 1)$
c. $x^2 + y^2 - 6x - 8y = 0$; $(0, 0)$
d. $x^2 + y^2 - 10x = 0$; $(9, 3)$

4. Consider the function $f(x) = -x^2$.

    a. Copy and complete the following tables; P and Q are points on the graph of $f(x)$.

P	Q	Slope of secant line PQ	P	Q	Slope of secant line PQ
(1,)	(2,)		(1,)	(0,)	
(1,)	(1.5,)		(1,)	(0.5,)	
(1,)	(1.1,)		(1,)	(0.9,)	
(1,)	(1.01,)		(1,)	(0.99,)	

    b. Use the results of part (a) to approximate the slope of the tangent line to the graph of $f(x)$ at the point P.

    c. Calculate the slope of the secant line PR, where the x-coordinate of R is $1 + h$. Simplify your answer.

    d. Use the result of part (c) to calculate the slope of the tangent line to the graph of $f(x)$ at the point P.

    e. Compare your answers to parts (b) and (d).

    f. Sketch the graph of $f(x)$ and the tangent line to the graph at the point P.

5. Consider the function $f(x) = x^3$.

    a. Copy and complete the following tables; P and Q are points on the graph of $f(x)$.

P	Q	Slope of secant line PQ	P	Q	Slope of secant line PQ
(2,)	(3,)		(2,)	(1,)	
(2,)	(2.5,)		(2,)	(1.5,)	
(2,)	(2.1,)		(2,)	(1.9,)	
(2,)	(2.01,)		(2,)	(1.99,)	

    b. Use the results of part (a) to approximate the slope of the tangent line to the graph of $f(x)$ at the point P.

    c. Calculate the slope of the secant line PR, where the x-coordinate of R is $2 + h$. Simplify your answer.

    d. Use the result of part (c) to calculate the slope of the tangent line to the graph of $f(x)$ at the point P.

    e. Compare your answers to parts (b) and (d).

    f. Sketch the graph of $f(x)$ and the tangent line to the graph at the point P.

6. Find the slope of the tangent line to the graph of $f(x) = 2x^2$ at the points determined by the given x values. Sketch the graph and the tangent line in each case.

    a. $x = 1$ **b.** $x = -2$ **c.** $x = 0$

7. Find the slope of the tangent line to each curve at the given point. Sketch the curve and tangent line, and find the equation of the tangent line.

a. $y = 2x$; (1, 2)

b. $y = x^2 - 9$; (2, −5)

c. $y = x^2 - 3x$; (2, −2)

d. $y = x^2 - 3x$; (0, 0)

e. $y = \dfrac{1}{x}$; $\left(\dfrac{1}{3}, 3\right)$

f. $y = \dfrac{4}{x}$; (−2, −2)

g. $y = 3x^3$; (1, 3)

h. $y = -x^2 + 2x + 3$; (−2, −5)

8. Show that the slopes of the tangent lines to the curve $y = -x^2 + 2x + 3$ at the points $x = 3$ and $x = -1$ are equal in magnitude but opposite in sign. Illustrate this result by sketching the graph.

Problems 1.2

1. Find the coordinates of the point on the curve $y = 3x^2 - 4x$ where the tangent line is parallel to the line $y = 8x$.

2. Show that at the point(s) of intersection of the curves $y = x^2$ and $y = \dfrac{1}{2} - x^2$, the tangent lines to each curve are perpendicular.

3. A tangent line is drawn to the rectangular hyperbola $y = \dfrac{1}{x}$ at the point $\left(b, \dfrac{1}{b}\right)$. This line, together with the x-axis and the y-axis, determines a triangle. Prove that the area of this triangle is the same for every choice of b.

4. Prove that the tangent line to the curve $y = x^3$ at the point (a, a^3) intersects this curve again at $x = -2a$. Illustrate with a sketch.

5. Suppose that the flight path of an airplane is represented by the curve $y = 4x^2 + 6$. When the airplane is at the point (−1, 10) and moving so that x increases, it fires a missile in the direction of the tangent line. If the missile travels along the tangent line, will it hit a target located at $\left(\dfrac{1}{4}, 0\right)$? Illustrate with a sketch.

1.3 Rates of Change

Many relationships of practical importance can be modelled by means of functions. For example:

- the price of gasoline varies with time
- air temperature varies with elevation
- the fuel consumption of a car depends on its speed

These and many other relationships can be described either graphically or by means of an equation of the form

$$y = f(x)$$

where $f(x)$ is a function. The variable y (which can represent price, air temperature, etc.) is called **the dependent variable**, and the variable x (which can represent time, elevation, etc.) is called **the independent variable**.

One is often interested in how rapidly y changes when there is a change in x. This concept is "rate of change." For example, one speaks of the rate of change of the price of gasoline as time passes, the rate of change of the temperature as elevation varies, and so on. In this section, we shall show that a rate of change can be calculated in the same way that the slope of a tangent line is calculated—by finding the limit of a difference quotient.

We begin by considering a familiar rate of change—the velocity of a moving object. For example, a truck that travels a distance of 300 km in 4 h has an average velocity of $\frac{300}{4} = 75$ km/h, since

$$\text{average velocity} = \frac{\text{distance travelled}}{\text{time elapsed}}$$

However, the velocity of the truck would certainly not be constant, and hence the average velocity would not give detailed information about the motion of the truck. For example, one might be interested in knowing whether the truck had exceeded the speed limit of 100 km/h at any time during the trip. To answer such questions, one would need to know the velocity at particular instants of time. The velocity at an instant of time is called the **instantaneous velocity**. For brevity the word "instantaneous" is often omitted. Thus velocity and instantaneous velocity mean the same thing.

Example 1 below illustrates average velocity.

Example 1. A pebble is dropped from a cliff of height 80 m. After t seconds, it has fallen a distance of s metres, where

$$s(t) = 5t^2, \quad 0 \leq t \leq 4$$

a. Find the average velocity of the pebble between times $t = 1$ s and $t = 3$ s.
b. Find the average velocity of the pebble during the time interval from $t = 1$ to $t = 1 + \Delta t$.

Solution.

a. The displacement at time t is

$$s(t) = 5t^2$$

The displacement after one second is

$$s(1) = 5$$

and the displacement after three seconds is

$$s(3) = 45$$

It follows that the distance fallen between the times $t = 1$ and $t = 3$ is

$$\Delta s = s(3) - s(1)$$
$$= 45 - 5$$
$$= 40$$

Since the elapsed time is

$$\Delta t = 3 - 1$$
$$= 2$$

the average velocity is $\frac{40}{2} = 20$ m/s

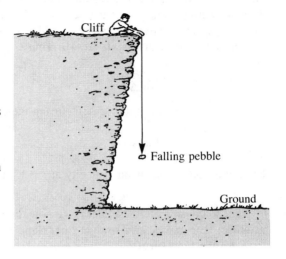

Cliff

Falling pebble

Ground

b. The distance fallen between $t = 1$ and $t = 1 + \Delta t$ is

$$\Delta s = s(1 + \Delta t) - s(1)$$
$$= 5(1 + \Delta t)^2 - 5(1)^2$$
$$= 10 \Delta t + 5(\Delta t)^2$$

Thus, during the interval of time Δt,

$$\text{average velocity} = \frac{\Delta s}{\Delta t}$$
$$= \frac{10 \Delta t + 5(\Delta t)^2}{\Delta t}$$
$$= 10 + 5 \Delta t$$

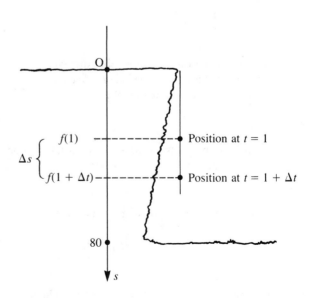

O

$\Delta s \begin{cases} f(1) & \\ \\ f(1 + \Delta t) & \end{cases}$

Position at $t = 1$

Position at $t = 1 + \Delta t$

80

s

The formula for the average velocity found in Example 1(b) can now be used to calculate the (instantaneous) velocity v of the pebble at time $t = 1$. To do this, find the limiting value of the average velocity over the interval of time Δt, starting at $t = 1$, as the time interval becomes shorter and shorter, that is, as $\Delta t \rightarrow 0$. Thus,

$$v = \lim_{\Delta t \to 0} \frac{\Delta s}{\Delta t}$$

$$= \lim_{\Delta t \to 0} (10 + 5\Delta t) \quad \text{(using the expression from Example 1(b))}$$

$$= 10 \text{ m/s}$$

Therefore, the instantaneous velocity at $t = 1$ s is $v = 10$ m/s.

In order to consolidate these ideas, we now discuss motion in more general terms. Consider an object that moves in a straight line. Suppose that the position of the object at time t is given by the function $s(t)$.

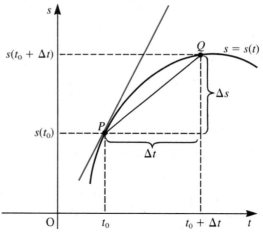

The change in position during an interval of time Δt starting at time t_0 is

$$\Delta s = s(t_0 + \Delta t) - s(t_0)$$

Thus, the average velocity over the interval of time Δt is

$$\frac{\Delta s}{\Delta t} = \frac{s(t_0 + \Delta t) - s(t_0)}{\Delta t}$$

From the diagram, it follows that the average velocity during the time interval Δt equals the slope of the secant line PQ.

As in Example 1, the velocity at a particular time t_0 is calculated by finding the limiting value of the average velocity as $\Delta t \rightarrow 0$.

The velocity of an object, with position function $s(t)$, at time t_0 is

$$v(t_0) = \lim_{\Delta t \to 0} \frac{\Delta s}{\Delta t} = \lim_{\Delta t \to 0} \frac{s(t_0 + \Delta t) - s(t_0)}{\Delta t}$$

Referring to the figure, note that **the velocity $v(t_0)$ equals the slope of the tangent line to the graph of $s(t)$ at $t = t_0$.**

We now give an example showing how to calculate the velocity at an instant of time.

Example 2. A dragster races down a 400 m strip in 10 s. Its distance in metres from the starting time after t seconds is

$$s(t) = 3t^2 + 10t$$

Find its velocity as it crosses the finish line.

Solution. First find an expression for the average velocity. The dragster crosses the finish line at time $t = 10$. The change in position Δs between times $t = 10$ and $t = 10 + \Delta t$ is

$$
\begin{aligned}
\Delta s &= s(10 + \Delta t) - s(10) \\
&= [3(10 + \Delta t)^2 + 10(10 + \Delta t)] - [3(10)^2 + 10(10)] \\
&= 3[20\Delta t + (\Delta t)^2] + 10\Delta t \\
&= 70\,\Delta t + 3(\Delta t)^2
\end{aligned}
$$

It follows that the average velocity over the time interval between $t = 10$ and $t = 10 + \Delta t$ is

$$
\begin{aligned}
\frac{\Delta s}{\Delta t} &= \frac{70\,\Delta t + 3(\Delta t)^2}{\Delta t} \\
&= 70 + 3\,\Delta t
\end{aligned}
$$

Thus, the velocity at time $t = 10$ is

$$
\begin{aligned}
v(10) &= \lim_{\Delta t \to 0} \frac{\Delta s}{\Delta t} \\
&= \lim_{\Delta t \to 0} (70 + 3\,\Delta t) \\
&= 70
\end{aligned}
$$

since $\Delta t \to 0$ implies that $3\,\Delta t \to 3(0) = 0$. Thus, the dragster crosses the finish line with a velocity of 70 m/s. $\square$

Velocity is only one example of the concept of **rate of change**. In general, suppose that a quantity y depends on a variable x according to the equation

$$y = f(x)$$

As the independent variable x changes from a to $a + \Delta x$, the corresponding change in the dependent variable y is

$$\Delta y = f(a + \Delta x) - f(a)$$

The difference quotient

$$\frac{\Delta y}{\Delta x} = \frac{f(a + \Delta x) - f(a)}{\Delta x}$$

is called **the average rate of change of** y **with respect to** x **over the interval from** $x = a$ **to** $x = a + \Delta x$. From the diagram, it follows that the average rate of change equals the slope of the secant line PQ of the graph of $f(x)$.

The **rate of change of** y **with respect to** x **when** $x = a$ is defined to be the limiting value of the average rate of change as $\Delta x \to 0$.

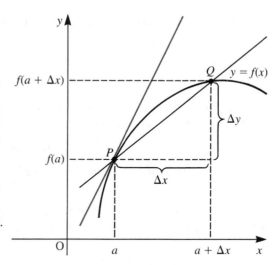

The rate of change of $y = f(x)$ **with respect to** x **when** $x = a$ **is**

$$\lim_{\Delta x \to 0} \frac{\Delta y}{\Delta x} = \lim_{\Delta x \to 0} \frac{f(a + \Delta x) - f(a)}{\Delta x}$$

Referring to the figure, observe that **the rate of change of the function** $f(x)$ **at** $x = a$ **equals the slope of the tangent line to the graph of** $f(x)$.

For example, if x represents height above sea level (in kilometres) and y represents air temperature (in degrees Celsius) at height x, then $\lim_{\Delta x \to 0} \frac{\Delta y}{\Delta x}$ is **the rate of change of temperature with respect to height** (in degrees Celsius per kilometre). As a second example, if x represents time (in days) and y represents the volume of water in a reservoir (in kilolitres) at time x, then $\lim_{\Delta x \to 0} \frac{\Delta y}{\Delta x}$ is the **rate of change of volume with respect to time** (in kilolitres per day).

If the independent variable represents time, it is customary to omit the phrase "with respect to time" and to speak simply of "the rate of change." Thus we say that the velocity of an object is the rate of change of its position.

The next two examples illustrate the general concept of rate of change.

Example 3. A medicine is administered to a patient. The amount M of the medicine (in mg) in one millilitre of the patient's blood t hours after the injection is given by

$$M(t) = t - \tfrac{1}{3}t^2, \text{ where } 0 \leq t \leq 3$$

Find the rate of change of the amount M one hour after the injection.

Solution. The change ΔM in the amount of medicine when t changes from 1 to $1 + \Delta t$ is

$$\Delta M = M(1 + \Delta t) - M(1)$$

$$= [(1 + \Delta t) - \tfrac{1}{3}(1 + \Delta t)^2] - [1 - \tfrac{1}{3}(1)^2]$$

$$= \Delta t - \tfrac{1}{3}[2\,\Delta t + (\Delta t)^2]$$

$$= \tfrac{1}{3}\,\Delta t - \tfrac{1}{3}(\Delta t)^2$$

The average rate of change is

$$\frac{\Delta M}{\Delta t} = \frac{\tfrac{1}{3}\,\Delta t - \tfrac{1}{3}(\Delta t)^2}{\Delta t}$$

$$= \tfrac{1}{3} - \tfrac{1}{3}\,\Delta t$$

Thus, the rate of change of M when $t = 1$ is

$$\text{rate of change} = \lim_{\Delta t \to 0} \frac{\Delta M}{\Delta t}$$

$$= \lim_{\Delta t \to 0} \left(\tfrac{1}{3} - \tfrac{1}{3}\,\Delta t\right)$$

$$= \tfrac{1}{3}$$

Thus after one hour the rate of change in the amount of medicine is $\tfrac{1}{3}$ mg/h.　　□

Since the rate of change in Example 3 is **positive**, the amount of medicine in the bloodstream is **increasing** after one hour.

Example 4. A circular oil slick on the ocean spreads outwards. Find the rate of change of the area of the oil slick with respect to its radius when the radius is 100 m.

Solution. The area A (in square metres) of an oil slick of radius r metres is

$$A = \pi r^2$$

The change ΔA in the area when the radius changes from 100 to $100 + \Delta r$, which is represented by the shaded region in the diagram, is

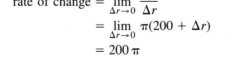

$$\Delta A = \pi(100 + \Delta r)^2 - \pi(100)^2$$
$$= \pi[200\,\Delta r + (\Delta r)^2]$$

The average rate of change of area with respect to radius is

$$\frac{\Delta A}{\Delta r} = \frac{\pi[200\,\Delta r + (\Delta r)^2]}{\Delta r}$$
$$= \pi(200 + \Delta r)$$

Hence, the instantaneous rate of change is

$$\text{rate of change} = \lim_{\Delta r \to 0} \frac{\Delta A}{\Delta r}$$
$$= \lim_{\Delta r \to 0} \pi(200 + \Delta r)$$
$$= 200\,\pi$$

Thus, when the radius is 100 m, the rate of change of area with respect to radius is 200π m²/m. Observe that this rate of change equals the circumference of the oil slick when $r = 100$ m (see Problem 1 in problems section 1.3).   □

Exercises 1.3

1. The function $s(t) = 6t(t + 1)$ describes the distance (in kilometres) that a car has travelled after a time t (in hours), for $0 \le t \le 6$.

   a. Find the average velocity of the car during the following intervals.
   (i)   from $t = 2$ to $t = 3$
   (ii) from $t = 2$ to $t = 2.1$
   (iii) from $t = 2$ to $t = 2.01$

   b. Use the results of part (a) to approximate the instantaneous velocity of the car when $t = 2$.

   c. Find the average velocity of the car from $t = 2$ to $t = 2 + \Delta t$.

   d. Use the result of part (c) to find the (instantaneous) velocity when $t = 2$.

2. A construction worker drops a wrench while working on a high-rise building 320 m above the ground. After t seconds the wrench has fallen a distance s, where

$$s(t) = 5t^2, \quad 0 \le t \le 8.$$

   a. Find the average velocity during each of the first four seconds.
   b. Find the average velocity during an interval of time Δt starting at $t = 2$, $t = 4$, and $t = 6$.
   c. Using the results of part (b), find the velocity of the wrench at times $t = 2$, $t = 4$, and $t = 6$.

3. A motorboat coasts towards a dock with its engine off. Its distance s (in metres) from the dock t seconds after the engine is cut is

$$s(t) = \frac{90}{3 + t} - 10, \quad 0 \le t \le 6$$

   a. Find the average velocity during an interval of time Δt starting at $t = 1$, $t = 3$, and $t = 5$.
   b. Find the velocity of the motorboat at times $t = 1$, $t = 3$, and $t = 5$.

4. Refer to Example 3.

   a. Find the rate of change of the amount M of the medicine two hours after the injection.
   b. What is the significance of the fact that your answer is negative?

5. Find the average rate of change of the function $y = f(x)$ with respect to x over the given interval. In each case, sketch the graph of the function and draw the secant line that has a slope equal to the average rate of change.

   a. $f(x) = 3x^2, \quad 1 \le x \le 3$
   b. $f(x) = (2 + x)^2, \quad -3 \le x \le 1$
   c. $f(x) = 5 - x^2, \quad -2 \le x \le 2$
   d. $f(x) = \frac{3}{x}, \quad -\frac{3}{2} \le x \le -\frac{1}{2}$

6. Find the rate of change of $y = f(x)$ with respect to x at the given x-value. In each case sketch the graph of the function and draw the tangent line that has a slope equal to the rate of change.

   a. $f(x) = 3x^2, \quad x = 1$
   b. $f(x) = (2 + x)^2, \quad x = -3$
   c. $f(x) = 5 - x^2, \quad x = 2$
   d. $f(x) = \frac{3}{x}, \quad x = \frac{1}{2}$

7. An oil tank is being drained for cleaning. After t minutes there are V litres of oil left in the tank, where

$$V(t) = 50(30 - t)^2, \quad 0 \le t \le 30.$$

   a. Find the average rate of change of volume during the first 20 minutes.
   b. Find the rate of change of volume at the time $t = 20$.

8. Suppose that the air temperature T (in degrees Celsius) varies with the height h (in kilometres) above the earth's surface according to the equation

$$T(h) = \frac{60}{2 + h}$$

Find the rate of change of temperature with respect to height at a height of 1 km.

9. A funnel has the shape of a right circular cone. The volume of liquid in the funnel (in millilitres) when the depth is h centimetres is

$$V(h) = \frac{1}{3}\pi h^3$$

Find the rate of change of volume with respect to depth when $h = 5$ cm.

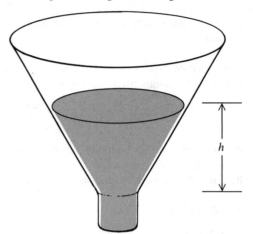

Problems 1.3

1. a. Show that the rate of change of the area of a circle with respect to its radius equals the circumference of the circle.
  b. Show that the rate of change of the volume V of a sphere with respect to its radius r equals the surface area S of the sphere. (Note that $V(r) = \frac{4}{3}\pi r^3$ and $S(r) = 4\pi r^2$).

2. The diagram shows how fuel consumption (in L/100 km) for a certain model of car depends on speed, between speeds of 40 km/h and 120 km/h.

  a. Will an increase in speed increase or decrease fuel consumption when the speed is (i) 50 km/h? (ii) 100 km/h?
  b. For what speeds is the rate of change of fuel consumption with respect to velocity (i) positive? (ii) negative?
  c. At what speed is fuel consumption lowest? What is the rate of change in fuel consumption at this speed?

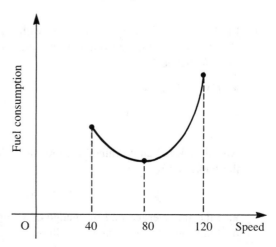

3. A person of height 2 m standing a distance x from a light pole of height 10 m has a shadow of length y. Find the rate of change in the length of the shadow with respect to distance x.

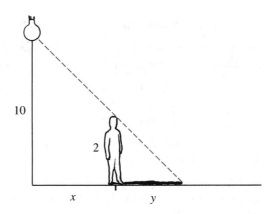

1.4 The Limit Concept

In the previous sections we showed that in order to calculate the slope of a tangent line, or a rate of change, it is necessary to evaluate **the limit of a difference quotient**. This is one of the ways in which limits have a fundamental place in Calculus. We now begin a careful examination of the concept of the "limiting value of a function."

To begin, consider the limiting value of the function

$$f(x) = 3x - 5$$

as x approaches 2. As $x \to 2$,

$$3x \to 3(2) = 6$$

and therefore

$$3x - 5 \to 6 - 5 = 1$$

We say that **"the limit of** $3x - 5$ **as** x **approaches** 2 **equals** 1," and we write

$$\lim_{x \to 2} (3x - 5) = 1$$

Observe that $f(2) = 1$, so that in this case

$$\lim_{x \to 2} f(x) = f(2)$$

In words, as x approaches 2, $f(x)$ approaches $f(2)$. This means that the graph passes through the point $(2, f(2))$ without a "break". We say that the function $f(x)$ is **continuous at** $x = 2$.

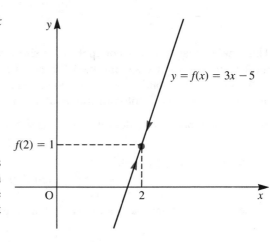

In retrospect it follows that $\lim\limits_{x \to 2} f(x)$ could have been evaluated simply by substituting $x = 2$ into the formula for $f(x)$. It is essential to note, however, that **not all limits can be evaluated by substitution**. For example, consider the function

$$f(x) = \begin{cases} x - 1, & \text{if } x < 1 \\ 1, & \text{if } x = 1 \\ x + 1, & \text{if } x > 1 \end{cases}$$

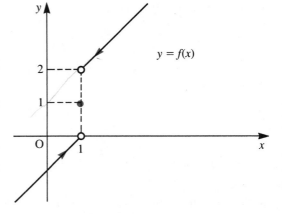

whose graph consists of two open rays and the single point (1, 1).

By studying the graph of $f(x)$, observe that the limiting value of $f(x)$ as $x \to 1$ depends on whether $x > 1$ or $x < 1$. If $x \to 1$ and $x > 1$, then $f(x)$ approaches the limiting value of 2. We say that "the limit of $f(x)$ as x approaches 1 **from the right** equals 2," which is written as

$$\lim_{x \to 1^+} f(x) = 2$$

However, if $x \to 1$ and $x < 1$, then $f(x)$ approaches the limiting value of 0. We say that "the limit of $f(x)$ as x approaches 1 **from the left** equals 0", which is written as

$$\lim_{x \to 1^-} f(x) = 0$$

These two limits are referred to as **one-sided** limits, because in each case only values of x on one side of $x = 1$ are considered.

It should be noted that the function value at $x = 1$, $f(1) = 1$, played no role in determining the one-sided limits. The essential point is that **the one-sided limits are unequal**:

$$\lim_{x \to 1^+} f(x) \neq \lim_{x \to 1^-} f(x)$$

This implies that $f(x)$ does not approach a **single value** as $x \to 1$, and hence we say that "**the limit of $f(x)$ as $x \to 1$ does not exist**." Since the one-sided limits are unequal, the graph has a "break" or "discontinuity" at the point where $x = 1$. (See the previous diagram.) We say that the function $f(x)$ is **discontinuous at $x = 1$**.

We now summarize the ideas that we have introduced in the previous examples.

The Limit of a Function

$$\lim_{x \to a} f(x) = L$$

means that $f(x)$ approaches the value L as x approaches the value a.

This is an intuitive explanation of the concept of limit. It is possible to define limits using inequalities (see Problem 7 in this section). This precise definition is important for advanced work but is not necessary for our purposes.

We next illustrate the concept of one-sided limits and summarize the way in which they can be used to determine whether a limit exists.

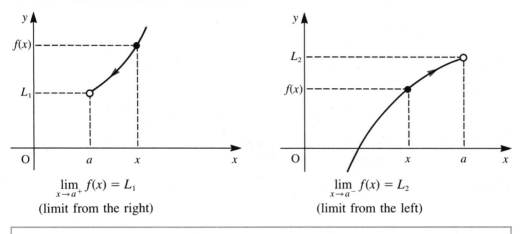

$$\lim_{x \to a^+} f(x) = L_1$$
(limit from the right)

$$\lim_{x \to a^-} f(x) = L_2$$
(limit from the left)

If $\lim_{x \to a^+} f(x) \neq \lim_{x \to a^-} f(x)$, then $\lim_{x \to a} f(x)$ does not exist.

If $\lim_{x \to a^+} f(x) = L = \lim_{x \to a^-} f(x)$, then $\lim_{x \to a} f(x) = L$.

In Example 1, one-sided limits must be used to find the limit of a function.

Example 1. Consider the function

$$f(x) = \begin{cases} x^2 - 3, & \text{if } x \leq -1 \\ x - 1, & \text{if } x > -1 \end{cases}$$

By evaluating one-sided limits, determine whether $\lim_{x \to -1} f(x)$ exists. Sketch the graph of $f(x)$.

Solution. For $x > -1$, $f(x) = x - 1$ and

$$\lim_{x \to -1^+} f(x) = \lim_{x \to -1^+} (x - 1)$$
$$= -1 - 1$$
$$= -2$$

For $x < -1$, $f(x) = x^2 - 3$ and

$$\lim_{x \to -1^-} f(x) = \lim_{x \to -1^-} (x^2 - 3)$$
$$= 1 - 3$$
$$= -2$$

These one-sided limits can be confirmed by inspecting the graph of $f(x)$. This graph is obtained by sketching the line $y = x - 1$ for $x > -1$, and the parabola $y = x^2 - 3$ for $x \leq -1$. Since the one-sided limits are equal, $\lim_{x \to -1} f(x)$ exists and

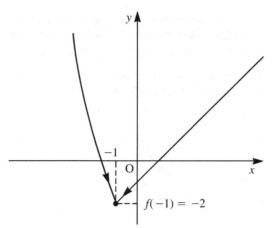

$$\lim_{x \to -1} f(x) = -2$$

Note that $f(-1) = -2$ and hence

$$\lim_{x \to -1} f(x) = f(-1)$$

This equality describes the fact that the separate parts of the graph meet at $x = -1$ without a break, so that $f(x)$ is continuous at $x = -1$. ☐

We now define and illustrate geometrically the notion of a continuous function.

If $f(a)$ is defined and if

$$\lim_{x \to a} f(x) = f(a),$$

we say that **the function $f(x)$ is continuous at** $x = a$. Otherwise, we say that $f(x)$ **is discontinuous at** $x = a$.

There are many ways in which a function can fail to be continuous at $x = a$. Two such possibilities are illustrated.

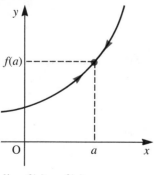

$$\lim_{x \to a} f(x) = f(a)$$

f is continuous at $x = a$

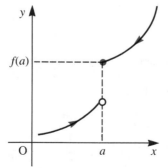

$$\lim_{x \to a^+} f(x) \neq \lim_{x \to a^-} f(x)$$

f is discontinuous at $x = a$

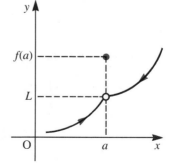

$$\lim_{x \to a} f(x) = L \neq f(a)$$

f is discontinuous at $x = a$

The essential geometric point about continuity is that if a function is discontinuous at $x = a$, its graph has a "break" at $x = a$.

Example 2 shows a function that is discontinuous.

Example 2. By sketching the graph of the function

$$f(x) = \begin{cases} x^2, & \text{if } x < 1 \\ 2, & \text{if } x \geq 1 \end{cases}$$

find all x values at which the function is discontinuous.

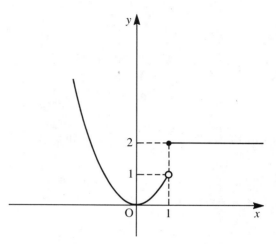

Solution. The graph of $f(x)$ consists of the parabola $y = x^2$ for $x < 1$, and the horizontal line $y = 2$ for $x \geq 1$. Since there is a "break" in the graph at $x = 1$, $f(x)$ is discontinuous at $x = 1$. (However, $f(x)$ is continuous for all other values of x.)

It follows from the graph that

$$\lim_{x \to 1^-} f(x) = 1 \quad \text{and} \quad \lim_{x \to 1^+} f(x) = 2$$

This confirms that $\lim_{x \to 1} f(x)$ does not exist and that $f(x)$ is discontinuous at $x = 1$. ☐

We conclude this section by summarizing the main points concerning limits:

- $\lim_{x \to a} f(x)$ is determined by the values of $f(x)$ when x is close to but not equal to a.

- $\lim_{x \to a} f(x)$ may exist even if $f(a)$ is not defined. (See section 1.6.)

- $\lim_{x \to a} f(x)$ can be equal to $f(a)$. (See section 1.5.) In this case the graph of $f(x)$ passes through the point $(a, f(a))$ without a break and $f(x)$ is continuous at $x = a$.

- $\lim_{x \to a} f(x)$ does not exist if the one-sided limits are not equal:

$$\lim_{x \to a^+} f(x) \neq \lim_{x \to a^-} f(x)$$

In this case the graph of $f(x)$ has a break at $x = a$, and $f(x)$ is discontinuous at $x = a$.

Exercises 1.4

1. Evaluate each limit and illustrate your result with a graph indicating the limiting value.

a. $\lim_{x \to 3} (2x - 8)$ **b.** $\lim_{x \to -1} (2x - 8)$

c. $\lim_{x \to 2} (x^2 - 1)$ **d.** $\lim_{x \to -1} (9 - 4x^2)$

e. $\lim_{x \to 1} (x^2 - 2x - 3)$ **f.** $\lim_{x \to -2} (x^2 - 2x - 3)$

2. By evaluating one-sided limits, find the indicated limit **if it exists**. Sketch the graph of the function and state whether the function is continuous.

a. $f(x) = \begin{cases} x + 2, & \text{if } x < -1 \\ -x + 2, & \text{if } x \geq -1 \end{cases}$; $\lim\limits_{x \to -1} f(x)$

b. $f(x) = \begin{cases} x^2, & \text{if } x \leq 1 \\ -x + 3, & \text{if } x > 1 \end{cases}$; $\lim\limits_{x \to 1} f(x)$

c. $f(x) = \begin{cases} -x + 4, & \text{if } x \leq 2 \\ -2x + 6, & \text{if } x > 2 \end{cases}$; $\lim\limits_{x \to 2} f(x)$

d. $f(x) = \begin{cases} 4 - x^2, & \text{if } x < 1 \\ x, & \text{if } x \geq 1 \end{cases}$; $\lim\limits_{x \to 1} f(x)$

e. $f(x) = \begin{cases} 4x, & \text{if } x \geq \dfrac{1}{2} \\ \dfrac{1}{x}, & \text{if } x < \dfrac{1}{2} \end{cases}$; $\lim\limits_{x \to \frac{1}{2}} f(x)$

f. $f(x) = \begin{cases} x + 3, & \text{if } x < 2 \\ \dfrac{4}{x}, & \text{if } x \geq 2 \end{cases}$; $\lim\limits_{x \to 2} f(x)$

g. $f(x) = \begin{cases} 1, & \text{if } x < -\dfrac{1}{2} \\ x^2 - \dfrac{1}{4}, & \text{if } x \geq -\dfrac{1}{2} \end{cases}$; $\lim\limits_{x \to -\frac{1}{2}} f(x)$

h. $f(x) = \begin{cases} 2 + x^2, & \text{if } x < 0 \\ 2 - x^2, & \text{if } x \geq 0 \end{cases}$; $\lim\limits_{x \to 0} f(x)$

3. By sketching the graph of the function

$$f(x) = \begin{cases} x + 1, & \text{if } x < -1 \\ -x + 1, & \text{if } -1 \leq x \leq 1 \\ x - 2, & \text{if } x > 1 \end{cases}$$

find all x values at which the function is discontinuous.

4. Sketch the graph of any function that satisfies the given conditions in each case.

a. $\lim\limits_{x \to 1^+} f(x) = 3$, $\lim\limits_{x \to 1^-} f(x) = 2$, $f(1) = 1$

b. $\lim\limits_{x \to 2} f(x) = 0$, $f(2) = 1$

c. $\lim\limits_{x \to 0^-} f(x) = 1$, $\lim\limits_{x \to 0^+} f(x) = -1$, $f(0) = 1$

d. $f(x) = 1$, if $x < 1$ and $\lim\limits_{x \to 1^+} f(x) = 2$

e. $\lim\limits_{x \to -1} f(x) = \dfrac{1}{2}$ and f is discontinuous at $x = -1$

5. Let $f(x) = Ax + B$, where A and B are constants. If $\lim\limits_{x \to 1} f(x) = -2$ and $\lim\limits_{x \to -1} f(x) = 4$, find A and B.

6. The electrical power $p(t)$ (in kilowatts) being used by a household, as a function of time t (in hours), is modelled by the graph, where $t = 0$ corresponds to 6:00 a.m. The graph indicates peak use at 8:00 a.m. and a power failure between 9:00 a.m. and 10:00 a.m.

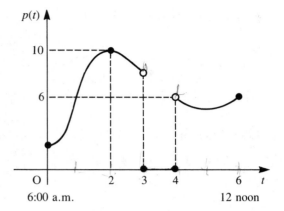

a. Evaluate $\lim\limits_{t \to 2} p(t)$.

b. Evaluate $\lim\limits_{t \to 4^+} p(t)$ and $\lim\limits_{t \to 4^-} p(t)$.

c. For what values of t is $p(t)$ discontinuous?

Problems 1.4

1. a. Sketch the graph of the function

$$f(x) = \begin{cases} 1 - x^2, & \text{if } |x| \leq 1 \\ x^2 - 4, & \text{if } |x| > 1 \end{cases}$$

b. Identify all x-values at which the function is discontinuous.

c. Evaluate the one-sided limits at each point of discontinuity in part (b).

2. The fish population (in thousands) in a lake at time t (in years) is modelled by the function

$$p(t) = \begin{cases} 3 + \frac{1}{12}t^2, & \text{if } 0 \leq t < 6 \\ 2 + \frac{1}{18}t^2, & \text{if } 6 < t \leq 12 \end{cases}$$

This function describes a sudden change in the population at time $t = 6$, due to a chemical spill.

a. Sketch the graph of $p(t)$.

b. Evaluate $\lim\limits_{t \to 6^-} p(t)$ and $\lim\limits_{t \to 6^+} p(t)$.

c. Determine how many fish were killed by the spill.

d. At what time did the population recover to the level it was at before the spill?

3. Consider the function

$$f(x) = \begin{cases} \dfrac{x|x - 1|}{x - 1}, & \text{if } x \neq 1 \\ 0, & \text{if } x = 1 \end{cases}$$

a. Evaluate $\lim\limits_{x \to 1^+} f(x)$ and $\lim\limits_{x \to 1^-} f(x)$ and then determine whether $\lim\limits_{x \to 1} f(x)$ exists.

b. Sketch the graph of $f(x)$ and identify any points of discontinuity.

4. Sketch the graph of the function f defined by

$$f(x) = \begin{cases} -x^2, & \text{if } |x| < 1 \\ x^2 - 2, & \text{if } |x| > 1 \end{cases}$$

Note that f is not defined at $x = 1$ and $x = -1$ and is therefore discontinuous at these points. Can values of $f(1)$ and $f(-1)$ be assigned so as to make f continuous at $x = 1$ and $x = -1$?

5. Consider the function f defined by

$$f(x) = \begin{cases} A, & \text{if } x < -2 \\ 2|x - 1|, & \text{if } -2 \leq x \leq 3 \\ B, & \text{if } x > 3 \end{cases}$$

when A and B are constants. Find A and B so that the function f is continuous at $x = 3$ and $x = -2$. Sketch the graph of the function.

6. Consider the greatest-integer function

$$f(x) = [x]$$

where $[x]$ is defined to be the greatest integer that does not exceed x (for example, $[-3.2] = -4$, and $[5.9] = 5$).

a. Sketch the graph of $f(x)$.
b. Find all points at which $f(x)$ is discontinuous.
c. What realistic situation could this graph represent?

7. In the text we have given an intuitive and simplified explanation of the concept of limit. The following is a more precise explanation in words:

The statement $\lim_{x \to a} f(x) = L$ means that there is a unique number L such that the value of $f(x)$ is arbitrarily close to L for all values of x sufficiently close to a but not equal to a.

The formal definition of a limit is:

Definition: The statement $\lim_{x \to a} f(x) = L$ means that for any real number $\epsilon > 0$ there exists a real number $\delta > 0$ such that

$$0 < |x - a| < \delta \text{ implies } |f(x) - L| < \epsilon.$$

Consider the function $f(x) = 2x - 3$, and suppose that we wish to prove that

$$\lim_{x \to 2} (2x - 3) = 1$$

using this definition. If we are given any number $\epsilon > 0$, we have to find a number $\delta > 0$ such that

$$0 < |x - 2| < \delta \text{ implies } |f(x) - 1| < \epsilon$$

Find an acceptable value of δ for each value of ϵ.

a. $\epsilon = \frac{1}{10}$ **b.** $\epsilon = \frac{1}{100}$ **c.** $\epsilon = 10^{-6}$

8. Prove the following theorem:
If f is continuous, then

$$\lim_{x \to a} \left[f(g(x)) \right] = f\left(\lim_{x \to a} g(x) \right)$$

provided that both limits exist.

1.5 Properties of Limits

In the previous section, the concept of a limit was developed intuitively. In this section we discuss some of the fundamental properties of limits. These properties, which can be proved by using the definition of a limit (see section 1.4, Problem 7), will provide the basis for developing techniques used to evaluate limits.

Consider the function $h(x) = 3x^3 + 5x^2$.
As $x \to -1$, observe that

$$3x^3 + 5x^2 \to 3(-1)^3 + 5(-1)^2 = -3 + 5$$
$$= 2$$

This can be written in limit notation as

$$\lim_{x \to -1} (3x^3 + 5x^2) = 2$$

The function $h(x)$ is the sum of two parts, $3x^3$ and $5x^2$. As $x \to -1$, $3x^3 \to 3(-1)^3 = -3$, and $5x^2 \to 5(-1)^2 = 5$. In limit notation,

$$\lim_{x \to -1} 3x^3 = -3 \text{ and } \lim_{x \to -1} 5x^2 = 5$$

We thus reach the expected conclusion that

$$\lim_{x \to -1} (3x^3 + 5x^2) = \lim_{x \to -1} 3x^3 + \lim_{x \to -1} 5x^2$$

In other words, the limit of a sum equals the sum of the individual limits.

This result is true in general, and similar results hold for products, quotients and nth roots. Here is a summary of the basic properties of limits.

Properties of Limits

Sum

$$\lim_{x \to a} [f(x) + g(x)] = \lim_{x \to a} f(x) + \lim_{x \to a} g(x)$$

Product

$$\lim_{x \to a} [f(x) g(x)] = \left[\lim_{x \to a} f(x)\right]\left[\lim_{x \to a} g(x)\right]$$

Constant Multiple

$$\lim_{x \to a} [Cf(x)] = C\left[\lim_{x \to a} f(x)\right]$$

Quotient

$$\lim_{x \to a} \left[\frac{f(x)}{g(x)}\right] = \frac{\lim_{x \to a} f(x)}{\lim_{x \to a} g(x)}, \text{ provided that } \lim_{x \to a} g(x) \neq 0$$

nth Root

$$\lim_{x \to a} \sqrt[n]{f(x)} = \sqrt[n]{\lim_{x \to a} f(x)}, \text{ provided that } \lim_{x \to a} f(x) \geq 0 \text{ if } n \text{ is}$$

an even integer

Limits such as

$$\lim_{x \to 2} (3x - 5) \text{ and } \lim_{x \to 3} (x^2 - 3)$$

are easy to evaluate, because the values $x = 2$ and $x = 3$ can be substituted into the corresponding function to obtain

$$\lim_{x \to 2} (3x - 5) = 1 \text{ and } \lim_{x \to 3} (x^2 - 3) = 6$$

Keep in mind, however, that not all limits can be evaluated in this way. In the previous section we considered examples of limits that do not exist, and in the next section we shall evaluate limits of the form $\lim_{x \to a} f(x)$ in cases where $f(a)$ is undefined. It is thus important to know which limits can be evaluated by substitution—that is, for which functions the statement

$$\lim_{x \to a} f(x) = f(a)$$

is valid.

For example, consider **the power function**

$$f(x) = x^n$$

where n is a positive integer. For $n = 2$, the limit property for products implies that

$$\lim_{x \to a} x^2 = \lim_{x \to a} (x)(x)$$
$$= \left[\lim_{x \to a} x\right]\left[\lim_{x \to a} x\right]$$
$$= (a)(a)$$
$$= a^2$$

This can be extended to all positive integers n by repeated application of the product property.

Hence,

$$\lim_{x \to a} x^n = a^n$$

and therefore we can use substitution to evaluate limits of power functions.

The next three examples illustrate other types of functions for which substitution can be used to evaluate limits.

Example 1. Evaluate

$$\lim_{x \to a} (2x^3 - 7x^2 + 5x)$$

by using the properties of limits.

Solution. Apply the sum and constant multiple properties to obtain

$$\lim_{x \to a} (2x^3 - 7x^2 + 5x) = \lim_{x \to a} (2x^3) + \lim_{x \to a} (-7x^2) + \lim_{x \to a} (5x)$$

$$= 2 \lim_{x \to a} x^3 - 7 \lim_{x \to a} x^2 + 5 \lim_{x \to a} x$$

$$= 2a^3 - 7a^2 + 5a \quad \text{(limit of power functions)} \qquad \square$$

We have thus shown that the limit in Example 1 can be evaluated by substitution. The function

$$f(x) = 2x^3 - 7x^2 + 5x$$

is an example of a **polynomial function**—that is, a function that is a sum of terms of the form

$$kx^n$$

where n is a positive integer or zero and k is a real number. The method of solution of Example 1 can be applied to any polynomial function. Hence, the limit of any polynomial function can be evaluated by substitution. For example,

$$\lim_{x \to -1} (3x^5 - 7x) = 3(-1)^5 - 7(-1)$$

$$= 4$$

Example 2. Use the properties of limits to evaluate

$$\lim_{x \to a} \frac{5x^3 + 7x - 2}{3x^2 - 12}$$

if $a \neq 2$ and $a \neq -2$.

Solution. By the substitution property for polynomial functions,

$$\lim_{x \to a} (5x^3 + 7x - 2) = 5a^3 + 7a - 2$$

and

$$\lim_{x \to a} (3x^2 - 12) = 3a^2 - 12.$$

Note that $3a^2 - 12 \neq 0$, since $a \neq 2$ and $a \neq -2$. Thus, by the quotient property for limits,

$$\lim_{x \to a} \frac{5x^3 + 7x - 2}{3x^2 - 12} = \frac{\lim_{x \to a} (5x^3 + 7x - 2)}{\lim_{x \to a} (3x^2 - 12)}$$

$$= \frac{5a^3 + 7a - 2}{3a^2 - 12} \qquad \square$$

We have thus shown that the limit in Example 2 can be evaluated by substitution **for all numbers** a **for which the denominator is non-zero**. The function

$$f(x) = \frac{5x^3 + 7x - 2}{3x^2 - 12}$$

is an example of a **rational function**—that is, a function that is a quotient of two polynomials. The method of solution of Example 2 can be applied to any rational function. Hence, for any rational function

$$f(x) = \frac{p(x)}{q(x)}$$

$\lim_{x \to a} f(x)$ can be evaluated by substitution, provided that $q(a) \neq 0$ (so that $f(a)$ is defined). For example,

$$\lim_{x \to 3} \frac{x^3 - 21}{2x + 3} = \frac{3^3 - 21}{2(3) + 3}$$

$$= \frac{6}{9}$$

$$= \frac{2}{3}$$

Example 3. Use the properties of limits to evaluate

$$\lim_{x \to a} \sqrt{\frac{x - 1}{3x^2 + 4}}$$

if $a \geq 1$.

Solution. By the substitution property for rational functions,

$$\lim_{x \to a} \frac{x - 1}{3x^2 + 4} = \frac{a - 1}{3a^2 + 4}$$

since $3a^2 + 4 \neq 0$. Since $a \geq 1$, it follows that

$$\frac{a - 1}{3a^2 + 4} \geq 0$$

Hence, by the nth root property,

$$\lim_{x \to a} \sqrt{\frac{x - 1}{3x^2 + 4}} = \sqrt{\lim_{x \to a} \frac{x - 1}{3x^2 + 4}}$$

$$= \sqrt{\frac{a - 1}{3a^2 + 4}} \qquad \square$$

We have thus shown that the limit in Example 3 can be evaluated by substitution. The function

$$f(x) = \sqrt{\frac{x - 1}{3x^2 + 4}}$$

is an example of an **algebraic function**. By this we mean any function that is defined using roots and the arithmetic operations. Other examples of algebraic functions are

$$f(x) = \sqrt{x + \sqrt{x}} \quad \text{and} \quad f(x) = x^{\frac{1}{3}} \sqrt{x^2 + 4}$$

The method for solving Example 3 can be applied to any algebraic function. Hence for any algebraic function, $\lim_{x \to a} f(x)$ can be evaluated by substitution, provided that $f(a)$ is defined. For example,

$$\lim_{x \to 5} \sqrt{\frac{x + 11}{x - 4}} = \sqrt{\frac{5 + 11}{5 - 4}}$$

$$= \sqrt{16}$$

$$= 4$$

To summarize: for the following types of functions

- polynomial functions
- rational functions
- algebraic functions

we can evaluate $\lim_{x \to a} f(x)$ by substitution:

$$\lim_{x \to a} f(x) = f(a)$$

provided that $f(a)$ is defined.

Note that this result has the geometric interpretation that all functions of the above types are **continuous** at each point of their domain. This means that the graph of the function passes through the point $(a, f(a))$ without a "break."

Exercises 1.5

1. State whether each of the following functions is a polynomial function, a rational function, or an algebraic function.

    a. $x^2 + \pi^2$ **b.** $\sqrt{x^3 + 1}$

    c. $\dfrac{\sqrt{x} + 4}{\sqrt{x} - 4}$ **d.** $\dfrac{x^2 + 4}{x^2 - 4}$

    e. $(x^2 + 2x + 2)^3$ **f.** $(\sqrt{x} + 1)^2$

    g. $\left[\dfrac{x - 2}{x + 1}\right]^3$ **h.** $\left[\dfrac{x^{\frac{1}{2}} + x^{\frac{1}{3}}}{x + 1}\right]^6$

2. Evaluate each limit, using substitution where appropriate.

    a. $\lim_{x \to 2} \dfrac{3x}{x^2 + 2}$ **b.** $\lim_{x \to 3} \sqrt{x^3 + \dfrac{27}{x - 1}}$

    c. $\lim_{x \to -1} (x^4 + x^3 + x^2)$ **d.** $\lim_{x \to 4} \left(\sqrt{x} + \dfrac{1}{\sqrt{x}}\right)^2$

    e. $\lim_{x \to 2\pi} (x^3 + \pi^2 x - 5\pi^3)$ **f.** $\lim_{x \to a} \dfrac{(x + a)^2}{x^2 + a^2}$

    g. $\lim_{x \to 0} (\sqrt{1 + \sqrt{1 + x}})$ **h.** $\lim_{h \to 0} \dfrac{1}{\sqrt{x} + \sqrt{x + h}}$

    i. $\lim_{x \to -3} \sqrt{\dfrac{x - 3}{2x + 4}}$ **j.** $\lim_{x \to -1} \dfrac{2x^3 - 5}{2x^2 + 3}$

    k. $\lim_{x \to 4} (\sqrt{x} + 2)^3$ **l.** $\lim_{\Delta x \to 0} [5(\Delta x)^3 - 3\,\Delta x + 2]$

3. If $\lim\limits_{x \to 2} f(x) = 3$, use the properties of limits to evaluate each limit.

a. $\lim\limits_{x \to 2} [f(x)]^2$

b. $\lim\limits_{x \to 2} \dfrac{x^2 + 5}{f(x)}$

c. $\lim\limits_{x \to 2} \dfrac{[f(x)]^3 - x^3}{f(x) + x}$

d. $\lim\limits_{x \to 2} \sqrt{[f(x)]^2 + x^4}$

e. $\lim\limits_{x \to 2} \left[x^2 f(x) - \dfrac{6}{f(x)} \right]$

f. $\lim\limits_{x \to 2} \sqrt{3f(x) - 2x}$

Problems 1.5

1. Suppose that the function $f(x)$ satisfies the inequality

$$\frac{2}{1 + x^2} \le f(x) \le 2 + x^2$$

for all $x \ne 0$. Evaluate $\lim\limits_{x \to 0} f(x)$ and illustrate graphically.

2. If $\lim\limits_{x \to 0} \dfrac{f(x)}{x} = 1$ and $\lim\limits_{x \to 0} \dfrac{g(x)}{x} = 2$,

evaluate each limit.

a. $\lim\limits_{x \to 0} f(x)$

b. $\lim\limits_{x \to 0} g(x)$

c. $\lim\limits_{x \to 0} \dfrac{f(x)}{g(x)}$

1.6 Limits of Indeterminate Forms

In this section, we consider limits in which the function is undefined at the limiting value of x. For example, the function

$$f(x) = \frac{9 - x^2}{3 - x}$$

is undefined at $x = 3$, and the function

$$g(x) = \frac{\sqrt{1 + 4x} - \sqrt{1 + x}}{x}$$

is undefined at $x = 0$. If we attempt to evaluate the limits

$$\lim_{x \to 3} \frac{9 - x^2}{3 - x} \quad \text{and} \quad \lim_{x \to 0} \frac{\sqrt{1 + 4x} - \sqrt{1 + x}}{x}$$

by substituting $x = 3$ and $x = 0$, respectively, we obtain the result

$$\text{``}\frac{0}{0}\text{''}$$

which has no meaning. We cannot conclude that these limits do not exist, only that they cannot be evaluated by substitution. A quotient that has the property that both the numerator and denominator are zero when the limiting value of x is substituted is said to be **indeterminate of the form** "$\frac{0}{0}$". We use the quotation marks because $\frac{0}{0}$ is not mathematically defined.

Notice that the difference quotient

$$\frac{f(a + h) - f(a)}{h}$$

is indeterminate of the form "$\frac{0}{0}$" when $h = 0$. Because it is interpreted as a rate of change, the limit of the difference quotient as $h \to 0$

$$\lim_{h \to 0} \frac{f(a + h) - f(a)}{h}$$

is of fundamental importance in Calculus, and motivates the study of limits of indeterminate forms.

In order to obtain a clue as to the possible limiting value of

$$f(x) = \frac{9 - x^2}{3 - x}$$

as $x \to 3$, consider this table of values for $f(x)$, where x is close to 3 but not equal to 3.

x	2.9	2.99	2.999	2.9999	3.0001	3.001	3.01	3.1
$\dfrac{9 - x^2}{3 - x}$	5.9	5.999	5.999	5.9999	6.0001	6.001	6.01	6.1

This table suggests that the limiting value is 6. In Example 1 we show that this is the case by rearranging the function algebraically.

Example 1. Evaluate $\lim\limits_{x \to 3} \dfrac{9 - x^2}{3 - x}$ and illustrate the result geometrically.

Solution. The function can be simplified by factoring the numerator to obtain

$$9 - x^2 = (3 - x)(3 + x)$$

Therefore,

$$\frac{9 - x^2}{3 - x} = \frac{(3 - x)(3 + x)}{3 - x}$$
$$= 3 + x \quad \text{where } x \neq 3$$

Since

$$\lim_{x \to 3} (3 + x) = 3 + 3$$
$$= 6$$

by substitution it follows that

$$\lim_{x \to 3} \frac{9 - x^2}{3 - x} = \lim_{x \to 3} (3 + x)$$
$$= 6$$

Thus the limit of the indeterminate form $\dfrac{9 - x^2}{3 - x}$ as $x \to 3$ exists and equals 6.

Because $\dfrac{9 - x^2}{3 - x} = 3 + x$ when $x \ne 3$, the graph of the function

$$f(x) = \frac{9 - x^2}{3 - x}, \text{ where } x \ne 3$$

is the line $y = 3 + x$ with the point $(3, 6)$ deleted. ☐

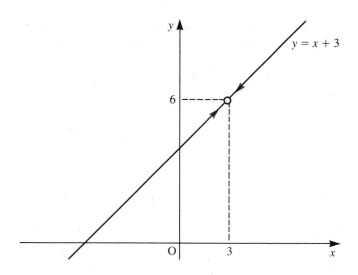

In evaluating the limit of an indeterminate quotient, one should attempt to rearrange the expression so as to eliminate the factor in the denominator that becomes zero on substitution. This was achieved in the previous example by **factoring**. The next example illustrates the technique of **rationalizing** in order to simplify a quotient that includes a difference of radicals.

Example 2. Evaluate

$$\lim_{x \to 0} \frac{\sqrt{1 + 4x} - \sqrt{1 + x}}{x}$$

if it exists.

Solution. This quotient is indeterminate of the form "$\frac{0}{0}$" when we try to substitute $x = 0$.

To rationalize the numerator, multiply both the numerator and denominator by $\sqrt{1 + 4x} + \sqrt{1 + x}$. We obtain

$$\frac{\sqrt{1 + 4x} - \sqrt{1 + x}}{x} = \frac{(\sqrt{1 + 4x} - \sqrt{1 + x})}{x} \cdot \frac{(\sqrt{1 + 4x} + \sqrt{1 + x})}{(\sqrt{1 + 4x} + \sqrt{1 + x})}$$

$$= \frac{(1 + 4x) - (1 + x)}{x(\sqrt{1 + 4x} + \sqrt{1 + x})}$$

$$= \frac{3x}{x(\sqrt{1 + 4x} + \sqrt{1 + x})}$$

$$= \frac{3}{\sqrt{1 + 4x} + \sqrt{1 + x}} \qquad \text{if } x \neq 0$$

Since we have eliminated the factor x from the denominator and the resulting expression is an algebraic function, we can now evaluate the required limit by substituting $x = 0$. Thus

$$\lim_{x \to 0} \left(\frac{\sqrt{1 + 4x} - \sqrt{1 - x}}{x} \right) = \lim_{x \to 0} \left(\frac{3}{\sqrt{1 + 4x} + \sqrt{1 + x}} \right)$$

$$= \frac{3}{\sqrt{1 + 4(0)} + \sqrt{1 + 0}}$$

$$= \frac{3}{2} \qquad \qquad \square$$

For some indeterminate limits, the use of one-sided limits is required.

Example 3. Evaluate the limit if it exists. Illustrate the result graphically.

$$\lim_{x \to 2} \frac{x|x - 2|}{x - 2}$$

Solution. Observe that the quotient is indeterminate of the form "$\frac{0}{0}$" at $x = 2$. In order to simplify this quotient, we have to consider the two cases that result from writing

$$|x - 2| = \begin{cases} x - 2, & \text{if } x > 2 \\ -(x - 2), & \text{if } x < 2 \end{cases}$$

and we have to use one-sided limits.

First, if $x > 2$, then

$$\frac{x|x - 2|}{x - 2} = \frac{x(x - 2)}{x - 2}$$
$$= x$$

Hence the limit from the right is

$$\lim_{x \to 2^+} \frac{x|x - 2|}{x - 2} = \lim_{x \to 2^+} x$$
$$= 2$$

Second, if $x < 2$, then

$$\frac{x|x - 2|}{x - 2} = \frac{-x(x - 2)}{x - 2}$$
$$= -x$$

The limit from the left is

$$\lim_{x \to 2^-} \frac{x|x - 2|}{x - 2} = \lim_{x \to 2^-} (-x)$$
$$= -2$$

Since the one-sided limits are not equal, it follows that

$$\lim_{x \to 2} \frac{x|x - 2|}{x - 2}$$

does not exist. From the calculations above, note that the graph of the function is given by $y = x$ if $x > 2$, and by $y = -x$ if $x < 2$.

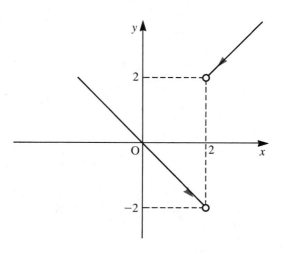

The final example illustrates the use of a **change of variable** to evaluate the limit of an indeterminate quotient.

Example 4. Evaluate $\displaystyle\lim_{x \to 0} \frac{(x + 8)^{\frac{1}{3}} - 2}{x}$ if it exists.

Solution. This quotient is indeterminate of the form "$\frac{0}{0}$" when $x = 0$. In order to eliminate the factor of x in the denominator, introduce a new variable u by letting

$$u = (x + 8)^{\frac{1}{3}}$$

It follows that $u^3 = x + 8$, and therefore

$$x = u^3 - 8$$

If $x \neq 0$ and hence $u \neq 2$, the given function can be expressed in terms of u, resulting in

$$\frac{(x + 8)^{\frac{1}{3}} - 2}{x} = \frac{u - 2}{u^3 - 8}$$

$$= \frac{u - 2}{(u - 2)(u^2 + 2u + 4)}$$

$$= \frac{1}{(u^2 + 2u + 4)}$$

Since $u = (x + 8)^{\frac{1}{3}}$, as $x \to 0$ it follows that $u \to 8^{\frac{1}{3}} = 2$. Thus

$$\lim_{x \to 0} \frac{(x + 8)^{\frac{1}{3}} - 2}{x} = \lim_{u \to 2} \frac{1}{u^2 + 2u + 4}$$

$$= \frac{1}{2^2 + 2(2) + 4} \quad \text{(by substitution)}$$

$$= \frac{1}{12} \qquad\qquad \square$$

In this section, algebraic methods for evaluating limits have been developed. The examples in this section have illustrated four techniques for evaluating the limit of an indeterminate quotient:

- factoring
- rationalizing
- one-sided limits
- change of variable.

Exercises 1.6

1. Evaluate the limit of each indeterminate quotient. Illustrate the result geometrically by sketching the graph of each function.

   a. $\lim_{x \to 2} \dfrac{4 - x^2}{2 - x}$

   b. $\lim_{x \to -2} \dfrac{4 - x^2}{2 + x}$

   c. $\lim_{x \to 1} \dfrac{x^3 - 1}{x - 1}$

   d. $\lim_{x \to -2} \dfrac{x^3 + 2x^2 - 4x - 8}{x + 2}$

   e. $\lim_{x \to -\frac{3}{2}} \dfrac{8x^3 + 27}{2x + 3}$

   f. $\lim_{x \to -1} \dfrac{2x^2 + 5x + 3}{x + 1}$

   g. $\lim_{x \to -\frac{4}{3}} \dfrac{3x^2 + x - 4}{3x + 4}$

   h. $\lim_{x \to 2} \dfrac{2x^3 - 5x^2 + 3x - 2}{2x - 4}$

2. Evaluate the limit of each indeterminate quotient.

   a. $\lim_{x \to 0} \dfrac{\sqrt{1 + x} - 1}{x}$

   b. $\lim_{x \to 0} \dfrac{\sqrt{4 + x} - 2}{x}$

   c. $\lim_{x \to 4} \dfrac{\sqrt{x} - 2}{x - 4}$

   d. $\lim_{x \to 0} \dfrac{\sqrt{4 - x} - \sqrt{4 + x}}{x}$

   e. $\lim_{x \to 1} \dfrac{\sqrt{5 - x} - \sqrt{3 + x}}{x - 1}$

   f. $\lim_{x \to 9} \dfrac{x - 9}{\sqrt{x} - 3}$

   g. $\lim_{x \to 0} \dfrac{\sqrt{x + 1} - \sqrt{2x + 1}}{\sqrt{3x + 4} - \sqrt{2x + 4}}$

   h. $\lim_{x \to \frac{1}{4}} \dfrac{1 - 4x}{\sqrt{x} - 2x}$

3. By using one-sided limits determine whether the limit of each indeterminate quotient exists. Illustrate the results geometrically by sketching the graph of each function.

   a. $\lim_{x \to 3} \dfrac{|x - 3|}{x - 3}$

   b. $\lim_{x \to \frac{5}{2}} \dfrac{(x - 1)|2x - 5|}{2x - 5}$

   c. $\lim_{x \to 1} \dfrac{x^2 + x - 2}{|x - 1|}$

   d. $\lim_{x \to -2} \dfrac{(x + 2)^3}{|x + 2|}$

4. Evaluate the limit

$$\lim_{x \to 1} \dfrac{\sqrt{x} - 1}{x - 1}$$

   a. by rationalizing
   b. by making the change of variable $u = \sqrt{x}$.

5. Evaluate each limit by making the suggested change of variable.

a. $\lim\limits_{x \to 27} \dfrac{x^{\frac{1}{3}} - 3}{x - 27}$, $\quad u = x^{\frac{1}{3}}$

b. $\lim\limits_{x \to 1} \dfrac{x^{\frac{1}{6}} - 1}{x - 1}$, $\quad u = x^{\frac{1}{6}}$

c. $\lim\limits_{x \to 4} \dfrac{\sqrt{x} - 2}{\sqrt{x^3} - 8}$, $\quad u = \sqrt{x}$

d. $\lim\limits_{x \to 1} \dfrac{x^{\frac{1}{6}} - 1}{x^{\frac{1}{3}} - 1}$, $\quad u = x^{\frac{1}{6}}$

6. Evaluate the limit of each difference quotient. In each case, interpret the limit as the slope of the tangent line to a curve at a specific point.

a. $\lim\limits_{h \to 0} \dfrac{(2 + h)^2 - 4}{h}$

b. $\lim\limits_{h \to 0} \dfrac{\dfrac{1}{3 + h} - \dfrac{1}{3}}{h}$

c. $\lim\limits_{h \to 0} \dfrac{\sqrt{4 + h} - 2}{h}$

d. $\lim\limits_{h \to 0} \dfrac{\dfrac{1}{\sqrt{9 + h}} - \dfrac{1}{3}}{h}$

e. $\lim\limits_{h \to 0} \dfrac{(8 + h)^{\frac{1}{3}} - 2}{h}$

f. $\lim\limits_{h \to 0} \dfrac{(1 + h)^{\frac{1}{6}} - 1}{h}$

7. Evaluate each limit, if it exists, using any appropriate technique.

a. $\lim\limits_{u \to 4} \dfrac{u^2 - 16}{u^3 - 64}$

b. $\lim\limits_{t \to -2} \dfrac{t + 2}{\sqrt{6 + t} - \sqrt{2 - t}}$

c. $\lim\limits_{x \to 4} \dfrac{x^2 - 5}{x^2 - 5x + 6}$

d. $\lim\limits_{x \to -3} \sqrt{\dfrac{x + 3}{x^3 + 27}}$

e. $\lim\limits_{x \to 1} \dfrac{x^3 + x^2 - 5x + 3}{x^2 - 2x + 1}$

f. $\lim\limits_{t \to 4^-} \dfrac{2 - \sqrt{t}}{\sqrt{4 - t}}$

g. $\lim\limits_{x \to -1} \dfrac{x^2 + x}{|x + 1|}$

h. $\lim\limits_{u \to 1} \dfrac{\sqrt{1 + u} - \sqrt{1 + u^2}}{u - 1}$

i. $\lim\limits_{v \to 2} \dfrac{\sqrt{2v} - \sqrt{3 - v}}{\sqrt{2v} + \sqrt{3 - v}}$

j. $\lim\limits_{x \to 0} \dfrac{(1 + 2x)^{\frac{1}{3}} - 1}{x}$

k. $\lim\limits_{t \to -1} \dfrac{t^3 - 2t}{t - 1}$

l. $\lim\limits_{x \to 0} \dfrac{x^2 - 3x}{4x^3 + 6x}$

m. $\lim\limits_{y \to 3} \dfrac{\dfrac{1}{y} - \dfrac{1}{3}}{y - 3}$

n. $\lim\limits_{x \to 3^+} x\sqrt{x - 3}$

o. $\lim\limits_{x \to 3} \dfrac{6x^3 - 5x^2 + 3}{2x^3 + 4x - 7}$

p. $\lim\limits_{x \to 9} \dfrac{x - 4\sqrt{x} + 3}{\sqrt{x} - 3}$

q. $\lim\limits_{x \to 1} \left(\dfrac{1}{x - 1}\right)\left(\dfrac{1}{x + 3} - \dfrac{2}{3x + 5}\right)$

r. $\lim\limits_{t \to 0} \dfrac{|t^3|}{t^3}$

Problems 1.6

1. Does $\lim\limits_{x \to 1} \dfrac{x^2 + |x - 1| - 1}{|x - 1|}$ exist? Illustrate your result by sketching the graph of the function.

2. For what value of A does this limit exist?

$$\lim_{x \to 1} \frac{x^2 + Ax - 3}{x - 1}$$

3. For what values of A and B is this statement correct?

$$\lim_{x \to 0} \frac{\sqrt{Ax + B} - 3}{x} = 1$$

4. Consider the function $f(x) = \dfrac{2x - 2}{x^2 + x - 2}$.

    a. For what values of x is f discontinuous?

    b. At each point where f is discontinuous, determine the limit of $f(x)$ if it exists.

5. Evaluate

$$\lim_{x \to a} \frac{x^3 - a^3}{x - a}$$

for any number a. Interpret this limit in terms of the tangent line to the curve $y = x^3$.

6. Evaluate

$$\lim_{x \to a} \frac{x^{\frac{1}{3}} - a^{\frac{1}{3}}}{x - a}$$

for any number a. Interpret this limit in terms of the tangent line to the curve $y = x^{\frac{1}{3}}$.

7. Evaluate each limit, where n is a positive integer and a is any number.

    a. $\lim\limits_{x \to a} \dfrac{x^n - a^n}{x - a}$
        b. $\lim\limits_{x \to a} \dfrac{x^{\frac{1}{n}} - a^{\frac{1}{n}}}{x - a}$

1.7 The Derivative

In sections 1.2 and 1.3 we discussed the limiting value of the difference quotient

$$\lim_{h \to 0} \frac{\Delta y}{\Delta x} = \lim_{h \to 0} \frac{f(a + h) - f(a)}{h}$$

as the increment $\Delta x = h$ tends to zero. This limit was interpreted both as the slope of the tangent line to the curve $y = f(x)$ at the point $(a, f(a))$ and as the rate of change of y with respect to x.

Since this limit plays a central role in Calculus, it is given a name and a concise notation. This limit is called **the derivative of** $f(x)$ **at** a, is denoted by $f'(a)$, and read as "f prime of a."

The **derivative of** $f(x)$ **at** a, denoted by $f'(a)$, is defined by

$$f'(a) = \lim_{h \to 0} \frac{f(a + h) - f(a)}{h}$$

provided that this limit exists.

Note that the difference quotient is indeterminate of the form "$\frac{0}{0}$" as $h \to 0$. It is thus necessary to rearrange the difference quotient so that the limit is of a form that can be evaluated by substitution (as in section 1.6).

We now illustrate this definition with an example. The calculation in Example 1 is similar to the calculations of slopes and rates of change that were done in sections 1.2 and 1.3.

Example 1. Find the derivative of $f(x) = x^2$ at $x = -2$.

Solution. The difference quotient at $x = -2$ is

$$\frac{f(-2 + h) - f(-2)}{h} = \frac{(-2 + h)^2 - (-2)^2}{h}$$

$$= \frac{-4h + h^2}{h}$$

$$= -4 + h$$

Thus, by the definition of the derivative,

$$f'(-2) = \lim_{h \to 0} \frac{f(-2 + h) - f(-2)}{h}$$

$$= \lim_{h \to 0} (-4 + h)$$

$$= -4 + 0$$

$$= -4 \qquad \qquad \square$$

Some of the concepts that were studied in sections 1.2 and 1.3 can now be restated in terms of derivatives:

- The slope m of the graph of $y = f(x)$ at the point $(a, f(a))$ is

$$m = f'(a)$$

- If $s(t)$ is the position of a moving object, then the velocity of the object at time $t = t_0$ is

$$v(t_0) = s'(t_0)$$

- In general, $f'(a)$ is the rate of change of the function $y = f(x)$ with respect to x, when $x = a$.

In many applications of Calculus, it is not sufficient to calculate the derivative at a specific value of x (or t), as in Example 1. One needs to know the derivative **at an arbitrary value of the independent variable**. For example, consider a baseball that is hit vertically upwards. Its height at time t is given by the function $s(t)$. The maximum height is attained when the (instantaneous) velocity is zero. (If the velocity were not zero at the highest point, the ball would continue to travel upwards.) To determine when this occurs, one would find the velocity $v(t) = s'(t)$ at an arbitrary time t, and then solve the equation $v(t) = 0$ for t.

The next example illustrates the efficiency of calculating the derivative at an arbitrary value of x instead of at specific values.

Example 2.

a. Find the derivative of $f(x) = x^2$ at an arbitrary value of x.
b. Calculate the slope of the tangent line to the parabola $y = x^2$ at $x = -2$, $x = 0$, and $x = 2$.

Solution.
a. Form the difference quotient at an arbitrary value of x.

$$\frac{f(x + h) - f(x)}{h} = \frac{(x + h)^2 - x^2}{h}$$
$$= \frac{2xh + h^2}{h}$$
$$= 2x + h$$

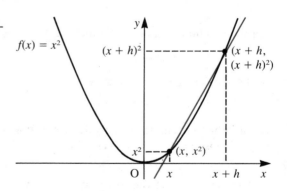

By the definition of the derivative,

$$f'(x) = \lim_{h \to 0} \frac{f(x + h) - f(x)}{h}$$
$$= \lim_{h \to 0} (2x + h)$$
$$= 2x$$

Note that x is treated as a constant when the limit is evaluated as $h \to 0$.

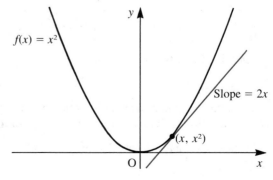

b. The required slopes of the tangent lines of $y = x^2$ are obtained by evaluating the derivative $f'(x) = 2x$ at the given x values. We obtain the following slopes:

$$f'(-2) = -4$$
$$f'(0) = 0$$
$$f'(2) = 4.$$

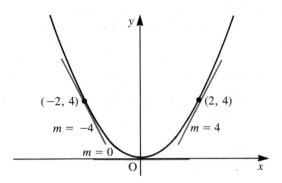

For the function f defined in Example 2 by

$$f(x) = x^2$$

we have calculated the derivative as

$$f'(x) = 2x$$

for an arbitrary number x. This defines **a new function** called **the derivative of** f, denoted by f', whose value at x is $f'(x) = 2x$.

The **derivative of the function** $f : x \to f(x)$ is the function $f' : x \to f'(x)$ where

$$f'(x) = \lim_{h \to 0} \frac{f(x + h) - f(x)}{h}$$

provided that this limit exists.

One should keep in mind the distinction between **the derivative of f at** a, which is the **number** $f'(a)$, and **the derivative of** f, which is the **function** f'.

The next example of calculating a derivative requires the technique of rationalizing from section 1.6.

Example 3. Find the derivative f' of the function f, where

$$f(x) = \sqrt{x}, \qquad x > 0$$

Solution. Form the difference quotient at an arbitrary value of x, and simplify.

$$
\begin{aligned}
\frac{f(x + h) - f(x)}{h} &= \frac{\sqrt{x + h} - \sqrt{x}}{h} \\
&= \frac{(\sqrt{x + h} - \sqrt{x})(\sqrt{x + h} + \sqrt{x})}{h(\sqrt{x + h} + \sqrt{x})} \\
&= \frac{(x + h) - x}{h(\sqrt{x + h} + \sqrt{x})} \\
&= \frac{1}{\sqrt{x + h} + \sqrt{x}}, \qquad h \neq 0
\end{aligned}
$$

By the definition of the derivative,

$$
\begin{aligned}
f'(x) &= \lim_{h \to 0} \frac{f(x + h) - f(x)}{h} \\
&= \lim_{h \to 0} \frac{1}{\sqrt{x + h} + \sqrt{x}} \\
&= \frac{1}{\sqrt{x + 0} + \sqrt{x}} \\
&= \frac{1}{2\sqrt{x}}
\end{aligned}
$$

Thus the derivative f' is given by $f'(x) = \dfrac{1}{2\sqrt{x}}$, for $x > 0$. $\qquad\square$

So far we have used the prime notation (f') for the derivative of a function f. There is an alternative notation, which was introduced by Leibniz.

$$\text{If } y = f(x), \text{ we write } \frac{dy}{dx} = f'(x).$$

The symbol $\dfrac{dy}{dx}$ for the derivative is read "dee y by dee x." As an illustration, in Example 2 we showed that

$$\text{if } y = x^2, \text{ then } \frac{dy}{dx} = 2x$$

and in Example 3 we showed that

$$\text{if } y = \sqrt{x}, \text{ then } \frac{dy}{dx} = \frac{1}{2\sqrt{x}}.$$

The Leibniz notation has the advantage that it reminds one of the process by which the derivative is obtained—namely, as the limit of the difference quotient.

$$\frac{dy}{dx} = \lim_{\Delta x \to 0} \frac{\Delta y}{\Delta x}$$

It is important to realize that $\frac{dy}{dx}$ is **a single symbol** for the derivative of $y = f(x)$ and is **not a quotient**, unlike $\frac{\Delta y}{\Delta x}$, which is the quotient of two increments. The Leibniz notation is also convenient in that certain fundamental formulas, which will be developed in Chapter 2, are easier to remember and use when the derivatives are written in this notation.

The advantages of the prime notation are that it is more concise (one can write y' instead of $\frac{dy}{dx}$) and that it is convenient for expressing the numerical value of the derivative at a particular point, for example, $f'(2)$.

It is often helpful to think of the process of finding the derivative of a function as an operation that is performed on a function f to produce a new function, the derivative f'. From this point of view, the derivatives that were calculated in Examples 2 and 3 would be written as

$$\frac{d}{dx}(x^2) = 2x \quad \text{and} \quad \frac{d}{dx}(\sqrt{x}) = \frac{1}{2\sqrt{x}}$$

We think of $\frac{d}{dx}$ as the "derivative operator." It is not written by itself but always as acting on a function. The derivative operator can also be written as D_x; for example,

$$D_x(x^2) = 2x$$

If the independent variable is t, we would write

$$\frac{d}{dt}(t^2) = 2t \quad \text{or} \quad D_t(t^2) = 2t$$

Finally, note that the derivative of a function does not necessarily exist at all points. For example, consider the function

$$f(x) = |x|$$

at $x = 0$. The graph consists of two straight lines that meet at the origin. Observe that any secant line OP_1 drawn to the right has slope $+1$, whereas any secant line OP_2 drawn

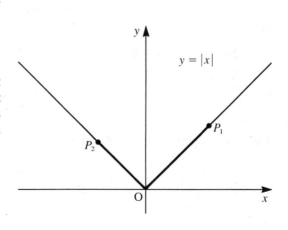

to the left has slope -1.

In this situation there are two limiting slopes, and hence the graph does not have a tangent line at $x = 0$. This analysis suggests that $f'(0)$ does not exist. This can be verified by using the definition of the derivative at $x = 0$ (see Problem 6).

In general, if the graph of a function $y = f(x)$ has a "corner" or "cusp" at a point $P(a, f(a))$, then the graph does not have a tangent line at P, and the derivative at that point, $f'(a)$, does not exist.

We have now introduced one of the main concepts of Calculus—the derivative of a function. The properties and applications of derivatives form one main branch of Calculus, called **differential Calculus**. We shall study this topic, which could be called the mathematics of change, in Chapters 2 to 6. In Chapters 7 and 8, we shall turn to anti-derivatives and the problem of areas and introduce the main ideas of **integral Calculus**.

Exercises 1.7

1. For each function, find the derivative $f'(a)$ for the given value of a.

a. $f(x) = x^2$; $a = 1$

b. $f(x) = x^2$; $a = -2$

c. $f(x) = 2 - x^2$; $a = 2$

d. $f(x) = 2 - x^2$; $a = 0$

e. $f(x) = \sqrt{x + 1}$; $a = 0$

f. $f(x) = \sqrt{x + 1}$; $a = 3$

2. Find the derivative $f'(x)$ of each function.

a. $f(x) = 4x^2$

b. $f(x) = x^2 + 3x$

c. $f(x) = 5x - 3$

d. $f(x) = \dfrac{3}{x + 2}$

e. $f(x) = (2 - x)^2$

f. $f(x) = -3x^2 + 2x + 5$

g. $f(x) = \sqrt{3x + 2}$

h. $f(x) = \dfrac{1}{\sqrt{x}}$

i. $f(x) = \sqrt{x^2 + 1}$

j. $f(x) = \dfrac{1}{x^2}$

3. In each case, find the derivative $\dfrac{dy}{dx}$.

a. $y = -3x^2$

b. $y = (x + 1)(x + 2)$

c. $y = 6 - 7x$

d. $y = \dfrac{5}{3 - 7x}$

e. $y = \dfrac{x + 1}{x - 1}$

f. $y = \sqrt{3 - 11x}$

g. $y = \dfrac{4}{x^2 + 3}$

h. $y = x + \dfrac{1}{x}$

4. Answer the following.

    a. Find the derivative of each of the following functions:
      (i) $f(x) = x^3$ (ii) $f(x) = x^4$
    b. In Example 2, we showed that the derivative of $f(x) = x^2$ is $f'(x) = 2x$. Referring to part (a), can you see a pattern developing?
    c. Use the pattern of part (b) to guess the derivative of $f(x) = x^{39}$.
    d. Guess a formula for the derivative of $f(x) = x^n$, where n is a positive integer.

5. Sketch the graph of $f(x) = 2x^2 - 4x$ and find the slope of the tangent line when $x = 0$, $x = 1$, and $x = 2$. Include the tangent lines on the sketch.

6. An object moves in a straight line with its position at time t seconds given by

$$s(t) = 8t - t^2$$

where s is measured in metres. Find the velocity when $t = 2$, $t = 4$, and $t = 6$.

7. Consider the parabola $y = 5x - x^2$. Determine at what point(s) the slope of the tangent line has the given value. Draw a sketch to illustrate the results.

    a. 1   **b.** 0   **c.** -1

8. The distance of a dragster from the starting line after t seconds is

$$s(t) = 3t^2 + 10t$$

where s is measured in metres. Determine when its velocity is 40 m/s.

9. For any constant function

$$f(x) = C$$

the graph is a horizontal line, and hence the slope is 0. This suggests that the derivative is

$$f'(x) = 0$$

Verify this by using the definition of the derivative.

10. Consider any straight line function

$$f(x) = mx + b$$

where m and b are constants. Since the tangent line coincides with the graph, its slope is constant and equals m. Hence, the derivative should be

$$f'(x) = m.$$

Verify this by using the definition of the derivative.

11. Often when a new product is marketed, the sales initially grow rapidly, and then level off with time. For a certain product, this situation can be modelled by the equation

$$S(t) = 1000 - \frac{1000}{t + 1}$$

where t is time in months, and $S(t)$ represents sales.

   a. Find the number of sales and the rate of change of sales at the end of the first month and at the end of the second year.
   b. Referring to part (a), discuss the difference in the results in the two cases.

12. Sketch the graph of the function $f(x) = 2 + |x - 3|$ and use it to find $f'(2)$ and $f'(4)$.

13. Sketch the graph of a function that satisfies all of the given conditions.

   a. $f'(x) > 0$ if $x > 1$, $f'(x) < 0$ if $x < 1$, $f'(1) = 0$
   b. $f'(x) = 2$ if $x > 0$, $f'(x) = -1$ if $x < 0$, $f(0) = -1$

Problems 1.7

1. The flight path of a spacecraft is represented by the parabola $y = x^2$. If the engine is shut down at the point $P(a, a^2)$, the spaceship will fly off along the tangent line at P. If the spaceship is moving from left to right, at what point should the engine be shut down in order for it to reach the point $(4, 7)$?

2. Find the slope of the tangent line to the curve

$$\frac{1}{x} + \frac{1}{y} = 1$$

   at the point $(2, 2)$.

3. **a.** By sketching the graph of a typical function $f(x)$ and a secant line at the point $(a, f(a))$, verify that

$$\lim_{x \to a} \frac{f(x) - f(a)}{x - a} = f'(a)$$

   b. If $\lim_{x \to \pi} \frac{f(x)}{x - \pi} = 3$ and $f(x)$ is continuous at π, what can be said about $f(\pi)$ and $f'(\pi)$?

4. If $f(a) = 0$ and $f'(a) = 6$, find $\lim_{h \to 0} \frac{f(a + h)}{2h}$.

5. Consider the nearest-integer function

$$f(x) = \{x\}$$

where $\{x\}$ is defined to be the distance of x from the nearest integer (for example $\{2.7\} = 0.3$ and $\{-5.4\} = 0.4$).

a. Sketch the graph of $f(x)$.
b. At what points (if any) is $f(x)$ discontinuous?
c. At what points (if any) does $f'(x)$ not exist?

6. a. For the function $f(x) = |x|$, show that $f'(0)$ does not exist by evaluating the one-sided limits of the difference quotient at $x = 0$:

$$\lim_{h \to 0^+} \frac{f(0 + h) - f(0)}{h} \quad \text{and} \quad \lim_{h \to 0^-} \frac{f(0 + h) - f(0)}{h}$$

b. Repeat part (a) for the function $f(x) = x|x|$ and show that $f'(0)$ does exist. What is its value?
c. Sketch the graph of the function in part (b), and show how the conclusion in part (b) can be reached graphically.

Review Exercises

1. Consider the graph of the function $f(x) = \frac{1}{2}x^2$.

a. Find the slope of the secant line that joins the points on the graph given by
   (i) $x = 1$ and $x = 2$
   (ii) $x = 1$ and $x = 1.1$
   (iii) $x = 1$ and $x = 1.01$
b. Find, in simplified form, the slope of the secant line that joins the points on the graph given by $x = 1$ and $x = 1 + h$.
c. Find the slope of the tangent line at $x = 1$.

2. The height (in metres) of a model rocket t seconds after launching is given by

$$h(t) = 3t^2$$

until the fuel runs out after 20 s.

a. Find the average velocity of the rocket during each of the first four seconds.
b. Find (in simplified form) the average velocity during an interval of time Δt starting at $t = 2$, $t = 6$, and $t = 18$.
c. Using the results of part (b), find the velocity at times $t = 2$, $t = 6$, and $t = 18$.

3. After t minutes of growth, a certain bacterial culture has a mass in grams of $M(t) = t^2$.

a. How much does it grow during the time interval $2 \le t \le 2.01$?
b. What is its average rate of growth during the time interval $2 \le t \le 2.01$?
c. What is its rate of growth when $t = 2$?

4. For each position function $s(t)$, find and simplify the average velocity $\dfrac{\Delta s}{\Delta t}$ at an arbitrary time t; then find the velocity $v(t)$.

a. $s(t) = 7t + 3$

b. $s(t) = 3t^2 - 2t$

c. $s(t) = 10 - \dfrac{3}{t + 1}$

d. $s(t) = \sqrt{9 + t}$

5. In each of the following cases, use a calculator to construct a table of nearby values and thus approximate the limit. Then evaluate the limit, using one of the algebraic methods discussed in the text.

a. $\displaystyle\lim_{x \to 5} \dfrac{x - 5}{x^2 - 25}$

b. $\displaystyle\lim_{x \to 3} \dfrac{\sqrt{x} - \sqrt{3}}{x - 3}$

c. $\displaystyle\lim_{x \to 0} \dfrac{2 + x^2}{1 + (1000x)^2}$

d. $\displaystyle\lim_{x \to 2} \dfrac{x^3 + x - 10}{x - 2}$

6. Evaluate each limit if it exists.

a. $\displaystyle\lim_{x \to -1} \dfrac{x^3 + x^2}{x + 1}$

b. $\displaystyle\lim_{x \to 3} \sqrt{\dfrac{x + 2}{x - 2}}$

c. $\displaystyle\lim_{x \to 2} \dfrac{x^3 - 3x^2 - 4x + 12}{x^3 - 2x^2 - x + 2}$

d. $\displaystyle\lim_{x \to 4} \left[\dfrac{4x^2 + \sqrt{x} + 6}{x - 2} \right]^{\frac{1}{3}}$

e. $\displaystyle\lim_{b \to 0} \dfrac{\sqrt{a + b} - \sqrt{a}}{b}$

f. $\displaystyle\lim_{x \to 0} \dfrac{x^2 + 3x}{|x|}$

g. $\displaystyle\lim_{x \to 2} \dfrac{x^2 - 4}{x^3 - 8}$

h. $\displaystyle\lim_{x \to 2} \dfrac{1}{\dfrac{1}{2} + \dfrac{1}{x}}$

i. $\displaystyle\lim_{x \to \frac{1}{4}} \dfrac{4x - 1}{\dfrac{1}{\sqrt{x}} - 2}$

j. $\displaystyle\lim_{x \to 1} \dfrac{\sqrt{1 + 4x} - \sqrt{2 + 3x}}{x^3 - 1}$

7. Sketch the graph of each function, and use it to determine whether the function is continuous. Evaluate the one-sided limits at the points where the function is discontinuous.

a. $f(x) = \begin{cases} 1 - 2x, & \text{if } x \le 2 \\ 5 - x, & \text{if } x > 2 \end{cases}$

b. $f(x) = \begin{cases} 1 - 2x, & \text{if } x \le 2 \\ 4 - x, & \text{if } x > 2 \end{cases}$

c. $f(x) = \begin{cases} 5 - x^2, & \text{if } x < 1 \\ 3, & \text{if } x \ge 1 \end{cases}$

d. $f(x) = \dfrac{x^2 + x}{|x|}$

8. Evaluate the limit of each difference quotient. In each case interpret the limit as the slope of the tangent line to a curve at a specific point.

a. $\displaystyle\lim_{h \to 0} \dfrac{(5 + h)^2 - 25}{h}$

b. $\displaystyle\lim_{h \to 0} \dfrac{\sqrt{3 + h} - \sqrt{3}}{h}$

c. $\displaystyle\lim_{h \to 0} \dfrac{\dfrac{4}{2 + h} - 2}{h}$

d. $\displaystyle\lim_{h \to 0} \dfrac{(1 + h)^{\frac{1}{3}} - 1}{h}$

9. Find the derivative $f'(x)$ of each function.

a. $f(x) = (1 - 2x)^2$

b. $f(x) = \dfrac{5}{x + 5}$

c. $f(x) = \sqrt{3 - 5x}$

d. $f(x) = 3 - 5x$

e. $f(x) = x(1 - x)$

f. $f(x) = \pi x^2$

g. $f(x) = \dfrac{1}{1 - \dfrac{x}{\pi}}$

h. $f(x) = \dfrac{1}{x(1 - x)}$

10. A speeding driver, trying to negotiate the curve $y = \frac{1}{8}x^2 + 2$, leaves the road at the point $\left(2, \frac{5}{2}\right)$, travelling in a straight line in the direction of the tangent. Will the driver hit a tree located at the point $(4, 8)$? Illustrate graphically.

11. The function

$$I(t) = 3\left[1 - \frac{|t - 1|}{t - 1}\right]$$

models the current flowing in an electrical circuit at time t. By sketching the graph, determine at what time the switch is opened.

12. The function $p(t)$ describes the production of unleaded gasoline in a refinery, in thousands of litres, where the time t is measured in days.

a. Evaluate $\lim\limits_{t \to 1} p(t)$.

b. Evaluate $\lim\limits_{t \to 3^-} p(t)$ and $\lim\limits_{t \to 3^+} p(t)$.

c. When was the refinery shut down for repairs? When did production begin again?

d. At what times is the production function $p(t)$ discontinuous?

e. At what time was the production highest? What was the rate of change of production at this time?

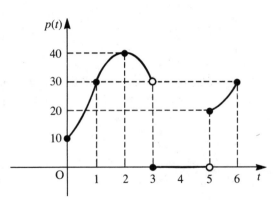

13. Suppose that at time t (in weeks) the mass (in kilograms) of a calf is modelled by the function

$$M(t) = 10 + t + \frac{1}{10}t^2,$$

where $0 \le t \le 10$

a. Find $M'(t)$.

b. Calculate each quantity and explain its meaning in words.
  (i) $M(0)$ (ii) $M'(0)$ (iii) $M'(3)$ (iv) $M(7)$

c. Draw a rough sketch of the graph of $M(t)$ and use it to help you make a general statement about the growth rate of the calf during the ten-week interval.

14. Consider the graph of the function $f(x)$.

a. For what numbers a does $\lim_{x \to a} f(x)$ not exist?

b. At which x values is $f(x)$ discontinuous?

c. At which x values does the graph not have a tangent line?

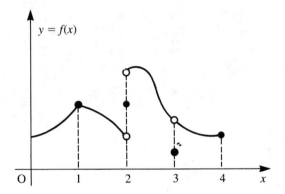

15. Consider the graph of the function $f(x)$.

a. Make a table to describe the derivative $f'(x)$ at the points $x_1, \ldots, x_6$. State whether $f'(x)$ is positive ($+$), negative ($-$), or zero, or whether the derivative does not exist (NE).

b. Use the results of part (a) and the graph of $f(x)$ to draw a rough sketch of the graph of $f'(x)$.

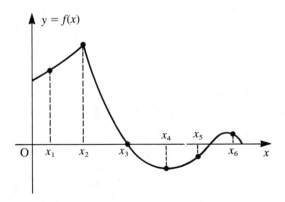

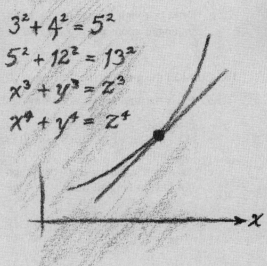

$$3^2 + 4^2 = 5^2$$
$$5^2 + 12^2 = 13^2$$
$$x^3 + y^3 = z^3$$
$$x^4 + y^4 = z^4$$

Pierre de Fermat *(1601–1665), one of the great mathematicians of the seventeenth century, was a jurist and a parliamentary counsellor to the king in the French town of Toulouse. He discovered a method for drawing tangents to curves and for finding maxima and minima (the elements of the Differential Calculus). In 1924 a letter written by Isaac Newton was discovered, wherein Newton acknowledged that his own early ideas came from Fermat's work. Jointly with Pascal, Fermat established the basics of the theory of probability, and (with Descartes) he was a founder of analytic geometry. One of the most famous problems in mathematics is "Fermat's Last Theorem":*

For integer $n > 2$, $x^n + y^n = z^n$ has no integer solutions x, y, z.

Of this theorem Fermat wrote in the margin of a book, "I have found a truly wonderful proof which this margin is too narrow to contain." Although all the great mathematicians tried hard, it remains unsolved to this day!

Differentiation

We have seen that derivatives of functions are of practical interest because they represent rates of change. In section 1.7 we calculated the derivatives of simple functions such as x^2, x^3, and $\sqrt{x}$ by using the definition of the derivative

$$f'(x) = \lim_{h \to 0} \frac{f(x + h) - f(x)}{h}$$

and the properties of limits.

Suppose, however, that we need to find the derivatives of more complicated functions such as

$$f(x) = \frac{2x^3 + x + 7}{x^2 - 3x + 5} \quad \text{or} \quad f(x) = \sqrt{1 + \sqrt{x}}$$

The thought of calculating the derivatives of these functions using the definition is not very inviting (try them!), and so we have an incentive to develop systematic rules that will make derivative calculations simpler and more direct. The process for calculating derivatives using these systematic rules is called **differentiation**.

2.1 The Power Rule and Polynomial Functions

In this section, we shall develop rules that are helpful in differentiating the simplest type of function, namely **polynomial functions**. Examples of polynomials are

$$f(x) = 2x^3 - 3x^2 + 7 \quad \text{and} \quad g(x) = \pi x^4 + 3x - \sqrt{2}$$

Polynomial functions are simply sums of terms of the form

$$kx^n$$

where n is a positive integer or zero and k is a real number. We shall thus proceed successively to show how to find

- the derivative of a **power function** $f(x) = x^n$, where n is a positive integer
- the derivative of a **constant function** $f(x) = k$
- the derivative of a **constant times a function** $f(x) = kg(x)$
- the derivative of the **sum of two functions** $f(x) = p(x) + q(x)$

In section 1.7 we found that

$$\text{if } f(x) = x^2, \text{ then } f'(x) = 2x$$

and in the exercises in section 1.7 you were asked to show that

$$\text{if } f(x) = x^3, \text{ then } f'(x) = 3x^2$$

and

$$\text{if } f(x) = x^4, \text{ then } f'(x) = 4x^3$$

These examples suggest the following general result.

The Power Rule

If $f(x) = x^n$, where n is a positive integer, then

$$f'(x) = nx^{n-1}$$

In Leibniz notation,

$$\frac{d}{dx}(x^n) = nx^{n-1}$$

For example, if

$$f(x) = x^5$$

then the derivative of f is

$$f'(x) = 5x^4$$

Alternatively, we can write

$$\frac{d}{dx}(x^5) = 5x^4$$

As a second example, if

$$y = t^{10}$$

then the derivative is

$$\frac{dy}{dt} = 10\,t^9$$

Example 1 shows an application of the Power Rule.

Example 1. Find the slope of the tangent line to the graph of $f(x) = x^4$ at the point where $x = 3$.

Solution. The slope of the tangent line to the graph of f at any point is the derivative $f'(x)$. Since $f(x) = x^4$, the Power Rule implies that

$$f'(x) = 4x^3$$

The slope of the tangent line when $x = 3$ is thus

$$\begin{aligned} m &= f'(3) \\ &= 4(3^3) \\ &= 108 \end{aligned}$$

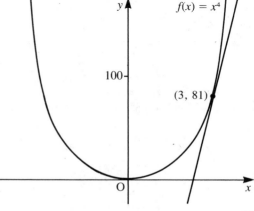

Proof of the Power Rule

The proof uses the factorization of a difference of nth powers:

$$a^n - b^n = (a - b)(a^{n-1} + a^{n-2}b + \ldots + ab^{n-2} + b^{n-1}) \tag{1}$$

This is a consequence of the factor theorem and can be verified by expanding the right side of the identity.

If we use the definition of the derivative, the derivative of $f(x) = x^n$ is

$$\begin{aligned} f'(x) &= \lim_{h \to 0} \frac{f(x+h) - f(x)}{h} \\ &= \lim_{h \to 0} \frac{(x+h)^n - x^n}{h} \\ &= \lim_{h \to 0} \frac{(x + h - x)[(x+h)^{n-1} + (x+h)^{n-2}x + \ldots + (x+h)x^{n-2} + x^{n-1}]}{h} \\ &= \lim_{h \to 0} [(x+h)^{n-1} + (x+h)^{n-2}x + \ldots + (x+h)x^{n-2} + x^{n-1}] \\ &= x^{n-1} + x^{n-1} + \ldots + x^{n-1} \quad \text{(by substituting } h = 0\text{)} \\ &= nx^{n-1} \quad \text{(since there are } n \text{ terms)} \end{aligned}$$

Note that, in reducing the difference quotient, the identity (1) was used with $a = x + h$ and $b = x$. □

Now consider a constant function, for example,

$$f(x) = 4$$

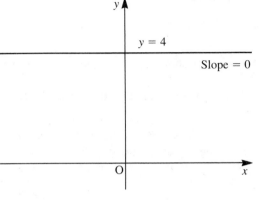

Since the graph of $f(x)$ is a horizontal line, the slope is zero at each point; hence, for all x,

$$f'(x) = 0$$

Alternatively, we can write

$$\frac{d}{dx}(4) = 0$$

The slope is also zero at each point on the graph of any constant function $f(x) = k$, and hence the derivative of any constant function is zero.

Derivative of a Constant Function

$$\frac{d}{dx}(k) = 0, \quad \text{where } k \text{ is a constant}$$

It seems plausible that if the value of one quantity is k times that of another quantity, where k is a constant, then the rate of change of the first quantity should be k times the rate of change of the second quantity.

The Constant Multiple Rule for Differentiation

If $f(x) = kg(x)$, where k is a constant, then

$$f'(x) = kg'(x)$$

In Leibniz notation,

$$\frac{d}{dx}(ky) = k\frac{dy}{dx}$$

For example,

$$\frac{d}{dx}(7x^2) = 7\frac{d}{dx}(x^2)$$
$$= 7(2x)$$
$$= 14x$$

Proof of the Constant Multiple Rule

Let $f(x) = kg(x)$. By the definition of the derivative,

$$f'(x) = \lim_{h \to 0} \frac{f(x + h) - f(x)}{h}$$

$$= \lim_{h \to 0} \frac{kg(x + h) - kg(x)}{h}$$

$$= \lim_{h \to 0} k \left[\frac{g(x + h) - g(x)}{h} \right]$$

$$= k \lim_{h \to 0} \frac{g(x + h) - g(x)}{h} \quad \text{(property of limits)}$$

$$= kg'(x) \qquad\qquad \square$$

Example 2. The distance (in metres) of a dragster from the starting line after t seconds is

$$s = 2t^3, \quad \text{for } 0 \le t \le 4$$

Find its velocity after 3 s.

Solution. The velocity of the dragster at time t is the rate of change of its position function. Therefore

$$v = \frac{ds}{dt}$$

$$= \frac{d}{dt}(2t^3)$$

$$= 2\frac{d}{dt}(t^3) \quad \text{(Constant Multiple Rule)}$$

$$= 2(3t^2) \quad \text{(Power Rule)}$$

$$= 6t^2$$

When $t = 3$,

$$v = 6(3^2)$$

$$= 54$$

Thus, after 3 s, the velocity of the dragster is 54 m/s. $\qquad \square$

A function such as $f(x) = x^2 + x^3$ is the sum of the functions x^2 and x^3. The **Sum Rule** of differentiation states that the derivative of a sum is the sum of the separate derivatives. For this example we have

$$\frac{d}{dx}(x^2 + x^3) = \frac{d}{dx}(x^2) + \frac{d}{dx}(x^3)$$

$$= 2x + 3x^2$$

If $f(x) = p(x) + q(x)$, then

$$f'(x) = p'(x) + q'(x)$$

In Leibniz notation, if u and v are functions of x, then

$$\frac{d}{dx}(u + v) = \frac{du}{dx} + \frac{dv}{dx}$$

Example 3. If $y = 2x^5 - 5x^2$, use the Sum Rule, the Constant Multiple Rule, and the Power Rule to find $\frac{dy}{dx}$.

Solution. Differentiation gives

$$\begin{aligned}
\frac{dy}{dx} &= \frac{d}{dx}(2x^5 - 5x^2) \\
&= \frac{d}{dx}(2x^5) + \frac{d}{dx}(-5x^2) \quad \text{(by the Sum Rule)} \\
&= 2(5x^4) + (-5)(2x) \quad \text{(by the Constant Multiple and Power Rules)} \\
&= 10x^4 - 10x
\end{aligned}$$

After some practice, it will be unnecessary to write all of the intermediate steps when calculating a derivative, as was done in Example 3. One simply applies the rules mentally and writes down the final derivative. In Example 3 it would be acceptable to go directly from

$$y = 2x^5 - 5x^2$$

to

$$\frac{dy}{dx} = 10x^4 - 10x$$

The Sum Rule can also be applied to the sum of any number of functions. Therefore, we are now able to differentiate any polynomial function. This is illustrated in the next example.

Example 4. Find $\frac{dy}{dx}$ if $y = x^4 + \pi x^3 + 6x^2 + 3x - \sqrt{2}$.

Solution. By differentiating each term separately and noting that $\frac{d}{dx}(-\sqrt{2}) = 0$, we obtain

$$\frac{dy}{dx} = 4x^3 + 3\pi x^2 + 12x + 3$$

Note also that π is a constant.

Proof of the Sum Rule

Let

$$f(x) = p(x) + q(x)$$

By the definition of the derivative,

$$f'(x) = \lim_{h \to 0} \frac{f(x + h) - f(x)}{h}$$

$$= \lim_{h \to 0} \frac{[p(x + h) + q(x + h)] - [p(x) + q(x)]}{h}$$

$$= \lim_{h \to 0} \left\{ \frac{[p(x + h) - p(x)]}{h} + \frac{[q(x + h) - q(x)]}{h} \right\}$$

$$= \lim_{h \to 0} \left\{ \frac{p(x + h) - p(x)}{h} \right\} + \lim_{h \to 0} \left\{ \frac{q(x + h) - q(x)}{h} \right\} \quad \text{(sum property of limits)}$$

$$= p'(x) + q'(x)$$

Exercises 2.1

1. Use the definition of the derivative to find $f'(x)$.

a. $f(x) = 3x - 5$ **b.** $f(x) = 2x^2 + x - 7$

c. $f(x) = -x^2 + 4x + 1$ **d.** $f(x) = x^3 - x^2$

e. $f(x) = 2 + 4x^3$ **f.** $f(x) = 3x^4$

2. By using the definition of the derivative, find the slope of the tangent line to each curve at the given point.

a. $y = x^2 - 6x$ at the point $(-1, 7)$

b. $y = -x^2 + 2x - 3$ at the point $(2, -3)$

c. $y = 2x^2 - 4x - 2$ at the point $(1, -4)$

d. $y = 4 - 3x^3$ at the point $(1, 1)$

3. a. Use the Power Rule and the Constant Multiple Rule to differentiate each function.

(i) $f(x) = 3x^5$ (ii) $f(x) = \frac{1}{\pi} x^3$

(iii) $f(t) = \frac{1}{3} t^9$ (iv) $f(x) = (4x)^2$

(v) $f(x) = \left(\frac{x}{2}\right)^4$ (vi) $f(t) = bt^7$, where b is a constant

b. For each function in part (a), find the equation of the tangent line to the graph of the function at the point $(1, f(1))$.

4. Differentiate each polynomial function. Use either the Leibniz notation $\dfrac{dy}{dx}$ or the prime notation $f'(x)$, depending on which is appropriate.

a. $y = x^2 - 4x + 3$

b. $f(x) = 2x^3 - 5x^2 + 4x - 3$

c. $g(m) = 6m^3 - 4m^5$

d. $p = 2q^4 + 5q^2 - 7$

e. $y = \dfrac{1}{5}x^5 + \dfrac{1}{3}x^3 - \dfrac{1}{2}x^2 + 1$

f. $f(x) = (2x - 1)(5 - x)$

g. $y = 3x^8 + x^7 - 7x^3 + 12x^2$

h. $f(t) = t^4 - \pi^4$

i. $s = (\pi t)^3 - 3\pi t$

j. $f(x) = x^2(x^2 - 2x)$

k. $g(x) = 5 - 7(x - 2)(x - 3)$

l. $v(x) = (2 + 5x)^2$

5. Let s represent the position of a moving object at time t. In each case find the velocity v at time t.

a. $s = 7t - 2t^2$

b. $s = 18 + 5t - \dfrac{1}{3}t^3$

c. $s = v_0 t + \dfrac{1}{2}at^2$

6. Tangents are drawn to the parabola $y = x^2$ at $(2, 4)$ and $\left(-\dfrac{1}{8}, \dfrac{1}{64}\right)$. Prove that these tangents are perpendicular. Illustrate this situation with a sketch.

7. Find a point on the parabola $y = -x^2 + 3x + 4$ where the slope of the tangent line is 5. Illustrate your answer with a sketch.

8. Find the equation of the normal line to the curve $y = -x^2 + 5x$ that has a slope of -2.

9. Show that there are two tangents to the curve $y = x^5 - 2x$ that have a slope of $-\dfrac{3}{4}$.

10. Show that there is no tangent line to the parabola $y = 4 - x^2$ that passes through the point $(1, 2)$.

11. Tangents are drawn from the point $(0, 3)$ to the curve $y = -3x^2$. Find the points at which these tangent lines touch the curve. Illustrate your answer with a sketch.

12. Find the equations of the tangent lines to the curve $y = 2x^2 + 3$ that pass through the point $(2, -7)$.

13. By finding the point at which the slope is zero, determine the coordinates of the vertex for each parabola.

a. $y = -3x^2 + 18x - 3$

b. $y = x^2 - 4x + 2$

c. $y = -\dfrac{1}{4}x^2 - 3x$

d. $y = ax^2 + bx + c, \quad a \neq 0$

14. A subway train travels from the Dundas station to the Queen station in 2 min. Its distance (in kilometres) from the Dundas station after t minutes is

$$s(t) = t^2 - \dfrac{1}{3}t^3$$

At what time(s) will the train have a velocity of $\dfrac{1}{2}$ km/min?

15. a. Prove that the curve $y = -2x^3 + x - 4$ has no tangent with a slope of 2.
   b. What is the maximum slope of any tangent drawn to this curve?

16. During a 90-day television advertising campaign promoting a new breakfast cereal, a daily survey was carried out in Lucknow. The number of people N who ate the cereal for breakfast was found to fit the formula

$$N = -3t^2 + 300t$$

where t represents the number of days from the beginning of the campaign.

   a. Find the rate of change of N with respect to t.
   b. At what rate is N changing after 30 days? After 70 days? Explain the difference in your answers.
   c. After how many days does the number of people eating the cereal stop increasing and begin to decline?
   d. Sketch a graph of N as a function of t, for $0 \le t \le 90$.

17. The flight path of a spaceship is described by the curve $y = x^3 - 8x, x > 0$. If the engine is shut down at point P, the spaceship will fly off along the tangent line at P. If the spaceship is moving from left to right, at what point should the engine be shut down in order to reach the point (4, 0)? Sketch the flight path.

Problems 2.1

1. The tangent line to the curve defined by $y = x^3 - 6x^2 + 8x$ at the point $A(3, -3)$, intersects the curve at another point B. Find the coordinates of B. Illustrate this situation with a sketch.

2. The surface area of a weather balloon as a function of time is given by

$$A = pt^3 - qt$$

where p and q are constants. At $t = 3$ min, the area of the balloon's surface is 25 m² and the area is changing at a rate of 39 m²/min. Find the values of p and q.

3. Let r and s be the unequal roots of the quadratic function $f(x) = ax^2 + bx + c$, where a, b, and c are constants. Show that

$$f'(r) = -f'(s).$$

Interpret this result geometrically. What happens if $r = s$?

4. For the power function $f(x) = x^n$, find the x-intercept of the tangent line at the point (1, 1). What happens to the intercept as n increases without bound ($n \to +\infty$)? Explain the result geometrically.

5. For each function f, sketch the graph of f and find an expression for $f'(x)$. Indicate at which points $f'(x)$ does not exist.

   a. $f(x) = \begin{cases} x^2, & \text{if } x < 3 \\ x + 6, & \text{if } x \ge 3 \end{cases}$ **b.** $f(x) = |3x^2 - 6|$ **c.** $f(x) = ||x| - 1|$

2.2 The Product Rule

In this section we shall show how to differentiate the product of two functions. This will enable us to differentiate functions such as

$$f(x) = (3x^2 - 1)(x^3 + 8) \quad \text{and} \quad f(x) = (x + 1)(x^2 + 3)^5$$

without multiplying out the brackets.

One might be tempted to guess that the derivative of a product is the product of the separate derivatives. However, a simple example shows that this is false.

Example 1. Let $f(x) = p(x)\,q(x)$, where $p(x) = 2x + 1$ and $q(x) = 3x^2$. Show that

$$f'(x) \neq p'(x)\,q'(x)$$

Solution. The expression for $f(x)$ must first be simplified.

$$f(x) = (2x + 1)(3x^2)$$
$$= 6x^3 + 3x^2$$

The derivative of $f(x)$ is

$$f'(x) = 18x^2 + 6x$$

and the derivatives of $p(x)$ and $q(x)$ are

$$p'(x) = 2$$

and

$$q'(x) = 6x$$

Thus,

$$p'(x)q'(x) = 12x$$

This does not give the correct derivative, which is $f'(x) = 18x^2 + 6x$. Thus we have shown that the derivative of $p(x)q(x)$ does not equal $p'(x)q'(x)$. □

Here is the correct formula for the derivative of a product, which is called the **Product Rule for differentiation**.

Product Rule

If $f(x) = p(x)q(x)$, then

$$f'(x) = p'(x)q(x) + p(x)q'(x)$$

In Leibniz notation,

$$\frac{d}{dx}(uv) = \frac{du}{dx}v + u\frac{dv}{dx}$$

You may find it helpful to remember the product rule by stating it partially in words:

$$(\text{Product})' = (\text{First})'(\text{Second}) + (\text{First})(\text{Second})'$$

Example 2 illustrates the Product Rule.

Example 2. Use the Product Rule to find the derivative of $y = (3x^2 - 1)(x^3 + 8)$.

Solution. Using the Product Rule,

$$\frac{dy}{dx} = \left[\frac{d}{dx}(3x^2 - 1)\right](x^3 + 8) + (3x^2 - 1)\frac{d}{dx}(x^3 + 8)$$
$$= 6x(x^3 + 8) + (3x^2 - 1)(3x^2)$$
$$= 6x^4 + 48x + 9x^4 - 3x^2$$
$$= 15x^4 - 3x^2 + 48x$$

We can of course differentiate the function in Example 2 by using the rules of section 2.1 if we first expand the product. The Product Rule will be essential, however, when we work with products of non-polynomial functions, such as

$$f(x) = x^2 \sin x, \quad \text{or} \quad f(x) = (x^2 + 9)\sqrt{1 + x^2}$$

Proof of the Product Rule

Let $f(x) = p(x)q(x)$; by the definition of the derivative,

$$f'(x) = \lim_{h \to 0} \frac{f(x + h) - f(x)}{h}$$
$$= \lim_{h \to 0} \frac{p(x + h)q(x + h) - p(x)q(x)}{h} \tag{1}$$

The purpose of the Product Rule is to express $f'(x)$ in terms of $p'(x)$ and $q'(x)$. Therefore, we would like to express the right side of equation (1) in terms of

$$\frac{p(x + h) - p(x)}{h} \quad \text{and} \quad \frac{q(x + h) - q(x)}{h}$$

This can be done by subtracting and adding the quantity $p(x)q(x + h)$ in the numerator in equation (1).

$$f'(x) = \lim_{h \to 0} \frac{p(x + h)q(x + h) - p(x)q(x + h) + p(x)q(x + h) - p(x)q(x)}{h}$$

$$= \lim_{h \to 0} \left\{\left[\frac{p(x + h) - p(x)}{h}\right]q(x + h) + p(x)\left[\frac{q(x + h) - q(x)}{h}\right]\right\}$$

$$= \left[\lim_{h \to 0} \frac{p(x + h) - p(x)}{h}\right]\left[\lim_{h \to 0} q(x + h)\right] + \left[\lim_{h \to 0} p(x)\right]\left[\lim_{h \to 0} \frac{q(x + h) - q(x)}{h}\right]$$

$$= p'(x)q(x) + p(x)q'(x)$$

Power of a Function Rule

Suppose that we now wish to differentiate functions such as

$$y = (x^2 - 3)^2 \quad \text{or} \quad y = (3x^2 - 2x + 5)^4$$

These functions are of the form

$$y = u^n \tag{2}$$

where n is a positive integer and $u = g(x)$ is a function whose derivative we can find. Using the product rule, we can develop an efficient method for differentiating such functions.

For the case $n = 2$, we write y as a product,

$$y = u^2 = (u)(u)$$

and apply the product rule to obtain

$$\frac{dy}{dx} = \frac{du}{dx}u + u\frac{du}{dx}$$

$$= 2u\frac{du}{dx}$$

Thus, if u is a function of x,

$$\frac{d}{dx}(u^2) = 2u\frac{du}{dx}$$

For example, if $y = (x^2 - 3)^2$, then

$$\frac{dy}{dx} = 2(x^2 - 3)\frac{d}{dx}(x^2 - 3)$$

$$= 4x(x^2 - 3)$$

If $n = 3$ in equation (2), we write

$$y = u^3 = (u^2)(u)$$

By the Product Rule,

$$\frac{dy}{dx} = \left[\frac{d}{dx}(u^2)\right]u + u^2\frac{du}{dx}$$

$$= \left[2u\frac{du}{dx}\right]u + u^2\frac{du}{dx}$$

$$= 3u^2\frac{du}{dx}$$

Thus, if u is a function of x,

$$\frac{d}{dx}(u^3) = 3u^2\frac{du}{dx}$$

These calculations suggest a generalization of the Power Rule.

The Power of a Function Rule

If u is a function of x, and n is a positive integer, then

$$\frac{d}{dx}(u^n) = nu^{n-1}\frac{du}{dx}$$

This result is called the **Power of a Function Rule** because it can be used to differentiate powers of a function. It is a special case of the so-called Chain Rule for differentiation, which we shall study in section 2.5.

We are now able to differentiate any polynomial function of the form $f(x) = (2 - 3x^2)^9$ or $f(t) = (t^2 - 1)(5t^3 + t - 1)^2$ without multiplying out the brackets.

Example 3. If $f(x) = (2 - 3x^2)^9$, find $f'(1)$.

Solution. By the Power of a Function Rule,

$$f'(x) = \frac{d}{dx}(2 - 3x^2)^9$$

$$= 9(2 - 3x^2)^8\frac{d}{dx}(2 - 3x^2)$$

$$= 9(2 - 3x^2)^8(0 - 6x)$$

$$= -54x(2 - 3x^2)^8$$

Hence,

$$f'(1) = -54 \qquad\qquad \square$$

With practice, one can omit the second line in the solution. Keep in mind, however, that the derivative of the function inside the parentheses $\left(\text{here } \dfrac{d}{dx}(2 - 3x^2), \text{ in general } \dfrac{du}{dx}\right)$ is part of the final expression; a common error when differentiating the power of a function is to omit this factor.

The next example requires the use of both the Product Rule and the Power of a Function Rule.

Example 4. The position (in centimetres) of an object moving in a straight line is given by

$$s = t(6 - 3t)^4, \quad t \geq 0$$

where the time t is measured in seconds. Determine at what times the object is at rest.

Solution. We have to find the values of t for which the velocity $v = \dfrac{ds}{dt}$ is zero. We have

$$v = \frac{d}{dt}[t(6 - 3t)^4]$$

$$= (1)(6 - 3t)^4 + t\frac{d}{dt}(6 - 3t)^4 \quad \text{(Product Rule)}$$

$$= (6 - 3t)^4 + t[4(6 - 3t)^3(-3)] \quad \text{(Power of a Function Rule)}$$

$$= (6 - 3t)^3[(6 - 3t) - 12t]$$

$$= 3(6 - 3t)^3(2 - 5t)$$

It follows that $v = 0$ (the object is at rest) when $t = 2$ or $t = \dfrac{2}{5}$. $\quad\square$

The expressions for derivatives that are obtained by using the Product Rule can be cumbersome. In Example 4 it was necessary to simplify the expression, but if the derivative is required only at a particular x value, it is not necessary to simplify before substituting for x.

The final example illustrates the extension of the Product Rule to more than two functions.

Example 5. Find an expression for $f'(x)$ if $f(x) = p(x)q(x)r(x)$.

Solution. We temporarily regard $p(x)q(x)$ as a single function.

$$f(x) = [p(x)q(x)]r(x)$$

By the Product Rule,

$$f'(x) = [p(x)q(x)]'r(x) + [p(x)q(x)]r'(x)$$

A second application of the Product Rule yields

$$f'(x) = [p'(x)q(x) + p(x)q'(x)]r(x) + p(x)q(x)r'(x)$$
$$= p'(x)q(x)r(x) + p(x)q'(x)r(x) + p(x)q(x)r'(x) \quad\square$$

Note the symmetric form of the result in Example 5. With practice, one can perform the differentiation in one step.

Exercises 2.2

1. Use the Product Rule to differentiate each function. Simplify your answers.

a. $f(x) = (3x + 1)(2x - 5)$
b. $y = (7 - x)(4 + 6x)$
c. $p = q(8q - 3)$
d. $g(t) = 5t^2(t + 7)$
e. $y = x^2(2x - 1)$
f. $y = (2x + 1)(4x^2 - 4x + 1)$
g. $s = (t^3 + 1)(3 - 2t^2)$
h. $f(x) = (5x^7 + 1)(x^2 - 2x)$
i. $m = n^5(n^3 - 7n^2 + 3n - 5)$
j. $f(x) = (3x^3 - 2x^2)(3x^2 + 2x)$

2. Find $\dfrac{dy}{dx}$ at the given value of x. (There is no need to simplify the expression for $\dfrac{dy}{dx}$ before substituting the given value.)

   a. $y = (2 + 7x)(x - 3), \quad x = 2$

   b. $y = (1 - 2x)(1 + 2x), \quad x = \dfrac{1}{2}$

   c. $y = (3 - 2x - x^2)(x^2 + x - 2), \quad x = -2$

   d. $y = (4x^2 + 2x)(3 - 2x - 5x^2), \quad x = 0$

   e. $y = (5 - 7x^3)(x^3 + 2x^2 - 7), \quad x = 1$

   f. $y = (x^4 - 4)(x^4 + 4), \quad x = 1$

3. Find the equation of the tangent line to the curve $y = (x^3 - 5x + 2)(3x^2 - 2x)$ at the point $(1, -2)$.

4. Let $f(x) = (2x - 1)^3$. Find $f'(x)$ by using the definition of the derivative. Try to use factoring methods in order to avoid expanding the cubic term. Verify your answer by using the Power of a Function Rule.

5. Differentiate each function. Do not expand any expression before differentiating.

   a. $f(x) = (2x + 1)^4$ **b.** $y = (5 - x)^6$

   c. $f(x) = (x^2 - 4)^3$ **d.** $y = (7 - x^3)^5$

   e. $f(x) = (2x^2 + 3x - 5)^4$ **f.** $y = (5x - x^2)^5$

   g. $f(x) = (\pi^2 - x^2)^3$ **h.** $y = (1 - x + x^2 - x^3)^4$

   i. $f(x) = [(2 - x)^4 + 16]^3$ **j.** $y = [(3x + 1)^3 - x]^5$

6. Differentiate each function. Express your answer in a simplified factored form.

   a. $f(x) = (x + 4)^3(x - 3)^6$ **b.** $y = (2x - 1)^4(2 - 3x)^4$

   c. $f(x) = x^3(3x - 5)^2$ **d.** $y = x^4(1 - 4x^2)^3$

   e. $f(x) = (x^2 + 3)^3(x^3 + 3)^2$ **f.** $y = (4 - 3x^3)^4(1 - 2x)^6$

7. Differentiate each function. Answers may be left in unsimplified form.

   a. $f(x) = x(x + 1)(x + 2)$ **b.** $f(x) = (2x - 3)(x^2 + 1)(x^3 - 3x)$

   c. $f(x) = x^3(7 + 2x)^4(1 - x)^2$ **d.** $f(x) = x^2(1 - x)^3(2x + 1)^4$

   e. $f(x) = 5x(1 - x^3)^3(2 + 3x)^2$ **f.** $f(x) = 3(1 - x^2)(2x^3 - 3)^2(2x - x^2)^3$

8. Find the equation of the normal line to the curve $y = (2x + 1)^3(4x - x^2)^2$ at the point $(-1, -25)$.

9. Prove that the y-axis is normal to the curve $y = (ax^2 + b)(cx^3 + d)$, where a, b, c, and d are non-zero constants.

10. The base b and height h of a triangle change with time t in such a way that

$$b = (t + 1)^2 \quad \text{and} \quad h = t^2 + 1.$$

Determine the rate of change of the area of the triangle when $t = 3$.

11. For what values of x do the curves $y = (1 + x^3)^2$ and $y = 2x^6$ have the same slope? Do the curves intersect at these points?

Problems 2.2

1. A 1000 L tank loses water so that, after t days, the remaining volume in litres is

$$V(t) = 1000\left(1 - \frac{t}{10}\right)^2$$

for $0 \le t \le 10$. How rapidly is water being lost when the tank is half full?

2. a. Find an expression for $f'(x)$ if

$$f(x) = p(x)q(x)r(x)s(x)$$

b. If $f(x) = (1 + x)(1 + 2x)(1 + 3x)(1 + 4x)$, find $f'(0)$.

3. Show that the tangent line to the curve $y = (x^2 + x - 2)^3 + 3$ at $(1, 3)$ is also tangent to the curve at another point.

4. In a local store the price of a tape deck is x dollars, where $100 \le x \le 400$, and the total number of tape decks sold per week (the "demand") is

$$D(x) = \left(300 - \frac{1}{2}x\right)^2$$

a. Write an expression for the total revenue $R(x)$ (that is, the total number of dollars resulting from the sales).
b. Use the Product Rule to find $R'(x)$.
c. Will the total revenue increase if the price per item is increased from
  (i) \$100 to \$105?   (ii) \$300 to \$305?

5. Let $f(x) = (x - a)g(x)$. Show that if the graph of g intersects the x-axis at $x = a$, then the graph of f is tangent to the x-axis at $x = a$.

6. Let $f(x) = \{[(1 - x)^4 + x^4]^4 + x^4\}^4$. Show that $f'(1) = 640$ and $f'(0) = -64$.

7. If $F(x) = (4 + x)(3 + 2x^2)^2(2 + 3x^3)^3$, find $F'(0)$.

Suggestion: Try to do this one mentally; most of the terms become zero when you substitute $x = 0$.

8. a. Find an expression for $f'(x)$ if

$$f(x) = p_1(x)p_2(x) \ldots p_{n-1}(x)p_n(x)$$

b. If $f(x) = (1 + x)(1 + 2x) \ldots (1 + nx)$, find $f'(0)$.

9. Use mathematical induction to prove that if u is a function of x and n is a positive integer, then

$$\frac{d}{dx}(u^n) = nu^{n-1}\frac{du}{dx}$$

2.3 The Quotient Rule

In this section we shall show how to differentiate the quotient of two functions—that is, functions of the form

$$f(x) = \frac{p(x)}{q(x)}$$

This will enable us to differentiate functions such as

$$f(x) = \frac{3x - 4}{x^2 + 5} \quad \text{and} \quad f(x) = \frac{(x - 1)^2}{(2x^2 + 5)^3}$$

The Quotient Rule

If $f(x) = \dfrac{p(x)}{q(x)}$ where $q(x) \neq 0$, then

$$f'(x) = \frac{q(x)p'(x) - p(x)q'(x)}{[q(x)]^2}$$

In Leibniz notation,

$$\frac{d}{dx}\left(\frac{u}{v}\right) = \frac{v\dfrac{du}{dx} - u\dfrac{dv}{dx}}{v^2}$$

Example 1. Let $f(x) = \dfrac{3x - 4}{x^2 + 5}$. Use the Quotient Rule to find $f'(x)$.

Solution. The function $f(x)$ can be expressed as

$$f(x) = \frac{p(x)}{q(x)}$$

where

$$p(x) = 3x - 4 \quad \text{and} \quad q(x) = x^2 + 5.$$

Thus, the Quotient Rule yields

$$f'(x) = \frac{(x^2 + 5)(3) - (3x - 4)(2x)}{(x^2 + 5)^2}$$

$$= \frac{-3x^2 + 8x + 15}{(x^2 + 5)^2} \qquad \square$$

You may find it helpful to remember the Quotient Rule by stating it partially in words:

$$\text{(Quotient)}' = \frac{\text{(Denominator)(Numerator)}' - \text{(Numerator)(Denominator)}'}{\text{(Denominator)}^2}$$

Note that in contrast to the Product Rule, which contains a sum, the order of the terms in the Quotient Rule is crucial, since it contains a difference. Our proof of the Quotient Rule makes use of the Product Rule rather than the definition of the derivative; this simplifies the calculation.

Proof of the Quotient Rule

We wish to find $f'(x)$, given that

$$f(x) = \frac{p(x)}{q(x)}, \quad q(x) \neq 0 \tag{1}$$

Begin by writing equation (1) as a product:

$$f(x)q(x) = p(x) \tag{2}$$

Now differentiate both sides of equation (2) to obtain

$$f'(x)q(x) + f(x)q'(x) = p'(x)$$

Solving for $f'(x)$, we get

$$f'(x) = \frac{p'(x) - f(x)q'(x)}{q(x)}$$

$$= \frac{p'(x) - \dfrac{p(x)}{q(x)}q'(x)}{q(x)}$$

$$= \frac{q(x)p'(x) - p(x)q'(x)}{[q(x)]^2} \qquad \square$$

In the next example, both the Quotient Rule and the Power of a Function Rule must be used.

Example 2. Differentiate $y = \left(\dfrac{2x - 1}{3x + 2}\right)^5$.

Solution. First use the Power of a Function Rule to obtain

$$\frac{dy}{dx} = 5\left(\frac{2x - 1}{3x + 2}\right)^4 \frac{d}{dx}\left(\frac{2x - 1}{3x + 2}\right) \tag{3}$$

The Quotient Rule yields

$$\frac{d}{dx}\left(\frac{2x - 1}{3x + 2}\right) = \frac{(3x + 2)(2) - (2x - 1)(3)}{(3x + 2)^2}$$

$$= \frac{7}{(3x + 2)^2}$$

On substituting this result in equation (3), we obtain

$$\frac{dy}{dx} = 5\left(\frac{2x-1}{3x+2}\right)^4 \frac{7}{(3x+2)^2}$$

which can be written as

$$\frac{dy}{dx} = \frac{35(2x-1)^4}{(3x+2)^6} \qquad \square$$

We are now able to differentiate any **rational function**, that is, any function that is the quotient of two polynomial functions. If the separate polynomials are written as products or powers, then the Product Rule or the Power of a Function Rule will have to be used in conjunction with the Quotient Rule.

In the proof of the Quotient Rule, an important operation was introduced that is used extensively in applications of calculus—we **differentiated both sides of an equation**. It is worth discussing this operation in more detail, because it can be a source of confusion. Consider an equation of the form

$$f(x) = g(x) \quad \text{for all } x \text{ such that } a < x < b \qquad (4)$$

We can differentiate both sides of equation (4) with respect to x and conclude that

$$f'(x) = g'(x) \quad \text{for all } x \text{ such that } a < x < b$$

(assuming that f and g have derivatives). In other words, if two functions are equal in an interval, then their derivatives are also equal in that interval. Contrast this with the following situation. Suppose that

$$f(c) = g(c) \quad \text{for some fixed number } c \qquad (5)$$

It does **not** follow that $f'(c) = g'(c)$; i.e, one cannot differentiate both sides of this equation. The reason is that equation (5) does not state that the functions f and g are equal in an interval but only that their values at $x = c$ are equal. If the graphs of f and g intersect at a single point, there is no reason to expect that their slopes should be equal at $x = c$. For example, consider the functions

$$f(x) = x^2 \quad \text{and} \quad g(x) = 2 - x^2$$

Note that

$$f(1) = g(1)$$

and

$$f'(1) \neq g'(1)$$

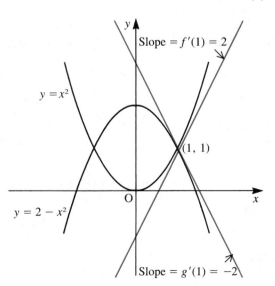

In sections 2.1 and 2.2 we developed the Power Rule and Power of a Function Rule for **positive integer exponents**. In order to differentiate functions with **negative integer exponents** such as

$$x^{-3} \quad \text{and} \quad (4x + 5)^{-2}$$

one could rewrite them as quotients,

$$\frac{1}{x^3} \quad \text{and} \quad \frac{1}{(4x + 5)^2}$$

and use the quotient rule. For example,

$$\frac{d}{dx}\left[\frac{1}{x^3}\right] = \frac{(x^3)(0) - (1)(3x^2)}{(x^3)^2}$$
$$= \frac{-3}{x^4}$$

and hence

$$\frac{d}{dx}(x^{-3}) = -3x^{-4}$$

Once again, we have the pattern of the Power Rule, but with a negative exponent, $n = -3$. Instead of using the Quotient Rule for each occurrence of a negative exponent, it is more efficient to show that the Power Rule holds for all negative integer exponents. This generalization of the Power Rule is stated here; it follows from the extended Power of a Function Rule on page 77.

Power Rule

$$\frac{d}{dx}(x^n) = nx^{n-1} \quad \text{for any integer } n$$

Example 3. Differentiate $y = \dfrac{1}{x} + \dfrac{1}{x^2} + \dfrac{1}{x^3}$

Solution. By the Sum Rule and the Power Rule,

$$\frac{dy}{dx} = \frac{d}{dx}(x^{-1} + x^{-2} + x^{-3})$$
$$= -x^{-2} - 2x^{-3} - 3x^{-4}$$
$$= -\frac{1}{x^2} - \frac{2}{x^3} - \frac{3}{x^4}$$

□

In order to differentiate functions such as

$$y = (4x + 5)^{-2}$$

we need to show that the Power of a Function Rule is true for negative exponents.

Power of a Function Rule

If u is a function of x, then

$$\frac{d}{dx}(u^n) = nu^{n-1}\frac{du}{dx} \quad \text{for any integer } n$$

For example,

$$\frac{d}{dx}(4x + 5)^{-2} = -2(4x + 5)^{-3}(4)$$
$$= -8(4x + 5)^{-3}$$

Proof of the Power of a Function Rule (negative integer exponents)

If n is a negative integer, let $m = -n$, so that m is a positive integer. Then if u is a function of x,

$$\frac{d}{dx}(u^n) = \frac{d}{dx}(u^{-m})$$
$$= \frac{d}{dx}\left[\frac{1}{u^m}\right]$$
$$= \frac{(u^m)(0) - (1)\left(mu^{m-1}\frac{du}{dx}\right)}{(u^m)^2}$$
$$= -mu^{-m-1}\frac{du}{dx}$$
$$= nu^{n-1}\frac{du}{dx}$$

Note that we have used the Power of a Function Rule, which was proved in section 2.2, for the positive integer m. $\qquad\square$

The Power Rule for negative integer exponents follows from the previous proof if we let $u = x$.

Example 4. Find the points at which the curve

$$y = \frac{1}{x^2 + 2x + 2}$$

has a horizontal tangent line.

Solution. Find the points at which the derivative equals zero. By the (extended) Power of a Function Rule,

$$\frac{dy}{dx} = \frac{d}{dx}(x^2 + 2x + 2)^{-1}$$

$$= -1(x^2 + 2x + 2)^{-2}\frac{d}{dx}(x^2 + 2x + 2)$$

$$= -(x^2 + 2x + 2)^{-2}(2x + 2)$$

This can be written as

$$\frac{dy}{dx} = \frac{-2(x + 1)}{(x^2 + 2x + 2)^2}$$

Thus $\frac{dy}{dx} = 0$ implies that $x + 1 = 0$ and hence that $x = -1$. It follows that the only point at which the tangent line is horizontal is $(-1, 1)$. $\quad\square$

It is of interest to illustrate the results of Example 4 graphically, although at this stage we do not expect you to sketch the graph of this function. (It can be obtained from the graph of the parabola $y = x^2 + 2x + 2$.)

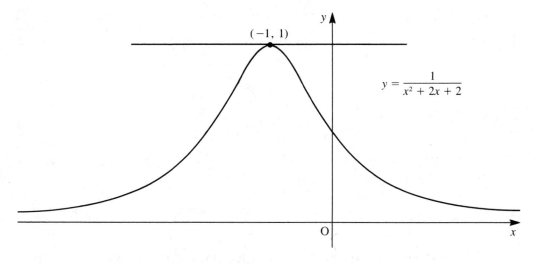

Note that when x takes on large positive or negative values, y is close to zero.

Exercises 2.3

1. Use the definition of the derivative to find $f'(x)$.

a. $f(x) = \dfrac{1}{x}$

b. $f(x) = \dfrac{1}{x^2}$

c. $f(x) = \dfrac{x}{x + 1}$

d. $f(x) = \dfrac{1}{(3x + 2)^2}$

2. Using the Quotient Rule, differentiate each function.

a. $f(x) = \dfrac{x^2}{x + 1}$

b. $f(x) = \dfrac{x^2}{1 - 2x}$

c. $y = \dfrac{2x - 1}{x + 3}$

d. $y = \dfrac{3x + 4}{5x + 6}$

e. $p = \dfrac{q^2 - 4q}{q + 2}$

f. $s = \dfrac{2t - 3}{t + 5}$

g. $m = \dfrac{n^3}{2n^2 - 1}$

h. $v = \dfrac{1 - w^3}{1 + w^3}$

3. Find $\dfrac{dy}{dx}$.

a. $y = \dfrac{1}{x^2 + 5}$

b. $y = \dfrac{x(3x + 5)}{1 - x^2}$

c. $y = \dfrac{x^2 - x + 1}{x^2 + 3}$

d. $y = \dfrac{2x^2 - 4}{x^3 + 3x + 4}$

e. $y = \dfrac{x^2 - 9}{x^2 + 9}$

f. $y = \dfrac{x^3}{8 - x^3}$

g. $y = \dfrac{x^2 - 1}{x(3x + 1)}$

h. $y = \dfrac{(2x - 3)(2x + 3)}{x + 1}$

4. Find $\dfrac{dy}{dx}$ and leave your answer in a simplified factored form.

a. $y = \dfrac{(2x - 1)^2}{(x - 2)^3}$

b. $y = \left[\dfrac{x^2 - 1}{x^2 + 1}\right]^2$

c. $y = \dfrac{x^2(1 - x)^3}{(1 + x)^3}$

d. $y = \dfrac{(5x - 3)^3}{(x + 2)^5}$

5. Use the Power Rule or the Power of a Function Rule to find $\dfrac{dy}{dx}$.

a. $y = 3x^{-2}$

b. $y = -2x^{-3}$

c. $y = \left(\dfrac{2}{x}\right)^2$

d. $y = -\dfrac{3}{x^5}$

e. $y = (2x - 1)^{-3}$

f. $y = 3(4 - x^2)^{-1}$

g. $y = \dfrac{1}{5x^2 + x}$

h. $y = \dfrac{\pi}{(x^3 - \pi)^2}$

6. Differentiate each function and simplify your answers where appropriate.

a. $f(x) = x^2 + x^{-2}$

b. $f(x) = \pi x + \left(\dfrac{\pi}{x}\right)^2$

c. $f(x) = 2x^{-3} - 3x^{-2}$

d. $f(x) = 3x^{-7} + x^7$

e. $f(x) = (2x^2 - 3x + 5)^{-1}$

f. $f(x) = \left(x - \dfrac{1}{3}x^{-3}\right)^3$

g. $f(x) = (1 - x)^{-2} - (2 - x)^{-1}$

h. $f(x) = \pi(x^2 + \pi^2)^{-3}$

7. Find $\dfrac{dy}{dx}$, first by using the Quotient Rule and then by using the Product Rule. Show that both methods lead to the same result.

a. $y = \dfrac{3x}{x + 2}$

b. $y = \dfrac{5x^2}{(4x - 3)^2}$

8. Find the slope of the tangent line to the curve at the given point.

a. $y = \dfrac{3x - 1}{x + 3}$, at $(-2, -7)$

b. $y = \dfrac{x^3}{x^2 - 6}$, at $(3, 9)$

c. $y = (3x + x^2)^{-2}$, at $\left(-2, \dfrac{1}{4}\right)$

d. $s = \dfrac{8t^5(t - 3)}{(t^2 - 1)^2}$, at the point where $t = 2$

9. Find the equation of the normal line to the curve at the given point.

a. $y = \dfrac{2 - 3x^2}{x^2 - 5}$, at the point where $x = 2$

b. $y = \dfrac{8}{(x + 5)^2}$, at the point where $x = -3$

c. $y = 2x^3 + x^{-3}$, at the point where $x = -1$

d. $y = \dfrac{(4x - 1)^3}{(2x + 3)^2}$, at the point where $x = -1$

10. Find the points on the graph of $y = \dfrac{3x}{x - 4}$ where the slope of the tangent line is $-\dfrac{3}{5}$.

11. Find the points where the tangent line to the curve is horizontal.

a. $y = \dfrac{2x^2}{x - 4}$

b. $y = \dfrac{x^2 - 1}{x^2 + 1}$

c. $y = \dfrac{x}{x^3 - 16}$

12. The number N of new SNAZ cars sold per week in Canada, t weeks after going on the market, is

$$N(t) = \frac{300t^2}{1 + t^2}, \quad 0 \le t \le 10$$

a. At what rate is the number of sales changing after one week? After five weeks?

b. Does the number of sales per week decrease at any time during this ten-week period? Explain.

13. At what values of x do the functions $f(x) = 2x^3 + 10x - 1$ and $g(x) = -\dfrac{4}{x}$ have equal derivatives? Do the graphs intersect at these points?

14. a. If $f(t) = g(t)$ for $1 \le t \le 3$, is it true that $f'(2) = g'(2)$? Explain.

b. If $f(2) = h(2)$, is it true that $f'(2) = h'(2)$? Explain.

15. Criticize the following incorrect statement: If $f(3) = 2$, then $f'(3) = 0$, since the derivative of a constant is zero.

Problems 2.3

1. A motorboat coasts towards a dock with its engine off. Its distance s (in metres) from the dock, t seconds after the engine is cut, is

$$s(t) = \frac{10(6 - t)}{3 + t} \quad \text{for } 0 \le t \le 6$$

a. How far is the boat from the dock initially?

b. Find the boat's velocity when it bumps into the dock.

2. Consider the function

$$f(x) = \frac{ax + b}{cx + d}, \quad x \ne -\frac{d}{c}$$

where a, b, c, and d are non-zero constants. What condition on a, b, c, and d ensures that each tangent line to the graph of f has positive slope?

3. The curves $y = \dfrac{4}{x} + 2$ and $y = ax^2 + bx + c$ intersect and have a common tangent at $x = 2$.

a. If the curves also intersect at $(1, 6)$, find the vertex of the parabola.

b. Prove that there are only two points of intersection of these curves.

c. Sketch graphs of both curves on the same axes, showing the common tangent and the points of intersection.

4. Consider any tangent line drawn to the curve $y = \dfrac{k}{x}$, where k is a constant. If A and B are the x- and y-intercepts of the tangent line and O is the origin, prove that the area of triangle AOB is the same for all tangent lines to the curve.

5. Prove the Quotient Rule using the definition of the derivative and the technique used in the proof of the Product Rule in section 2.2.

2.4 The Power Rule for Rational Exponents

In section 1.7 we used the definition of the derivative to show that

$$\frac{d}{dx}(\sqrt{x}) = \frac{1}{2\sqrt{x}}$$

This can be written in the form

$$\frac{d}{dx}\left(x^{\frac{1}{2}}\right) = \frac{1}{2}x^{-\frac{1}{2}}$$

We again recognize the pattern of the Power Rule but with a rational exponent $n = \frac{1}{2}$. In this section we shall prove and apply the Power Rule for rational exponents.

Power Rule

$$\frac{d}{dx}(x^r) = rx^{r-1} \text{ for any rational number } r$$

For example,

$$\frac{d}{dx}\left(x^{\frac{3}{2}}\right) = \frac{3}{2}x^{\frac{1}{2}}$$

When applying the Power Rule, first rewrite the function in exponent form.

Example 1. Differentiate $y = \sqrt{x} - x\sqrt{x}$.

Solution. Write in exponent form and apply the Power Rule.

$$\frac{dy}{dx} = \frac{d}{dx}\left(x^{\frac{1}{2}} - x^{\frac{3}{2}}\right)$$

$$= \frac{1}{2}x^{-\frac{1}{2}} - \frac{3}{2}x^{\frac{1}{2}}$$

$$= \frac{1}{2}\left(\frac{1}{\sqrt{x}} - 3\sqrt{x}\right) \qquad \square$$

In order to differentiate algebraic functions such as

$$\sqrt{5x + 7} \quad \text{and} \quad (3x^2 + 2)^{\frac{1}{3}}$$

we need to show that the Power of a Function Rule holds for rational exponents.

Power of a Function Rule

If u is a function of x, then

$$\frac{d}{dx}(u^r) = ru^{r-1}\frac{du}{dx} \quad \text{for any rational number } r.$$

We illustrate the rule with an example.

Example 2. Differentiate $y = (3x^2 + 2)^{\frac{1}{3}}$.

Solution. Apply the Power of a Function Rule.

$$\frac{dy}{dx} = \frac{1}{3}(3x^2 + 2)^{-\frac{2}{3}}\frac{d}{dx}(3x^2 + 2)$$

$$= \frac{1}{3}(3x^2 + 2)^{-\frac{2}{3}}(6x)$$

$$= \frac{2x}{(3x^2 + 2)^{\frac{2}{3}}} \qquad \square$$

When $u = x$, the Power of a Function Rule is simply the Power Rule. Thus it is only necessary to prove the more general rule.

Proof of the Power of a Function Rule (rational exponents)

Let

$$y = u^r$$

where u is a function of x. Since r is a rational number, we can write

$$r = \frac{m}{n}$$

where m and n are integers and $n \neq 0$. Then

$$y = u^{\frac{m}{n}}$$

and hence

$$y^n = u^m$$

Keeping in mind that u and y are functions of x, differentiate both sides of this equation, using the Power of a Function Rule for integers, to obtain

$$ny^{n-1}\frac{dy}{dx} = mu^{m-1}\frac{du}{dx}$$

Solve this equation for $\frac{dy}{dx}$ to get

$$\begin{aligned}
\frac{dy}{dx} &= \left(\frac{m}{n}\right)y^{1-n}u^{m-1}\frac{du}{dx} \\
&= \left(\frac{m}{n}\right)\left(u^{\frac{m}{n}}\right)^{1-n}u^{m-1}\frac{du}{dx} \quad (\text{since } y = u^{\frac{m}{n}}) \\
&= \left(\frac{m}{n}\right)u^{\frac{m}{n}-m}u^{m-1}\frac{du}{dx} \\
&= \left(\frac{m}{n}\right)u^{\frac{m}{n}-1}\frac{du}{dx} \\
&= ru^{r-1}\frac{du}{dx} \quad (\text{since } r = \frac{m}{n})
\end{aligned}$$

At this stage, we have at our disposal the following rules of differentiation:

- Sum Rule
- Constant Multiple Rule
- Product Rule
- Quotient Rule
- Power of a Function Rule

By using these rules, we are able to differentiate any function of the following types:

- polynomial functions
- rational functions
- algebraic functions

In order to consolidate the techniques of differentiation, we present two more examples.

Example 3. Differentiate $y = \dfrac{1}{\sqrt{4 + \sqrt{x}}}$.

Solution. Write the square roots as powers and use the Power of a Function Rule:

$$\frac{dy}{dx} = \frac{d}{dx}\left[\left(4 + x^{\frac{1}{2}}\right)^{-\frac{1}{2}}\right]$$

$$= -\frac{1}{2}\left(4 + x^{\frac{1}{2}}\right)^{-\frac{3}{2}}\frac{d}{dx}\left(4 + x^{\frac{1}{2}}\right)$$

$$= -\frac{1}{2}\left(4 + x^{\frac{1}{2}}\right)^{-\frac{3}{2}}\left(\frac{1}{2}x^{-\frac{1}{2}}\right)$$

$$= -\frac{1}{4\sqrt{x}(4 + \sqrt{x})^{\frac{3}{2}}} \qquad \square$$

Example 4. Find the slopes of the tangent lines to the curve

$$y = \frac{x^{\frac{3}{2}}}{2 - 3x}$$

at the points $(1, -1)$, $\left(2, -\frac{\sqrt{2}}{2}\right)$, and $\left(3, -\frac{3\sqrt{3}}{7}\right)$. Before doing the calculation use the graph to predict whether the slope will be positive, negative, or zero.

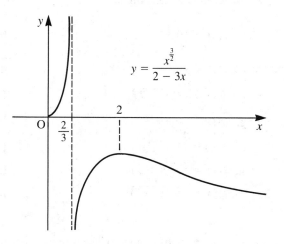

$$y = \frac{x^{\frac{3}{2}}}{2 - 3x}$$

Solution. From the graph, we expect a positive slope when $x = 1$, a zero slope when $x = 2$ (horizontal tangent line), and a negative slope when $x = 3$. By the Quotient and Power Rules,

$$\frac{dy}{dx} = \frac{(2 - 3x)\left(\frac{3}{2}x^{\frac{1}{2}}\right) - x^{\frac{3}{2}}(-3)}{(2 - 3x)^2}$$

$$= \frac{\frac{3}{2}x^{\frac{1}{2}}[(2 - 3x) + 2x]}{(2 - 3x)^2}$$

$$= \frac{3\sqrt{x}(2 - x)}{2(2 - 3x)^2}$$

The slopes of the tangent lines at the given points are shown in the table; their values agree with our prediction.

x	1	2	3
slope $= \dfrac{dy}{dx}$	$\dfrac{3}{2}$	0	$\dfrac{-3\sqrt{3}}{98}$

$\square$

Exercises 2.4

1. Use the definition of the derivative to find $f'(x)$.

    a. $f(x) = \sqrt{x}, \quad x > 0$

    b. $f(x) = \dfrac{1}{\sqrt{x}}, \quad x > 0$

    c. $f(x) = (3x + 1)^{\frac{1}{2}}, \quad x > -\dfrac{1}{3}$

    d. $f(x) = \dfrac{1}{\sqrt{x} + 1}, \quad x > 0$

2. Differentiate each function.

    a. $f(x) = 10x^{\frac{1}{5}}$

    b. $f(x) = \dfrac{300}{x^{\frac{2}{3}}}$

    c. $f(x) = x^2 + 3 - \dfrac{1}{\sqrt{x}}$

    d. $y = \sqrt{x} + 6\sqrt{x^3}$

    e. $f(x) = \sqrt{5x + 7}$

    f. $f(x) = \sqrt{x^2 - 3}$

    g. $g(t) = \dfrac{1}{\sqrt{4 + t^2}}$

    h. $g(t) = \dfrac{1}{2\sqrt{t} + 3}$

    i. $h(u) = (1 + u^{\frac{1}{3}})^6$

    j. $h(u) = \sqrt{u} + u^{-1}$

    k. $f(x) = \sqrt{x}(4 - x)^2$

    l. $f(x) = \dfrac{5}{7}x^{\frac{7}{5}} - \dfrac{2}{3}x^{\frac{3}{2}} + 2x^{-\frac{1}{2}}$

    m. $f(x) = \sqrt{(2x - 5)^5}$

    n. $f(x) = (x^2 + 1)\sqrt{1 - x^2}$

3. Find the rate of change of each function at the given value of t. Leave your answers as rational numbers, or in terms of roots and the number π.

    a. $f(t) = (\sqrt{t} - 2)(3\sqrt{t} + 8), \quad t = 2$

    b. $f(t) = \dfrac{\sqrt{t}}{1 + t}, \quad t = 1$

    c. $f(t) = \sqrt{t}(1 + t), \quad t = 4$

    d. $f(t) = \dfrac{t}{\sqrt{1 + t^2}}, \quad t = 1$

    e. $f(t) = t^{\frac{1}{3}}(4t - 5)^{\frac{2}{3}}, \quad t = 8$

    f. $f(t) = t(4 + \sqrt{t})^{\frac{1}{3}}, \quad t = 16$

    g. $f(t) = \left(\dfrac{\pi - t}{6\pi + t}\right)^{\frac{1}{3}}, \quad t = 2\pi$

    h. $f(t) = (t^2 + 3\pi^2)^{\frac{5}{2}}, \quad t = \pi$

4. Find $\dfrac{dy}{dx}$ by using the Quotient Rule and by using the Product Rule. Show that both methods lead to the same result.

    a. $y = \dfrac{\sqrt{1 - x}}{1 + x}$

    b. $y = \dfrac{x}{\sqrt{2x^2 - x}}$

5. Find the equation of

    a. the tangent line to the curve $y = \sqrt{16x^3}$ at the point (4, 32).
    b. the normal line to the curve $y = x\sqrt{x^2 - 3}$ at the point (2, 2).

    c. the tangent line to the curve $y = \sqrt{\dfrac{x - 1}{4x - 11}}$ at the point where $x = 5$.

By referring to the sketches of these curves, which are given below, check that your answers are reasonable.

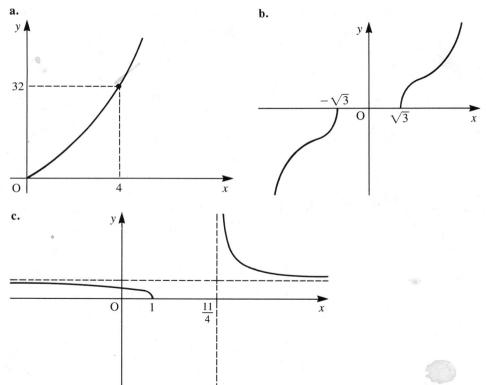

a.

b.

c.

6. Find the equation of the tangent line to the curve $y = \sqrt{7 + \sqrt{x}}$ at the point (4, 3).

7. It can be shown that from a height of h metres, a person can see a distance D kilometres to the horizon, where

$$D = 3.53 \sqrt{h}$$

    a. When the elevator of the CN Tower passes the 200 m height, how far can the passengers in the elevator see across Lake Ontario?
    b. Find the rate of change of this distance with respect to height when the height of the elevator is 200 m.

Problems 2.4

1. a. Let $P(a, b)$ be a point on the curve $\sqrt{x} + \sqrt{y} = 1$. Show that the slope of the tangent line at P is $-\sqrt{\dfrac{b}{a}}$.

  b. What happens to the slope of the tangent line as P approaches the points $(1, 0)$ and $(0, 1)$? Use this information to sketch the curve.

  c. Prove that the sum of the x-intercept and the y-intercept of the tangent line is a constant, independent of the point P.

2. Let $f(x) = \sqrt{2 + \sqrt{2 + \sqrt{2 + x}}}$ for $x > -2$. Verify that $f'(2) = \frac{1}{64}$. For what values of x, if any, does the derivative equal zero?

3. Consider the tangent line to the curve $y = \dfrac{1}{x^{\frac{1}{n}}}$ at the point $(1, 1)$, where n is an integer and $n \geq 2$. This tangent line intersects the curve $y = \dfrac{1}{x}$ at the point A, and it intersects the x-axis at the point B. If x_A and x_B are the x-coordinates of A and B, respectively, show that $x_B - x_A = 1$.

2.5 The Chain Rule

It is often helpful to regard complicated functions as being built up from simpler functions. For example, the function

$$y = f(x) = \sqrt{5 - x^2}$$

is built up by taking the square root of the function $5 - x^2$; that is,

$$y = \sqrt{u}, \quad \text{where} \quad u = 5 - x^2$$

If we let

$$g(u) = \sqrt{u} \quad \text{and} \quad h(x) = 5 - x^2$$

then

$$y = f(x) = g(h(x))$$

In words, the function value $f(x)$ is obtained by evaluating the function g at the value $h(x)$.

The function f, with values

$$f(x) = g(h(x))$$

is called **the composition of the functions g and h.** We say that f is a **composite function.**

For example, if

$$g(x) = \sqrt{x} + \frac{1}{\sqrt{x}} \quad \text{and} \quad h(x) = x^2 + 1$$

then the composition of g and h is

$$g(h(x)) = \sqrt{x^2 + 1} + \frac{1}{\sqrt{x^2 + 1}}$$

On the other hand, the composition of h and g is quite different:

$$h(g(x)) = \left(\sqrt{x} + \frac{1}{\sqrt{x}}\right)^2 + 1$$

Suppose that $y = g(u)$ and $u = h(x)$, so that y is a composite function of x, and suppose also that the derivatives of the functions g and h are known. How can we express $\frac{dy}{dx}$, the rate of change of y with respect to x, in terms of the known derivatives $\frac{dy}{du}$ and $\frac{du}{dx}$?

As a very simple example, if

$$y = 8u \quad \text{and} \quad u = \tfrac{1}{2}x$$

then

$$\frac{dy}{du} = 8 \quad \text{and} \quad \frac{du}{dx} = \frac{1}{2}$$

We can calculate $\frac{dy}{dx}$ directly by eliminating u.

$$\begin{aligned} y &= 8u \\ &= 8\left(\tfrac{1}{2}x\right) \\ &= 4x \end{aligned}$$

Thus, $\frac{dy}{dx} = 4$. Observe that, in this case,

$$\frac{dy}{dx} = \frac{dy}{du}\frac{du}{dx}$$

As a second example, if

$$y = u^r \quad \text{and} \quad u = g(x)$$

where r is a rational number, then

$$\frac{dy}{du} = ru^{r-1}$$

The Power of a Function Rule states that

$$\frac{dy}{dx} = ru^{r-1}\frac{du}{dx}$$

which can thus be written as

$$\frac{dy}{dx} = \frac{dy}{du}\frac{du}{dx}$$

These examples suggest the important Chain Rule of differentiation.

Chain Rule

If y is a function of u, and u is a function of x, then

$$\frac{dy}{dx} = \frac{dy}{du}\frac{du}{dx}$$

In words, the Chain Rule says:

If y is a function of u, and u is a function of x, then the derivative of y with respect to x is equal to the derivative of y with respect to u times the derivative of u with respect to x.

The following example illustrates the use of the Chain Rule for finding the derivative of a function that can be expressed as a composite function.

Example 1. Write

$$y = (1 - 2x^2)^3 - 4(1 - 2x^2)^2$$

as a composite function and use the Chain Rule to find $\frac{dy}{dx}$.

Solution. If we let

$$u = 1 - 2x^2$$

then

$$y = u^3 - 4u^2$$

Using the Chain Rule,

$$\frac{dy}{dx} = \frac{dy}{du}\frac{du}{dx}$$
$$= (3u^2 - 8u)(-4x)$$
$$= -4x[3(1 - 2x^2)^2 - 8(1 - 2x^2)] \qquad \square$$

In the previous example, we could have used the Power of a Function Rule to find the derivative. It should be noted, however, that the **Chain Rule is not restricted to power functions**. We shall use it extensively in Chapters 5 and 6 when we work with trigonometric, logarithmic, and exponential functions. In addition, the Chain Rule allows us to find derivatives of composite functions even if the functions that are being composed are not known. This is illustrated in the next example, where one of the functions is left unspecified. You could think of the unspecified function as the sine function or some other function whose derivative we do not yet know.

Example 2. If $y = f(u)$, and $u = \sqrt{x} + \dfrac{1}{\sqrt{x}}$, express $\dfrac{dy}{dx}$ in terms of $\dfrac{dy}{du}$.

Solution. By the Chain Rule,

$$\frac{dy}{dx} = \frac{dy}{du}\frac{du}{dx}$$

$$= \frac{dy}{du}\left[\frac{1}{2}x^{-\frac{1}{2}} - \frac{1}{2}x^{-\frac{3}{2}}\right]$$

$$= \frac{1}{2}\left(\frac{1}{\sqrt{x}} - \frac{1}{x\sqrt{x}}\right)\frac{dy}{du} \qquad \square$$

Proof of the Chain Rule

Let y be a function of u, such that $y = g(u)$ where u is a function of x, such that $u = h(x)$. A change Δx in x will produce a change Δu in u, which in turn will produce a change Δy in y.

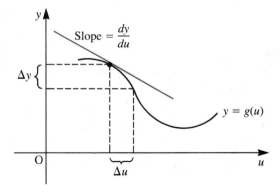

By the definition of the derivative,

$$\frac{dy}{dx} = \lim_{\Delta x \to 0} \frac{\Delta y}{\Delta x}$$

$$= \lim_{\Delta x \to 0} \left(\frac{\Delta y}{\Delta u}\frac{\Delta u}{\Delta x}\right)$$

(multiply and divide by Δu)

$$= \left(\lim_{\Delta x \to 0}\frac{\Delta y}{\Delta u}\right)\left(\lim_{\Delta x \to 0}\frac{\Delta u}{\Delta x}\right)$$

(product property of limits)

$$= \left(\lim_{\Delta u \to 0}\frac{\Delta y}{\Delta u}\right)\left(\lim_{\Delta x \to 0}\frac{\Delta u}{\Delta x}\right)$$

(since $\Delta u \to 0$ as $\Delta x \to 0$)

$$= \frac{dy}{du}\frac{du}{dx}$$

(by the definition of the derivative)

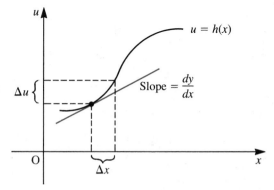

This proof is not valid in all circumstances, since in dividing by Δu we assumed that $\Delta u \neq 0$ whenever $\Delta x \neq 0$, as is the case in the situation illustrated in the diagram. A more advanced proof is needed to avoid this difficulty. $\qquad \square$

The next example illustrates an application of the Chain Rule.

Example 3. The radius of a circular oil slick on a body of water is increasing at a rate of 2 m/min. Find the rate of change of area of the oil slick when its radius is 50 m.

Solution. The area A of the oil slick is

$$A = \pi r^2$$

where r is a function of time t. By the Chain Rule,

$$\frac{dA}{dt} = \frac{dA}{dr}\frac{dr}{dt}$$

$$= 2\pi r\frac{dr}{dt}$$

It is given that $\dfrac{dr}{dt} = 2$. Thus when $r = 50$, the rate of change of area is

$$\frac{dA}{dt} = 2\pi(50)(2)$$

$$= 200\pi \text{ m}^2/\text{min} \qquad \square$$

"The Chain Rule" owes its name to the fact that a composite function describes a "chain of dependence,"

$$x \to u \to y,$$

such that the independent variable x determines u, which in turn determines the dependent variable y. The Chain Rule states that the derivative of the dependent variable y with respect to the independent variable x is the product of the derivatives of the separate "links" in the chain:

$$\frac{dy}{dx} = \frac{dy}{du}\frac{du}{dx}$$

One can have a chain of variables with more links, for example

$$x \to v \to u \to y$$

and the Chain Rule can be applied in succession to find $\dfrac{dy}{dx}$, as is illustrated in Example 4.

Example 4. If

$$y = \frac{1}{6}u^3 - 4\sqrt{u}, \quad u = 16 + v + v^2, \quad \text{and } v = x - \frac{1}{x}$$

find $\dfrac{dy}{dx}$ when $x = 1$.

Solution. **By the Chain Rule,**

$$\frac{dy}{dx} = \frac{dy}{du}\frac{du}{dx}$$

Since u is a composite function of x, we apply the Chain Rule again, obtaining

$$\frac{du}{dx} = \frac{du}{dv}\frac{dv}{dx}$$

which leads to

$$\frac{dy}{dx} = \frac{dy}{du}\frac{du}{dv}\frac{dv}{dx}$$

On differentiating the given functions, we get

$$\frac{dy}{dx} = \left(\frac{1}{2}u^2 - \frac{2}{\sqrt{u}}\right)(1 + 2v)\left(1 + \frac{1}{x^2}\right)$$

When $x = 1$, it follows that $v = 0$ and $u = 16$, so that

$$\frac{dy}{dx} = \left(\frac{256}{2} - \frac{1}{2}\right)(1)(2)$$

$$= 255 \qquad \qquad \square$$

Although the derivative $\frac{dy}{dx}$ should normally be expressed as a function of the variable x, the previous example shows that it can be convenient to leave $\frac{dy}{dx}$ in terms of the "intermediate variables" u and v.

For some purposes, it is more convenient to express the Chain Rule in the prime notation for derivatives. Let $y = g(u)$ and $u = h(x)$; then the composition of g and h is the function

$$y = g(h(x))$$

In this composite function we refer to g as the "outer" function and to h as the "inner" function.

The derivatives that appear on the right side of the Chain Rule are

$$\frac{dy}{du} = g'(u) = g'(h(x))$$

and

$$\frac{du}{dx} = h'(x)$$

The Chain Rule thus assumes the form given below.

Chain Rule (prime notation)

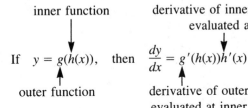

For example, if

$$y = (5 - 2x^6)^4$$

the inner function is $h(x) = 5 - 2x^6$ and the outer function is $g(u) = u^4$. Since

$$g'(u) = 4u^3 \quad \text{and} \quad h'(x) = -12x^5$$

the derivative of the composite function is

$$\frac{dy}{dx} = g'(h(x))h'(x) = 4(5 - 2x^6)^3(-12x^5)$$

The final example illustrates the use of the Chain Rule with prime notation.

Example 5. Find a formula for $\dfrac{dy}{dx}$ when $x = 2$, if

a. $y = f(x^2)$ **b.** $y = [f(x)]^2$

Solution.
a. By the Chain Rule,

$$\frac{dy}{dx} = f'(x^2)(2x)$$

When $x = 2$,

$$\frac{dy}{dx} = 4f'(4)$$

b. By the Chain Rule,

$$\frac{dy}{dx} = 2f(x)f'(x)$$

When $x = 2$,

$$\frac{dy}{dx} = 2f(2)f'(2)$$

We encourage you to become familiar with both forms of the Chain Rule. The prime notation has the advantage of specifically showing the functional dependence. On the other hand, the Leibniz notation

$$\frac{dy}{dx} = \frac{dy}{du}\frac{du}{dx}$$

is convenient in that it suggests the correct form of the Chain Rule: one can imagine the du's as cancelling. The cancellation is of course not a valid operation, since $\frac{dy}{du}$ is not the quotient of the symbols dy and du but is a single symbol for the derivative.

We end this section by reiterating that the Power of a Function Rule is a special case of the Chain Rule. For example, if

$$y = (1 + x^2)^{\frac{1}{2}}$$

then

$$\frac{dy}{dx} = \frac{1}{2}(1 + x^2)^{-\frac{1}{2}}(2x)$$

which is of the form

$$\frac{dy}{dx} = \frac{dy}{du}\frac{du}{dx}$$

where $\frac{dy}{du} = \frac{1}{2}u^{-\frac{1}{2}}$ is the derivative of the "outer function" and $\frac{du}{dx} = 2x$ is the derivative of the "inner function." From now on, when we use the Power of a Function Rule we shall refer to the more general Chain Rule.

Exercises 2.5

1. Write each function as a composition of two functions.

a. $y = (3x^3 + x - 2)^4 + 4(3x^3 + x - 2)^2$

b. $y = 2(\sqrt{x^2 + 1})^3 - 3\sqrt{x^2 + 1} + 5$

c. $y = \dfrac{(1 - 2x^{\frac{5}{2}})^2}{1 + (1 - 2x^{\frac{5}{2}})^3}$

d. $y = \left(3 - \dfrac{2}{\sqrt{x}}\right)^2 \sqrt{1 + \left(3 - \dfrac{2}{\sqrt{x}}\right)^3}$

2. Use the Chain Rule to find $\dfrac{dy}{dx}$ at the indicated value of x.

a. $y = 2u^3 + 3u^2, \quad u = x + \dfrac{1}{\sqrt{x}}; \quad x = 1$

b. $y = \dfrac{1-u}{1+u}, \quad u = \sqrt{x^2 + 5}; \quad x = -2$

c. $y = \sqrt{u^2 + 5}, \quad u = \dfrac{1-x}{1+x}; \quad x = -2$

d. $y = \dfrac{1}{(1+u^2)^2}, \quad u = \sqrt{x} - 1; \quad x = 4$

3. a. If $y = f(u)$ and $u = \sqrt{5 - x^2}$, so that y depends on x, express $\dfrac{dy}{dx}$ in terms of $\dfrac{dy}{du}$.

b. If $y = g(x)$ and $x = t^2\sqrt{t+1}$, so that y depends on t, express $\dfrac{dy}{dt}$ in terms of $\dfrac{dy}{dx}$.

c. If $u = h(v)$ and $v = (w^{\frac{1}{3}} + 1)^3$, so that u depends on w, express $\dfrac{du}{dw}$ in terms of $\dfrac{du}{dv}$.

4. If y is a function of x, find an expression for each derivative in terms of $\dfrac{dy}{dx}$.

a. $\dfrac{d}{dx}(y^2)$ **b.** $\dfrac{d}{dx}(y^{\frac{1}{3}})$ **c.** $\dfrac{d}{dx}(x^2 + y^2)$ **d.** $\dfrac{d}{dx}(xy^3)$

5. Use the Chain Rule to find $\dfrac{dy}{dx}$ at the indicated value of x.

a. $y = u^5 + u^3, \quad u = 4v + 3v^{-1}, \quad v = 3 - x^2; \quad x = 2$

b. $y = \dfrac{12}{(1 + 2u)^3}, \quad u = 1 - \dfrac{2}{v^2}, \quad v = 2x - 3\sqrt{x}; \quad x = 4$

c. $y = \sqrt{2 + u}, \quad u = \sqrt{2 + v}, \quad v = \sqrt{2 + x}; \quad x = 2$

6. The radius of a circle is increasing at a rate of 3 cm/s. Find the rate of change of the area of the circle when the radius is 10 cm.

7. The volume of a spherical balloon of radius r is $V = \dfrac{4}{3}\pi r^3$. If the radius is increasing at a rate of 0.03 m/s when the radius is 3 m, find the rate of change of volume with respect to time, at that instant.

8. The temperature T of a metal rod decreases with respect to distance x from the rod's left end, at a rate of 3°C/cm. An ant, which is trying to get cooler, crawls along the rod from left to right at a rate of 2 cm/s.

a. Write the given rates of change as derivatives.

b. Use the Chain Rule to find the rate of change of temperature, as felt by the ant, with respect to time t.

9. Water flows into a bathtub at a rate of 20 L/min, and the level rises 0.1 cm for each litre added.

   a. Write the given rates of change as derivatives. Use V to denote volume, h to denote the height of the water surface, and t to denote time.
   b. Use the Chain Rule to find how fast the water level is rising.

10. Find a formula for $\frac{dy}{dx}$ when $x = \frac{1}{2}$ if

   a. $y = f(x^3)$ **b.** $y = [f(x)]^3$ **c.** $y = (1 + f(x))^2$

11. Let $y = f(x^2 + 3x - 5)$. Find $\frac{dy}{dx}$ when $x = 1$, given that $f'(-1) = 2$.

12. a. Let $y = g(h(x))$ where $h(x) = \frac{x^2}{x + 2}$. If $g'\left(\frac{9}{5}\right) = -2$, find $\frac{dy}{dx}$ when $x = 3$.

   b. Let $p = q(r(t))$ where $r(t) = (t^2 + t + 2)^{-\frac{1}{3}}$. If $q'\left(\frac{1}{2}\right) = 3$, find $\frac{dp}{dt}$ when $t = 2$.

   c. Let $v = h(p(u))$ where $p(u) = u^{\frac{5}{2}} - 2u$. If $h'(24) = -\frac{1}{2}$, find $\frac{dv}{du}$ when $u = 4$.

13. Suppose that $f'(u) = \frac{u}{\sqrt{1 + 12u^2}}$ and that $g(x) = \frac{1}{1 + x^3}$. If $y = f(g(x))$, find $\frac{dy}{dx}$ when $x = 1$.

14. Let $y = \sqrt{x + f(x^2 - 1)}$. Find $\frac{dy}{dx}$ when $x = 3$, given that $f(8) = 0$ and $f'(8) = 3$.

Problems 2.5

1. A skydiver jumps from an airplane at 3000 m. The distance fallen (in metres) after t seconds is approximated by

$$s = 5t^2$$

As he falls, he experiences a change in air pressure p that will cause his ears to "pop" if the rate of change of pressure $\frac{dp}{dt}$ exceeds 2 pressure units/s. Suppose that the rate of change of pressure with respect to altitude (in metres) is 0.075 pressure units/m. At what time will the skydiver's ears pop? At what height will this occur?

2. Suppose that f and g are functions such that

$$f(1) = -\frac{1}{2}, \quad f'(1) = -\frac{2}{3}, \quad g(2) = 1, \quad \text{and } g'(2) = 3$$

   a. Find $h'(2)$ where h is the composite function $h(x) = f(g(x))$.
   b. What additional information would you need to find $k'(1)$ where k is the composite function $k(x) = g(f(x))$?

3. If $h(x) = f\left(\dfrac{p(x)}{q(x)}\right)$, express $h'(x)$ in terms of the derivatives f', p', and q'.

4. Given a function f_1, we define f_2, f_3, etc., by

$$f_2(x) = f_1(f_1(x)), \quad f_3(x) = f_1(f_1(f_1(x))), \text{ etc.}$$

Let

$$f_1(x) = \frac{1}{2 - 4x}$$

a. Show that $f_2(x) = \dfrac{1}{2} - \dfrac{1}{4x}$.

b. Find an expression for $f_{83}(x)$.

Review Exercises

1. Differentiate each function.

a. $y = 2x^5 - 7x^3 + 3x$

b. $y = -3x^{-6}$

c. $y = \dfrac{1}{5x^5}$

d. $y = 5x + \dfrac{3}{x^2}$

e. $y = (11t^2 + 1)^2$

f. $y = \dfrac{2}{(5 - x^2)^2}$

g. $y = \sqrt{t} + \sqrt{t^2}$

h. $y = \dfrac{1}{3u + 1} - \dfrac{1}{2u + 1}$

i. $w = \sqrt{9t^2 + 4}$

j. $w = (3t^4 - \pi)^4$

k. $w = (x^7 + 1)^{\frac{5}{9}}$

l. $w = (3x^5 - 2)^{\frac{2}{5}}$

2. Differentiate each function. In some cases it will save time to rearrange the function before you differentiate.

a. $y = \dfrac{x - 1}{x}$

b. $y = (x^3 - 3x)^2$

c. $y = \sqrt{x}(x^5 - x^3)$

d. $y = \dfrac{x^5 - x^3}{\sqrt{x}}$

e. $y = \sqrt{x - 1}(x + 1)$

f. $y = \dfrac{x^2 + x^{-1}}{x^2 - x^{-1}}$

g. $y = \dfrac{(2 - x^2)(2 + x^2)}{3 - x}$

h. $y = \dfrac{x^{\frac{4}{3}}}{2x - 5}$

i. $y = \sqrt{(x + 1)(2 - x)}$

j. $y = \dfrac{1}{1 + \dfrac{1}{x}}$

3. Find $\dfrac{dy}{dx}$ by using the Quotient Rule and by using the Product Rule. Show that both methods lead to the same result.

a. $y = \dfrac{1 - x^2}{1 + x^2}$

b. $y = \dfrac{x^2 + 2x - 7}{(x + 1)^2}$

4. Find the derivative, and give your answer in a simplified form.

a. $y = (x - 2)^3\left(\frac{1}{2}x + 1\right)^4$

b. $y = x^4(3x - 1)^6$

c. $y = \dfrac{(2x - 5)^3}{(x + 1)^4}$

d. $y = (9x - 1)^4(1 - 10x)^{\frac{3}{2}}$

e. $w = \dfrac{u^4}{(3u - 2)^3}$

f. $w = t^{\frac{5}{3}}(3 - t)^2$

g. $y = t(5t^2 + 7t - 2)$

h. $y = \dfrac{(t^2 - 1)^3}{(t^2 + 1)^3}$

i. $y = \left(\dfrac{\sqrt{x} - 1}{\sqrt{x} + 1}\right)^3$

j. $y = \dfrac{\sqrt{t - 1}}{t^2}$

5. a. If $y = 3u^2 + 5u - 7$ and $u = \dfrac{26}{x^3 + 5}$, find $\dfrac{dy}{dx}$ when $x = 2$.

b. If $y = \dfrac{u - 4}{u + 4}$ and $u = \dfrac{9}{\sqrt{x} + 1}$, find $\dfrac{dy}{dx}$ when $x = 4$.

c. If $y = f(\sqrt{x^2 + 9})$ and $f'(5) = -2$, find $\dfrac{dy}{dx}$ when $x = 4$.

d. If $y = u^3 - \dfrac{3}{u^3}$ and $u = \sqrt{2x + 5}$, find $\dfrac{dy}{dx}$ when $x = -2$.

e. If $y = 4u - u^2$ and $u = |x|$, find $\dfrac{dy}{dx}$ when $x = -3$.

6. If y is a function of x, find a formula for the following derivatives in terms of $\dfrac{dy}{dx}$.

a. $\dfrac{d}{dx}\left(\dfrac{x}{y}\right)$

b. $\dfrac{d}{dx}(xy^2 + x^2y)$

c. $\dfrac{d}{dx}\left[\dfrac{x}{x^2 + y^2}\right]$

d. $\dfrac{d}{dx}(\sqrt{x^2 + y^2})$

7. Find the equation of the tangent line to the curve $y = x + \dfrac{1}{x^2}$ that is parallel to the line $x + y + 3 = 0$.

8. Consider the graph of the function

$$f(x) = \frac{x^3}{x^2 - 6}$$

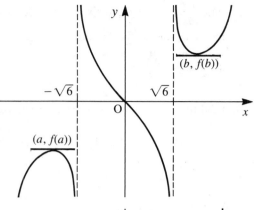

a. Find the slope of the tangent line to the graph at $(2, -4)$. Use the graph to verify that your answer is reasonable.

b. Find the values of a and b.

9. Consider the graph of the function

$$f(x) = 2x^{\frac{5}{3}} - 5x^{\frac{2}{3}}$$

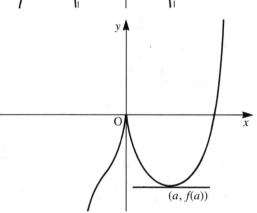

a. Find the slope of the tangent line when the graph crosses the x-axis.

b. Find the value of a.

10. Given the two parabolas $y = 2 - x^2$ and $y = 5 + x^2$, determine the equations of all common tangent lines. Illustrate with a sketch.

11. Let P be any point in the first quadrant on the hyperbola $y = \frac{1}{x}$. The tangent to the hyperbola at P meets the x-axis at A and the y-axis at B. If O is the origin, show that the area of $\triangle AOB$ is 2.

12. The radius of a sphere is

$$r = 3\sqrt{t} - t$$

at time t. Find the rate of change of the volume V of the sphere when $t = 1$ and $t = 4$. Is the volume increasing or decreasing at these times?

13. The lengths of the sides of a rectangle are

$$a = (1 + t^{\frac{1}{3}})^3 \quad \text{and} \quad b = (10 - \sqrt{t})^2$$

at time t. Find the rate of change of area when $t = 64$. Is the area increasing or decreasing at this time?

14. Consider the curve $y = x + \dfrac{1}{x}$. At what point(s) is the tangent line parallel

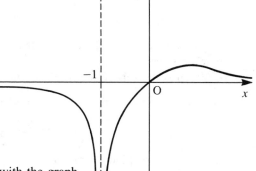

   a. to the line $y = -x$?
   b. to the line $y = x$?

15. Consider the graph of the function

$$y = \frac{x}{(x + 1)^2}$$

At what point(s) is the slope of the tangent line equal

   a. to 1?   **b.** to 0?

Check that your answers are compatible with the graph.

16. The radius of a circle is a function of time defined by $r = 4t^2 + 3t + 1$. Determine the rate of change of area of the circle when $\dfrac{dr}{dt} = 11$.

17. In order to make repairs to a retaining wall that is 40 m high, the water in a conservation reservoir is slowly drained out over a 4-week period. Starting at $t = 0$, the water is released so that after t days, the water depth D (in metres) is approximated by

$$D = 10\left(2 - \frac{t}{14}\right)^2$$

   a. Find the rate of change of depth D with respect to time t.
   b. At what rate is the depth changing after 1 week? 2 weeks?
   c. Find the rate of change of depth when the depth is 22.5 m.
   d. Sketch the graph of D for $0 \le t \le 28$.

18. The position (in metres) of a moving object at time t (in seconds) is given by

$$s(t) = 10t - \frac{3t}{t + 3}.$$

Find the velocity of the object initially ($t = 0$) and after 7 s.

19. The population P (in thousands) in the town of Powassan is given by the function

$$P(t) = 10\left(\frac{6t + 9}{3t + 7}\right)$$

where t is the time in years since 1955. Find the rate of change of the population in 1986.

20. The estimated number of houses in the Beechwood West subdivision after t months is given by the function

$$N(t) = \frac{1000t}{14 + t}$$

a. Find the number of houses and the rate of change of the number after 6 months and after 3 years.

b. When is the subdivision growing most rapidly?

21. Suppose that t hours after a side of beef is put in a freezer, its temperature (in °C) is

$$T(t) = 15 - 3t + \frac{4}{t + 1}$$

where $0 \le t \le 5$. Find the rate of change of temperature after one hour. Comment on the sign of the rate of change.

22. If the price of a racing bike is x dollars, where $400 \le x \le 900$, the total number of bikes sold at the Speedy Cycle Shop is

$$D(x) = \frac{1}{5}\left(30 - \frac{x}{50}\right)^2$$

a. Write a formula for the total revenue $R(x)$ generated when the price is x dollars.

b. Find the derivative $R'(x)$.

c. Hence determine whether the total revenue will increase if the price of a bike is increased from (i) \$450 to \$455 (ii) \$700 to \$705.

23. Suppose that the length of the base b and the height h of a triangle change with time.

a. Use the Product Rule to express the rate of change of area $\dfrac{dA}{dt}$ in terms of $\dfrac{db}{dt}$ and $\dfrac{dh}{dt}$.

b. The base of a triangle grows at a rate of 3 cm/min, and the height shrinks at a rate of 2 cm/min. Find the rate of change of area of the triangle when the base is 50 cm and the height is 30 cm. Is the area increasing or decreasing?

24. Suppose that the radius r and length h of a right circular cylinder change with time.

a. Express the rate of change of volume $\dfrac{dV}{dt}$ in terms of $\dfrac{dr}{dt}$ and $\dfrac{dh}{dt}$.

b. Suppose that the radius grows at a rate of 3 cm/min, and the length shrinks at a rate of 2 cm/min. Find the rate of change of the volume when the radius equals 20 cm and the height equals 12 cm. Is the volume increasing or decreasing?

25. A right circular cylinder of length 1 m and volume 0.1 m³, made of a pliable material, is being compressed between two metal plates so that its length decreases at 1 cm/min. If the volume of the cylinder stays constant, how fast is the radius increasing when the length of the cylinder is 50 cm?

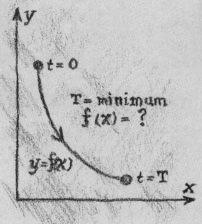

The Bernoulli Family

Jakob Bernoulli (1654–1705) taught himself the new Calculus of Newton and Leibniz, as did his younger brother Johann (1667–1748). Jakob invented polar coordinates and made significant contributions to the theory of probability. Johann first studied medicine (taking a doctor's degree at the University of Basel, Switzerland, with a thesis on muscle contraction). He soon became fascinated with Calculus, applying these new methods to a variety of problems in geometry, differential equations and mechanics. Both brothers became professors of mathematics at Basel (with Johann succeeding his older brother). There was a bitter rivalry between them which was aggravated when they worked on the same problem. In 1689 Johann posed the brachistochrone problem as a challenge to the mathematicians of the world: "A wire is bent in a curve which joins two given points. A bead slides down the wire without friction. What curve will give the minimum time of descent?" It is said that Newton, after a day at the Mint, learned of the problem and solved it the same afternoon. It was also solved by Jakob Bernoulli and Leibniz. Johann's son, Daniel (1700–1782), also gave up medicine for mathematics and went on to become an outstanding mathematical physicist. In three generations the Bernoulli family produced eight mathematicians and scientists, the above three being the most outstanding. (Note: The brachistochrone curve is the "cycloid": if a circle rolls without slipping on a flat surface, a point on its circumference traces a cycloid.)

Applications of the Derivative

Having developed the rules of differentiation in Chapter 2, we are now in a position to discuss a variety of applications of differential Calculus. In this chapter we consider the following concepts:

- implicit differentiation
- velocity and acceleration
- related rates of change
- maximum and minimum values
- tangent line approximation
- Newton's method for finding roots

3.1 Implicit Differentiation

Until now we have dealt with curves that are defined by an equation of the form

$$y = f(x)$$

in which y is defined **explicitly** in terms of x. Examples of functions defined explicitly are $y = x^2$, $y = \sqrt{1 - x^2}$, and $y = x^3 - 3x$.

However, curves may also be defined by a relation such as

$$\frac{x^2}{4} + y^2 = 1 \tag{1}$$

where y is not given explicitly in terms of x. In this case, we may solve for y to obtain either

$$y = \sqrt{1 - \frac{x^2}{4}} \tag{2}$$

or

$$y = -\sqrt{1 - \frac{x^2}{4}} \tag{3}$$

We say that the functions defined explicitly by equations (2) and (3) are defined **implicitly** by equation (1). Equation (1) represents an ellipse, equation (2) represents the upper half of this ellipse, and equation (3) represents the lower half of this ellipse.

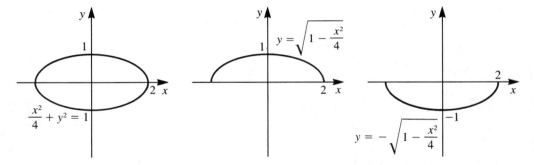

Consider the problem of finding the slope of the tangent line to the ellipse at the point $\left(1, -\frac{\sqrt{3}}{2}\right)$. Since this point lies on the lower half of the ellipse, we could differentiate the function

$$y = -\sqrt{1 - \frac{x^2}{4}}$$

in the usual way and substitute $x = 1$ into the resulting expression for $\frac{dy}{dx}$. An alternative, which avoids having to solve for y explicitly in terms of x, is to use the **method of implicit differentiation**. This method is illustrated in Example 1.

Example 1.

a. Let $y = f(x)$ be a function that satisfies the equation

$$\frac{x^2}{4} + y^2 = 1$$

Express $\frac{dy}{dx}$ in terms of x and y.

b. Find the slope of the tangent line to the ellipse $\dfrac{x^2}{4} + y^2 = 1$ at the points $\left(1, \dfrac{\sqrt{3}}{2}\right)$ and $\left(1, -\dfrac{\sqrt{3}}{2}\right)$.

Solution.

a. Since $y = f(x)$ satisfies the equation $\dfrac{x^2}{4} + y^2 = 1$, we have

$$\frac{x^2}{4} + [f(x)]^2 = 1$$

for all x in the domain of f. Differentiate both sides of this equation with respect to x to obtain

$$\frac{d}{dx}\left[\frac{x^2}{4} + [f(x)]^2\right] = \frac{d}{dx}(1)$$

which can be simplified to

$$\frac{x}{2} + 2f(x)f'(x) = 0$$

Therefore,

$$f'(x) = -\frac{x}{4f(x)}$$

Since $y = f(x)$,

$$\frac{dy}{dx} = -\frac{x}{4y}$$

Note that this result is valid for all points (x, y) on the ellipse, provided that $y \neq 0$.

b. At the point $\left(1, \dfrac{\sqrt{3}}{2}\right)$, the slope of the tangent line is

$$\frac{dy}{dx} = -\frac{1}{4\left(\dfrac{\sqrt{3}}{2}\right)}$$

$$= -\frac{1}{2\sqrt{3}}$$

At the point $\left(1, -\dfrac{\sqrt{3}}{2}\right)$, the slope of the

tangent line is

$$\frac{dy}{dx} = -\frac{1}{4\left(-\dfrac{\sqrt{3}}{2}\right)}$$

$$= \frac{1}{2\sqrt{3}}$$

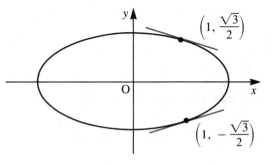

These values are compatible with the diagram. ☐

The function $f(x)$ in Example 1 can be thought of as being either

$$y = \sqrt{1 - \frac{x^2}{4}} \quad \text{or} \quad y = -\sqrt{1 - \frac{x^2}{4}}$$

The essential point is that implicit differentiation enables one to treat the relation as a whole, without focusing on either of the two functions and without even knowing their explicit form. In order to appreciate the efficiency of implicit differentiation, we suggest that you do part (b) of Example 1 by solving for y and differentiating in the usual way.

In practice, one streamlines the notation used in Example 1 by not substituting the function symbol $f(x)$ for y. Given the equation

$$\frac{x^2}{4} + y^2 = 1$$

one mentally views y as a function of x and differentiates both sides of the equation with respect to x to obtain

$$\frac{x}{2} + 2y\frac{dy}{dx} = 0$$

which yields

$$\frac{dy}{dx} = -\frac{x}{4y}$$

as before. This is **the method of implicit differentiation**.

In the next example we illustrate the efficiency of implicit differentiation by giving a simple proof of a well-known geometric property.

Example 2. If $x^2 + y^2 = 25$, express $\frac{dy}{dx}$ in terms of x and y. Using this result, verify that any tangent line to this circle is perpendicular to the radius at the point of tangency.

Solution. Treating y as a function of x, we differentiate both sides of the equation $x^2 + y^2 = 25$ with respect to x to obtain

$$2x + 2y\frac{dy}{dx} = 0$$

Thus, at any point on the circle where $y \neq 0$, the slope of the tangent line is

$$\frac{dy}{dx} = -\frac{x}{y}$$

On the other hand, the slope of the radius through the point (x, y) is $\frac{y}{x}$, provided that $x \neq 0$. The product of the slopes is $\left(\frac{-x}{y}\right)\left(\frac{y}{x}\right) = -1$, which proves that the tangent line and radius are perpendicular at all points **except** $(0, 5)$, $(0, -5)$, $(5, 0)$, and $(-5, 0)$. At $(0, 5)$ and $(0, -5)$ the tangent line is horizontal and the radius is vertical, and at $(5, 0)$ and $(-5, 0)$ the tangent line is vertical and the radius is horizontal. Therefore, the tangent line and radius are perpendicular at all points on the circle.

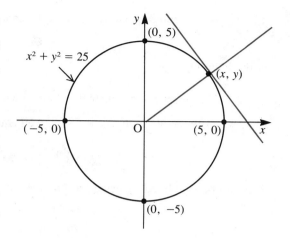

Many equations in x and y cannot be solved to obtain an explicit expression for y as a function of x. An example is

$$y^5 + x^2y - 2x^2 = -1$$

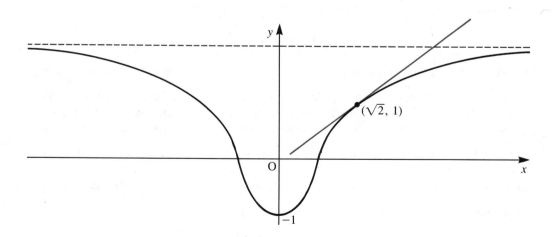

The curve defined by this equation is shown in the diagram (we do not expect you to be able to sketch such curves). This curve is the graph of a function, but one that is defined implicitly. Since we cannot solve the equation to obtain an explicit expression for y in terms of x, the only way to calculate the derivative $\frac{dy}{dx}$ is to use the method of implicit differentiation.

Example 3. Find the equation of the tangent line to the curve

$$y^5 + x^2y - 2x^2 = -1$$

at the point $(\sqrt{2}, 1)$.

Solution. We must first calculate the slope $\dfrac{dy}{dx}$ when $(x, y) = (\sqrt{2}, 1)$. Treating y as a function of x, we differentiate both sides of the given equation with respect to x to obtain

$$\frac{d}{dx}(y^5) + \frac{d}{dx}(x^2y) - \frac{d}{dx}(2x^2) = 0$$

This can be simplified by using the Product and Chain Rules to read

$$5y^4\frac{dy}{dx} + 2xy + x^2\frac{dy}{dx} - 4x = 0$$

On substituting $(x, y) = (\sqrt{2}, 1)$ we obtain

$$5\frac{dy}{dx} + 2\sqrt{2} + 2\frac{dy}{dx} - 4\sqrt{2} = 0$$

which yields

$$\frac{dy}{dx} = \frac{2\sqrt{2}}{7}$$

The equation of the required tangent line at the point $(\sqrt{2}, 1)$ is

$$y - 1 = \frac{2\sqrt{2}}{7}(x - \sqrt{2}) \qquad \square$$

Implicit differentiation provides us with a method for calculating the derivative $\dfrac{dy}{dx}$ for an implicitly defined function or for a relation. Note, however, that the expressions that result will usually involve both x and y. If a point on the graph of the function or relation is given (as in Example 3), then it is easy to calculate the value of the derivative. On the other hand, it is usually impossible to find the value of $\dfrac{dy}{dx}$ if only x is given. In Example 3, if we wish to find $\dfrac{dy}{dx}$ when $x = 2$, then we must also determine the y-value at $x = 2$. Substituting $x = 2$, the given equation reduces to

$$y^5 + 4y - 7 = 0$$

which cannot be solved exactly for y. There are, however, methods for finding an approximate solution of such an equation. One of these methods is discussed in section 3.7.

In the final example, we show that it can be convenient to use implicit differentiation to find $\dfrac{dy}{dx}$ even when y is given explicitly in terms of x.

Example 4. Find the slope of the tangent line to the curve

$$y = \sqrt[3]{6 + x^2}$$

at the point $(\sqrt{2}, 2)$.

Solution. Raise both sides of the equation to the third power to obtain

$$y^3 = 6 + x^2$$

Using the method of implicit differentiation, we obtain

$$3y^2 \frac{dy}{dx} = 2x$$

which yields

$$\frac{dy}{dx} = \frac{2x}{3y^2}$$

The slope of the tangent line at $(\sqrt{2}, 2)$ is thus

$$\frac{dy}{dx} = \frac{2(\sqrt{2})}{3(2)^2}$$

$$= \frac{\sqrt{2}}{6} \qquad \square$$

Exercises 3.1

1. Let $y = f(x)$ be a function that satisfies the given equation. Find $\dfrac{dy}{dx}$ in terms of x and y, using implicit differentiation.

   a. $4x^2 + y^2 = 8$
   b. $3x - 4y^2 = 2$
   c. $x^2 + y^2 + 5y = 10$
   d. $xy^2 = 4$
   e. $x^2 + 2xy - y^2 = 13$
   f. $y^3 + y = 4x$
   g. $y(x^2 + 3) = y^4 + 1$
   h. $(x - 1)^2 + (y - 1)^2 = 4$
   i. $xy^3 + x^3y = 2$
   j. $\sqrt{x} + \sqrt{y} = \sqrt{b}$ where b is a positive constant

2. Find the equation of the tangent line to the hyperbola $x^2 - 4y^2 = 5$ at the point $(3, -1)$.

   a. by using implicit differentiation,
   b. by solving explicitly for y.

3. For each curve, find the equations of the tangent line and the normal line at the given point.

   a. $\dfrac{x^2}{100} + \dfrac{y^2}{25} = 1$, $(-8, -3)$
   b. $4x^2 - 9y^2 = 36$, $\left(-5, \dfrac{8}{3}\right)$
   c. $xy = 64$, $(16, 4)$
   d. $x^3 + y^3 - 3xy = 17$, $(2, 3)$
   e. $y^2 = \dfrac{x^3}{2 - x}$, $(1, -1)$
   f. $y = \dfrac{75}{x^2 + y^2}$, $(4, 3)$
   g. $8\dfrac{y}{x^2} - 8\dfrac{x}{y^2} = 7$, $(2, 4)$

4. Write each function in an implicit form without radicals, and hence find $\dfrac{dy}{dx}$ in terms of x and y.

   a. $y = -2\sqrt{x}$ **b.** $y = \sqrt{3-x}$ **c.** $y = \sqrt[3]{x}$

   d. $y = -\sqrt{4-x^2}$ **e.** $y = \dfrac{3}{\sqrt{x}}$ **f.** $y = \sqrt{x} + 5$

5. Show that, if $15x = 15y + 5y^3 + 3y^5$, then

$$\frac{dy}{dx} = (1 + y^2 + y^4)^{-1}$$

6. Let $y = -(65 - x^6)^{\frac{1}{6}}$. Find the equation of the tangent line at $(1, -2)$ by expressing the curve in a simple implicit form, and then using implicit differentiation.

7. At what points on the curve $y^3 - 3x = 5$ is the slope of the tangent line equal to 1?

8. At what points on the ellipse

$$\frac{x^2}{9} + \frac{y^2}{16} = 1$$

   is the slope of the tangent line equal to 1? Illustrate your answer with a sketch.

9. For each of the following equations, find the indicated derivative by using implicit differentiation.

   a. $PV = 1000$; find $\dfrac{dV}{dP}$ **b.** $4h^2 + r^2 = 25$; find $D_r h$

   c. $s^2 - t^3 + 4t^{\frac{5}{2}} = 4t^2$; find $D_t s$ **d.** $u^2 x - u = 12$; find $\dfrac{du}{dx}$

Problems 3.1

1. A curve known as the strophoid is defined implicitly by the equation

$$x^3 + 4x^2 + xy^2 - 4y^2 = 0$$

and is shown in the diagram. Find the points at which the tangent line is horizontal.

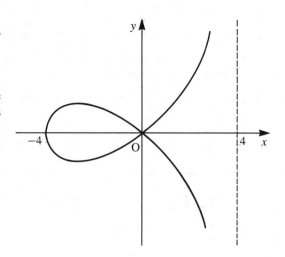

2. Find the equations of the lines that are tangent to the ellipse $x^2 + 4y^2 = 16$ and also pass through the point $(4, 6)$.

3. Prove that the curves defined by $x^2 - y^2 = k$ and $xy = p$ intersect orthogonally for all values of the constants k and p. Illustrate with a sketch.

4. Find the equation of the tangent line at an arbitrary point (a, b) on the curve

$$x^{\frac{2}{3}} + y^{\frac{2}{3}} = 1.$$

Show that the distance between the x-intercept and the y-intercept of the tangent line is independent of the point of tangency.

3.2 Velocity and Acceleration

One reason for introducing the derivative is the need to calculate rates of change. Two important rates of change are the velocity and acceleration of an object that moves in a straight line. In this section we shall discuss these concepts and use them to solve problems that involve motion.

Consider an object that moves in a straight line. Examples are a train moving along a straight track, a pebble falling from a building, and a rocket taking off vertically.

Choose an origin O and a positive direction on the line of motion, and let $s(t)$ denote the position of the object on the line relative to the origin. We shall call $s(t)$ the **position function** of the moving object. For a rocket launched vertically, one usually chooses the positive direction to be upward and the origin to be on the earth's surface, as shown in the diagram.

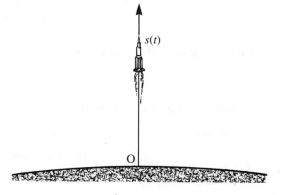

As explained in section 1.3, the velocity of an object that moves in a straight line is defined as the rate of change of the object's position with respect to time:

$$v(t) = s'(t)$$
$$= \lim_{\Delta t \to 0} \frac{s(t + \Delta t) - s(t)}{\Delta t}$$

The dimensions of velocity are length divided by time, and typical units are m/s or km/h.

Acceleration is associated with a change in velocity, just as velocity is associated with a change in position. When you press the gas pedal in a car, the car speeds up, but if you brake, the car slows down. In both cases, the velocity changes with time, so the car has a non-zero acceleration.

The **acceleration** at time t is defined as the rate of change of velocity with respect to time. More specifically, over the time interval from t to $t + \Delta t$, the average acceleration is

$$\frac{v(t + \Delta t) - v(t)}{\Delta t}$$

and the (instantaneous) acceleration $a(t)$ at time t is defined as

$$a(t) = v'(t)$$
$$= \lim_{\Delta t \to 0} \frac{v(t + \Delta t) - v(t)}{\Delta t}$$

The dimensions of acceleration are length divided by (time)^2; typical units are m/s^2.

For example, if the position function of a moving object is

$$s(t) = 6t^2 - t^3$$

then its velocity is

$$v(t) = s'(t)$$
$$= 12t - 3t^2$$

and its acceleration is

$$a(t) = v'(t)$$
$$= 12 - 6t$$

We now summarize these definitions.

Velocity $v(t)$ and Acceleration $a(t)$

For an object moving in a straight line with position function $s(t)$,

$$v(t) = s'(t) \quad \text{and} \quad a(t) = v'(t)$$

In Leibniz notation,

$$v = \frac{ds}{dt} \quad \text{and} \quad a = \frac{dv}{dt}$$

We recommend that you also know these definitions in word form, since you may encounter symbols other than s, v, and a for the above quantities.

Velocity = rate of change of position with respect to time
Acceleration = rate of change of velocity with respect to time

---

Example 1. A dragster races down a 400 m strip in 8 s. Its distance, in metres, from the starting line after t seconds is

$$s(t) = 6t^2 + 2t$$

a. Find the dragster's velocity and acceleration as it crosses the finish line.

b. How fast was it moving 60 m down the strip?

Solution.

a. The velocity $v(t)$ at time t is

$$v(t) = s'(t)$$
$$= 12t + 2$$

and the acceleration $a(t)$ at time t is

$$a(t) = v'(t)$$
$$= 12$$

Thus, as the dragster crosses the finish line at $t = 8$, the velocity is

$$v(8) = 98 \text{ m/s}$$

The acceleration is constant throughout the run and equals 12 m/s².

b. In order to find the velocity when the dragster has covered 60 m, we first need to find the value of t when $s(t) = 60$. We solve

$$6t^2 + 2t = 60$$

obtaining

$$3t^2 + t - 30 = 0$$

which yields

$$(3t + 10)(t - 3) = 0$$

Thus,

$$t = 3 \quad \text{or} \quad t = -\frac{10}{3}$$

We discard the root $t = -\frac{10}{3}$, since it represents a time before the start of the run. Thus the required velocity is $v(3) = 38$ m/s. □

To understand motion problems better, it is helpful to sketch the graph of the position function $s(t)$. In Example 1 the graph of $s(t)$ is part of a parabola, and the slope of the graph is positive, corresponding to the fact that the velocity is positive. And the slope of the graph, which equals the velocity, is increasing with time. This slope corresponds to the fact that the acceleration is positive.

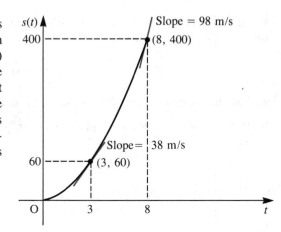

Keep in mind that the graph of $s(t)$ does not represent the path of the dragster. We think of the dragster as actually moving along the s-axis. Since the velocity is positive in this example, the dragster moves in the positive direction.

Example 2. A fly ball is hit vertically upward (a pop-up). The position function of the ball is

$$s(t) = -5t^2 + 30t$$

where the origin is at ground level and the positive direction is vertically up.

a. Find the maximum height reached by the ball.
b. Find the velocity of the ball as it strikes the ground.

Solution.
a. It is helpful to draw the graph of the position function $s(t)$, which is a parabola opening downward. The maximum height occurs when the velocity of the ball is zero—that is, when the slope of the graph is zero. The velocity function is

$$v(t) = s'(t)$$
$$= -10t + 30$$

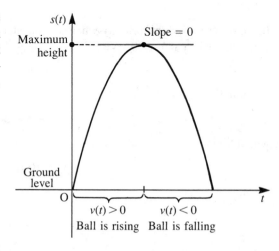

On solving $v(t) = 0$, we obtain $t = 3$. Therefore, the maximum height reached by the ball is

$$s(3) = 45 \text{ m}$$

b. When the ball strikes the ground, we have $s(t) = 0$.
To find the time at which this occurs, we solve the equation

$$-5t^2 + 30t = 0$$

to obtain

$$t = 0 \quad \text{or} \quad t = 6$$

Since $t = 0$ is the time at which the ball left the ground, the time at which the ball strikes the ground is $t = 6$. The velocity on impact is

$$v(6) = -30 \text{ m/s}$$

This negative value is reasonable, since the ball is falling (moving in the negative direction) when it strikes the ground.

We emphasize that the graph of $s(t)$ does not represent the path of the ball. We think of the ball as moving in a straight line along the s-axis, with the direction of motion reversing when $s = 45$. To see this, note that the ball is at the same height at $t = 1$ and $t = 5$:

$$s(1) = 25 \quad \text{and} \quad s(5) = 25.$$

The difference lies in the velocity:

$$v(1) = 20 \quad \text{and} \quad v(5) = -20$$

so that the ball is rising when $t = 1$ and falling when $t = 5$.

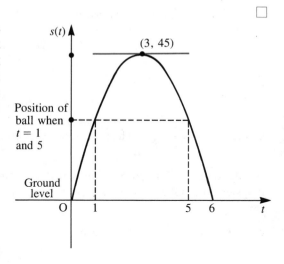

In Example 2 the acceleration is constant but negative:

$$a(t) = v'(t) = -10 \text{ m/s}^2$$

This value represents the acceleration that gravity imparts to any freely moving object. A more accurate value is -9.8 m/s^2, but for simplicity we shall use the value -10 m/s^2. The effect of this negative acceleration is to slow the ball down while it is rising (that is, moving in the positive direction) and to speed the ball up while it is falling.

CALCULUS

Example 3. Starting at time $t = 0$, a dragster accelerates down a strip and then brakes and comes to a stop. Its position function $s(t)$ (s is in metres, t is in seconds) is

$$s(t) = 6t^2 - \frac{1}{5}t^3$$

a. After how many seconds does the dragster stop?

b. What distance does the dragster travel?

c. At what time does the braking commence?

Solution.

a. The velocity of the dragster is

$$v(t) = s'(t)$$
$$= 12t - \frac{3}{5}t^2$$

To find when the dragster stops, we solve $v(t) = 0$:

$$12t - \frac{3}{5}t^2 = 0$$

or

$$\frac{3}{5}t(20 - t) = 0$$

so that $t = 0$ or $t = 20$. Thus the dragster stops after 20 s.

b. The dragster's initial position is $s(0) = 0$, and its final position is $s(20) = 800$. Since the dragster does not reverse its direction, the distance travelled is $s(20) - s(0) = 800$ m.

c. The acceleration of the dragster is

$$a(t) = v'(t)$$
$$= 12 - \frac{6}{5}t$$
$$= \frac{6}{5}(10 - t)$$

Observe that if $t < 10$ then $a(t) > 0$ and that if $t > 10$ then $a(t) < 0$. Thus the dragster accelerates (speeds up) from $t = 0$ to $t = 10$ and brakes (slows down) from $t = 10$ to $t = 20$. The braking begins after 10 s. ☐

The final example illustrates the significance of the signs of the position function and the velocity function.

Example 4. The position function of an object moving in a straight line is

$$s(t) = 3t^2 - \frac{1}{4}t^4$$

At time $t = 3$, is the object moving towards the origin or away from the origin?

Solution. The velocity of the object is

$$\begin{aligned} v(t) &= s'(t) \\ &= 6t - t^3 \end{aligned}$$

At time $t = 3$,

$$s(3) = \frac{27}{4} \quad \text{and} \quad v(3) = -9$$

In the diagram, let the positive direction be towards the right. Then $s(3) > 0$ implies that the object is **located** to the right of the origin when $t = 3$, and $v(3) < 0$ implies that the object is **moving** towards the left at $t = 3$. Therefore, the object is moving towards the origin when $t = 3$.

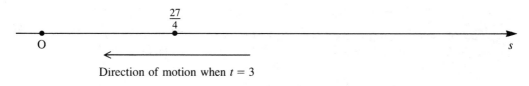

Direction of motion when $t = 3$

When we develop the techniques of curve sketching in chapter 4, we shall be able to draw and analyze the graphs of position functions that are more complicated than parabolas. In particular, we shall be able to interpret acceleration graphically.

Exercises 3.2

1. For each of the position functions, which describe motion in a straight line, find the velocity and acceleration as functions of time t.

   a. $s(t) = 5t^2 - 2t + 7$ **b.** $s(t) = 4t^4 - \frac{1}{2}t^2 + 3$

   c. $s(t) = 2t^3 - 15t^2 + 36t - 10$ **d.** $s(t) = t - 8 + \dfrac{6}{t}$

   e. $s(t) = \sqrt{t + 1} + \dfrac{1}{\sqrt{t + 1}}$ **f.** $s(t) = t(t - 3)^2$

   g. $s(t) = t + \dfrac{4}{t + 2}$ **h.** $s(t) = \dfrac{20t}{8 + t}$

2. An object moves in a straight line, and its position s (in metres) after t seconds is $s(t) = 8 - 7t + t^2$.

    a. Find the average velocity between $t = 3$ and $t = 4$.
    b. Find the velocity when $t = 3$.
    c. Find the average acceleration between $t = 3$ and $t = 4$.
    d. Find the acceleration when $t = 3$.

3. A ball is thrown upwards so that its height s (in metres) above the ground after t seconds is $s(t) = 24t - 5t^2$ where $t \geq 0$.

    a. Find the initial velocity.
    b. Find the maximum height reached by the ball.
    c. When does the ball strike the ground and what is its velocity at this time?

4. Each function describes the position of an object that moves along a straight line. Determine whether the object is moving towards or away from the origin at time $t = 1$ and at time $t = 4$.

    a. $s(t) = -\frac{1}{3}t^2 + t + 4$ **b.** $s(t) = t(t - 3)^2$
    c. $s(t) = t^3 - 7t^2 + 10t$ **d.** $s(t) = \sqrt{5t^2 + 4} - 2t - 2$

5. A pebble is thrown vertically upwards from the top of a cliff of height 30 m. The pebble's height h (in metres) in relation to the top of the cliff t seconds later is

$$h(t) = -5t^2 + 25t.$$

Find the pebble's velocity on impact at the base of the cliff.

6. A bullet shot straight up has a muzzle velocity of 650 m/s. After t seconds its height h (in metres) is

$$h(t) = 2 + 650t - 5t^2$$

    a. How long does it take gravity to reduce the velocity of the bullet to 100 m/s?
    b. When does the bullet reach its maximum height?
    c. What is the maximum height reached by the bullet? (Air resistence is being ignored.)

7. Each position function describes the motion of an object that accelerates from rest at $t = 0$ and subsequently brakes and comes to a stop. In each case, find the total distance travelled and the distance travelled before braking begins.

    a. $s(t) = 3t^2 - \frac{1}{4}t^3$ **b.** $s(t) = 9t^2(50 - t^2)$
    c. $s(t) = t^{\frac{5}{2}}(7 - t)$ **d.** $s(t) = t^2(10 - t)^3$

8. If the position function of an object is $s(t) = t^5 - 10t^2$, at what time will the acceleration be zero? Is the object moving towards or away from the origin at that instant?

9. Two particles have positions at time t given by the equations $s_1(t) = 4t - t^2$ and $s_2(t) = 6t^2 - t^3$ respectively. Find the velocities of the two particles when they have the same acceleration.

10. Starting at time $t = 0$, a train is halted by a braking deceleration of $\frac{1}{2}$ m/s², with the result that its position at time t is $s(t) = s_0 + v_0 t - \frac{1}{4}t^2$. Show that s_0 is the train's position when the brakes are applied and v_0 is its velocity at that time. Find the stopping distance if v_0 is 20 m/s.

11. The distance s (in metres) that a small airplane travels along a runway before take-off is given by $s(t) = 2t^2$, where t is measured in seconds from the time the brakes are released.

   a. If the velocity required for take-off is 160 km/h, how long after the brakes are released will the airplane become airborne?
   b. Could this plane take off on a runway 250 m long?

12. The distance-time relationship for a moving object is given by $s(t) = kt^2 + (6k^2 - 10k) t + 2k$, where k is a non-zero constant.

   a. Show that the acceleration is constant.
   b. Find the time at which the velocity is zero and determine the position of the object when this occurs.

Problems 3.2

1. An object moves so that its velocity v is related to its position s according to

$$v = \sqrt{b^2 + 2gs}$$

   where b and g are constants. Show that the acceleration of the object is constant.

2. The position function of an object that moves in a straight line is

$$s(t) = \begin{cases} t^2, & \text{if } 0 \le t \le 2 \\ 4t - 4, & \text{if } 2 < t < 8 \\ -68 + 20t - t^2, & \text{if } 8 \le t \le 10 \end{cases}$$

   a. Determine the velocity and acceleration at time t.
   b. Sketch the graphs of the position, velocity, and acceleration functions.
   c. Use your graphs to determine whether the velocity and acceleration are continuous functions.
   d. Use your graphs to find the maximum velocity and maximum acceleration.

3. An elevator is designed to start from rest without a jerk. It can do this if the acceleration function is continuous.

   a. Show that for the position function

$$s(t) = \begin{cases} 0, & \text{if } t < 0 \\ \dfrac{t^3}{1 + t^2}, & \text{if } t \ge 0 \end{cases}$$

   the acceleration is continuous at $t = 0$.
   b. What happens to the velocity and acceleration for very large values of t?

4. Point P moves along the curve
$$y = 3 + 3x - x^2$$
so that the projection of P on the x-axis has constant velocity. If $Q(a, b)$ is any fixed point on the curve, show that the slope of the line PQ changes at a constant rate.

3.3 Related Rates

Change is an essential feature of the real world. In many situations a change in one quantity causes a change in another quantity or occurs together with a change in another quantity, with the result that the two rates of change are related. Consider the following problem. An oil spill from a tanker spreads out in a circular pattern, centred at the tanker's position. If the edge of the spill is moving outwards at 2 m/s, find the rate of increase of the contaminated area when the radius is 500 m.

This is an example of a "related-rates" problem. We are given the rate of change of radius with respect to time, $\dfrac{dr}{dt}$, and wish to calculate the rate of change of area with respect to time, $\dfrac{dA}{dt}$. Since area and radius are related by $A = \pi r^2$, and since both depend on time t, we can calculate $\dfrac{dA}{dt}$ by differentiating both sides of the equation $A = \pi r^2$ with respect to t. Differentiating both sides of an equation that relates two or more time-dependent variables forms the basis for the method of solving related-rates problems. (See Example 3, section 2.5 for a solution of a similar problem.)

We now discuss some other examples.

Example 1. A ladder 5 m long is leaning against a vertical wall. If a person pulls the bottom of the ladder away from the wall at a rate of $\dfrac{1}{2}$ m/s, how fast is the top sliding down the wall when
a. the bottom of the ladder is 3 m from the wall?
b. the top of the ladder is touching the wall 2 m above the base of the wall?

Solution. Let A and B denote the positions of the ends of the ladder at an arbitrary time t, and let O denote the base of the wall. Denote the distances OA and OB by x and y. In order to emphasize that x and y depend on time, we write

$$x = x(t) \quad \text{and} \quad y = y(t)$$

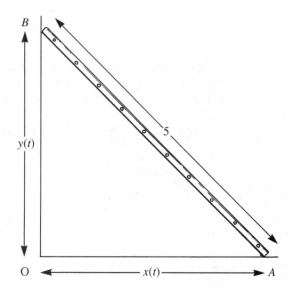

Since the wall meets the ground at right angles,

$$x^2 + y^2 = 25 \tag{1}$$

In addition, the given motion of the bottom of the ladder implies that

$$\frac{dx}{dt} = \frac{1}{2} \text{ m/s} \tag{2}$$

We wish to calculate $\frac{dy}{dt}$ for two different positions of the ladder. Since equation (1) is valid for arbitrary values of time t, we can differentiate both sides of the equation with respect to t to obtain

$$\frac{d}{dt}[(x(t))^2 + (y(t))^2] = \frac{d}{dt}(25)$$

which yields

$$2x\frac{dx}{dt} + 2y\frac{dy}{dt} = 0 \tag{3}$$

This equation relates the known rate of change $\frac{dx}{dt}$ and the unknown rate of change $\frac{dy}{dt}$.

To solve part (a), note that, when $x = 3$, it follows from equation (1) that $y = 4$. On substituting these values and the known rate of change $\frac{dx}{dt}$ in equation (3), we obtain

$$(2)(3)\left(\tfrac{1}{2}\right) + (2)(4)\frac{dy}{dt} = 0$$

and hence

$$\frac{dy}{dt} = -\frac{3}{8} \text{ m/s}$$

Note the minus sign, which indicates that $y(t)$ is **decreasing**. Thus the top of the ladder is sliding **down** the wall, at a rate of $\frac{3}{8}$ m/s.

To solve part (b), note that, when $y = 2$, it follows from equation (1) that $x = \sqrt{21}$. On substituting these values and the known rate of change $\frac{dx}{dt}$ in equation (3), we obtain

$$\frac{dy}{dt} = -\frac{\sqrt{21}}{4} \text{ m/s}$$

Comparing the answers to parts (a) and (b), note that, as the top of the ladder gets closer to the ground, it slides down the wall faster. $\qquad \square$

Before discussing more examples, we summarize the method that was used to solve the previous problem.

Guidelines for Related-Rate Problems

- Draw a diagram (if applicable).

- Introduce variables to represent the quantities that change.

- Express the unknown rate of change and the given rate of change as derivatives.

- Find an equation that relates the variables.

- Differentiate both sides of this equation with respect to time t, regarding all variables as functions of t.

- Evaluate the terms in the differentiated equation at the specified instant, using the given values and the given rate of change, and then solve for the unknown rate of change.

Example 2. Smoke is being emitted into the atmosphere from a smokestack. At any instant, the smoke-filled region forms an inverted right circular cone, the diameter of which is equal to its height. If the rate of smoke emission is 200 m³/min, how fast is the height increasing when the height is 50 m?

Solution. Let h denote the height of the cone at time t. The other quantities that change are the volume V and radius r of the "base" of the cone.

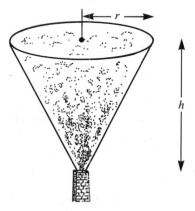

We are required to calculate $\dfrac{dh}{dt}$ and are given that

$$\frac{dV}{dt} = 200$$

The volume of the cone is

$$V = \frac{1}{3}\pi r^2 h$$

The radius r, which changes with time, can be eliminated from this equation. Since we are given that the diameter of the cone equals the height at any time, it follows that

$$2r = h$$

Substitute for r in the equation for V to obtain

$$V = \frac{1}{3}\pi \left(\frac{h}{2}\right)^2 h$$

which yields

$$V = \frac{1}{12}\pi h^3$$

This is the fundamental equation that relates the two time-dependent variables of interest, $V(t)$ and $h(t)$. Differentiate this equation with respect to t, using the Chain Rule, to obtain

$$\frac{dV}{dt} = \frac{\pi}{4}h^2\frac{dh}{dt}$$

To find $\frac{dh}{dt}$ at the specified instant, substitute $h = 50$ and the given rate of change $\frac{dV}{dt} = 200$ to obtain

$$200 = \frac{\pi}{4}(50)^2\frac{dh}{dt}$$

and hence

$$\frac{dh}{dt} = \frac{8}{25\pi}$$

Thus the height of the cone of smoke is increasing at a rate of $\frac{8}{25\pi} \approx 0.1$ m/min, when the height is 50 m. (The symbol $\approx$ means "is approximated by.") □

Where possible, one should use given information to eliminate unnecessary variables in the fundamental equation before differentiating. In the previous example, we eliminated the radius (using the given fact that the diameter of the cone equals the height). The fundamental equation then related two time-dependent variables, as in Example 1. In the next example, the fundamental equation relates **three** time-dependent variables.

Example 3. Two cars approach a right-angled intersection, one travelling south at 40 km/h and the other west at 70 km/h. When the faster car is 4 km from the intersection and the other car is 3 km from the intersection, how fast is the distance between the two cars changing?

Solution. Let s be the distance between the cars at an arbitrary time t. In the diagram, the x-axis and y-axis represent the roads, and the origin O represents the intersection. Let $(x, 0)$ be the position of the faster car at time t, and let $(0, y)$ be the position of the other car at the same time. We are given that

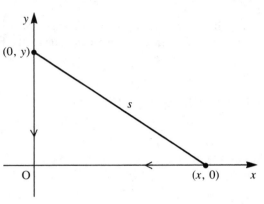

$$\frac{dx}{dt} = -70 \quad \text{and} \quad \frac{dy}{dt} = -40$$

and the minus signs indicate that the cars travel in the negative directions on the axes.

Since the roads intersect at right angles,

$$s^2 = x^2 + y^2$$

This equation is valid for any time t, so we can differentiate both sides of the equation with respect to t and use the Chain Rule to obtain

$$2s\frac{ds}{dt} = 2x\frac{dx}{dt} + 2y\frac{dy}{dt}$$

When $x = 4$, and $y = 3$, it follows from the equation $s^2 = x^2 + y^2$ that $s = 5$. When these values and the given rates of change are substituted in the previous equation, we obtain

$$(2)(5)\frac{ds}{dt} = (2)(4)(-70) + (2)(3)(-40)$$

and hence

$$\frac{ds}{dt} = -80 \text{ km/h}$$

Thus at the specified instant, the cars are approaching each other at a rate of 80 km/h; the minus sign means that the distance between them is decreasing. □

A note of caution is in order. The most common error in related-rates problems is to substitute the given data too soon, that is, to substitute before the basic equation is differentiated. In the preceding example, if we substitute $x = 4$ and $y = 3$ in the equation $s^2 = x^2 + y^2$, we obtain

$$s^2 = 4^2 + 3^2$$

This equation cannot be differentiated with respect to t, since it does not hold for arbitrary t. If one did take the invalid step of differentiating this equation, one would obtain the nonsensical result that $\frac{ds}{dt} = 0$.

To avoid this type of error, we recommend that you draw a diagram that represents the situation at an **arbitrary** time t. This will ensure that your basic equation holds for all t and hence can be differentiated.

Exercises 3.3

1. If A is the area of a circle of radius r, how is $\dfrac{dA}{dt}$ related to $\dfrac{dr}{dt}$?

2. The area of a circular oil slick on the surface of the sea is increasing at the rate of 150 m²/s. How fast is the radius changing when

   a. the radius is 25 m?
   b. the area is 1000 m²?

3. How fast is the side of a square shrinking when the length of the side is 2 m and the area is decreasing at 0.25 m²/s?

4. The hypotenuse of a right-angled triangle is of fixed length, but the lengths of the other two sides x and y depend on time. How fast is y changing when $\dfrac{dx}{dt} = 4$ and $x = 8$ if the length of the hypotenuse is 17?

5. A spherical balloon is inflated so that the volume is increasing at the rate of 5 m³/min.

   a. At what rate is the diameter increasing when the radius is 6 m?
   b. At what rate is the diameter increasing when the volume is 36 m³?

6. The trunk of a tree is approximately cylindrical in shape and has a diameter of 1 m when the height is 15 m. If the radius is increasing at 3 mm/a and the height is increasing at 0.4 m/a, find the rate of increase of the volume of the trunk.

7. Lumber in a spruce forest is valued at $1 million per square kilometre. If the radius of a circular-shaped forest fire is 4 km and is increasing at the rate of 0.1 km/h, find the rate at which money is being lost.

8. A conveyor belt system at a gravel pit pours washed sand onto the ground at the rate of 180 m³/h. The sand forms a conical pile with height one-third the diameter of the base. Find out how fast the height of the pile is increasing at the instant when the radius of the base is 6 m.

9. The head of a short-distance radar is set to sweep out an area of 18 000 km²/min. If the beam is set for a distance of 30 km, then find the rate of rotation (in rev/min) of the radar head.

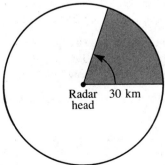

Radar 30 km
head

10. A ship K is sailing due north at 16 km/h, and a second ship R, which is 44 km north of K, is sailing due east at 10 km/h. At what rate is the distance between K and R changing 90 min later? Are they approaching one another or separating at this time? Explain.

11. Two cars approach an intersection, one travelling east and the other north. If both cars are travelling at 70 km/h, how fast are they approaching each other when they are both 0.5 km from the interesction?

12. At a certain instant, the area of a circular plate is increasing at the same rate as its radius is increasing. What is the radius at that instant?

13. An aircraft is 20 km east of a radar beacon and is travelling west at 250 km/h. At the same instant, a helicopter flying at the same altitude is 48 km south of the beacon and is travelling south at 100 km/h. How fast is the distance between the aircraft and helicopter changing at that instant?

14. The cross section of a water trough is an equilateral triangle with its top edge horizontal. If the trough is 5 m long and 25 cm deep, and if water is flowing in at a rate of 0.25 m³/min, how fast is the water level rising when the water is 10 cm deep at the deepest point?

15. A water trough is 6 m long, and its cross-section has the shape of an isosceles trapezoid that is 20 cm wide at the bottom, 50 cm wide at the top and 40 cm high. If the trough is being filled with water at the rate of 0.2 m³/min, how fast is the water level rising when the water is 25 cm deep?

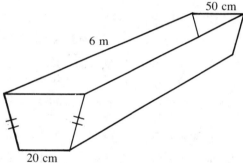

16. Suppose that a raindrop is a perfect sphere. Assume that through condensation the raindrop accumulates moisture at a rate proportional to its surface area. Show that the radius increases at a constant rate.

17. When a certain gas expands or contracts adiabatically, it obeys the law $PV^{1.4} = K$ where P is the pressure, V is the volume, and K is a constant. At a certain instant the pressure is 40 N/cm², the volume is 32 cm³, and the volume is increasing at the rate of 5 cm³ per second. At what rate is the pressure changing at this instant?

18. A woman 2 m tall walks away from a streetlight that is 6 m high at the rate of 1.5 m/s.
a. At what rate is her shadow lengthening when she is 3 m from the base of the light?
b. At what rate is her shadow lengthening when she is 30 m from the base of the light?

19. Referring to Exercise 18, calculate how fast the tip of the woman's shadow is moving when she is

a. 3 m from the base of the light.
b. 30 m away.

Problems 3.3

1. A light is at the top of a 30 m pole. A ball is dropped from the same height from a point 10 m from the light. The height of the ball (in metres) t seconds after it has been dropped is approximated by $h = 30 - 5t^2$. In which direction does the shadow of the ball move along the ground? How fast is the shadow of the ball moving along the ground 1 s later?

2. Liquid is being poured into the top of a funnel at a steady rate of 200 cm³/s. The funnel is in the shape of an inverted right circular cone with radius equal to its height, with a small hole in the bottom where the liquid flows out at a rate of 20 cm³/s.

   a. How fast is the height of the liquid changing when the height in the funnel is 15 cm?
   b. At the instant when the height of the liquid is 25 cm, the funnel becomes clogged at the bottom and no more liquid flows out. How fast does the height of the liquid change just after this occurs?

3. A ladder of length l standing on level ground is leaning against a vertical wall. The base of the ladder begins to slide away from the wall. Introduce a coordinate system so that the wall lies along the y-axis, the ground is on the x-axis, and the base of the wall is the origin.

   a. What is the equation of the path followed by the midpoint of the ladder?
   b. What is the equation of the path followed by any point on the ladder? (Hint: Let k be the distance from the top of the ladder to the point in question.)

4. A crystal is growing in the shape of a tetrahedron in such a way that its base is an equilateral triangle and its slant faces are isosceles triangles. The growth rate of each base edge is 1 mm/week and the growth rate of the vertical height is 1.5 mm/week.

   a. Find the rate of increase of the volume, in terms of the height h, at the instant when the vertical height is 3 times the length of a side of the triangular base.
   b. Find the growth rate of the volume at the instant when the area of the triangular base is $100\sqrt{3}$ mm².

5. A man 2 m tall strolls at 1 m/s along the edge of a road 10 m wide. A street light 6 m high stands on the opposite side of the road. How fast is the man's shadow lengthening when he is 10 m from the point opposite the light?

3.4 Maximum and Minimum Values

Optimization problems occur in practical situations in which a decision has to be made that will lead to the "best" outcome in some specified sense. For example, suppose a farmer has 600 m of fence and wishes to enclose a rectangular field along a straight section of a river. Find the dimensions of the field so that the largest possible area is enclosed.

The first step in solving an optimization problem is to translate the problem into mathematical language. This step will be studied in detail in the next section. The second step is to solve the resulting mathematical problem, which is often of this form: find the maximum (largest) value or minimum (smallest) value of a function on a given interval. The maximum values and minimum values of a function are collectively known as **extreme values**. In this section we show how differential calculus can be used to solve such problems.

We shall begin by discussing a simple example in which the maximum value and minimum value can be found by sketching the graph of the function. This will lead to a general algorithm for finding the maximum and minimum values of a function on a given interval.

Example 1.

a. Find the maximum value and the minimum value of the function

$$f(x) = -4x^2 + 12x + 7$$

on the interval $0 \leq x \leq 4$.

b. Repeat part (a) for the interval $2 \leq x \leq \frac{9}{2}$.

Solution.

a. The graph of this function is a parabola, opening downward. Since

$$f(x) = (2x + 1)(-2x + 7)$$

the x-intercepts are $x = -\frac{1}{2}$ and $x = \frac{7}{2}$. The vertex lies midway between the intercepts at $x = \frac{3}{2}$.

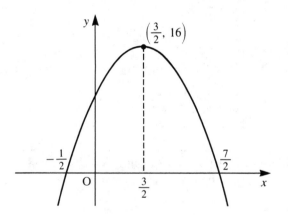

When the function f is restricted to the interval $0 \leq x \leq 4$, the second graph is obtained. The maximum value is

$$f\left(\frac{3}{2}\right) = 16$$

and the minimum value is

$$f(4) = -9$$

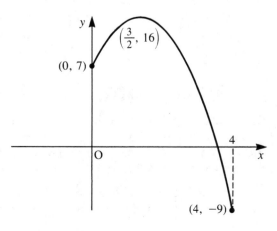

b. When the function f is restricted to the interval $2 \leq x \leq \frac{9}{2}$, the third graph is obtained. The maximum value is

$$f(2) = 15$$

and the minimum value is

$$f\left(\frac{9}{2}\right) = -20$$

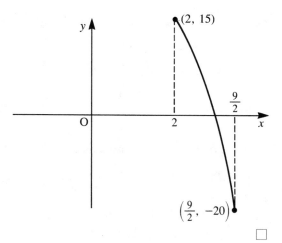

On the interval $0 \leq x \leq 4$, the maximum value $f\left(\frac{3}{2}\right) = 16$ occurs when the tangent line is horizontal, that is, when

$$f'\left(\frac{3}{2}\right) = 0,$$

as can be verified by differentiation. The minimum value $f(4) = -9$ occurs at an end point of the interval. On the interval $2 \leq x \leq \frac{9}{2}$, the tangent line is never horizontal ($f'(x) < 0$ for all x), and so the maximum value $f(2) = 15$ and the minimum value, $f\left(\frac{9}{2}\right) = -20$ both occur at the end points.

We now display three graphs for which the derivative equals zero at two points.

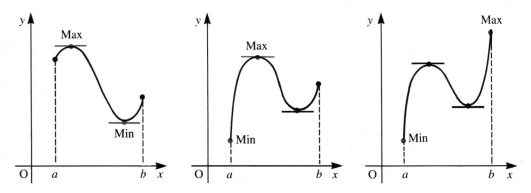

Note that in each case the maximum value occurs at a ''peak'' ($f'(c) = 0$) or at an end point, and the minimum value occurs at a ''valley'' ($f'(c) = 0$) or at an end point. This will be the case no matter how many peaks and valleys the graph has in the interval. To summarize, the extreme values occur at one of the following types of points:

- a point $x = c$ at which $f'(c) = 0$
- an end point of the interval

This observation leads to the following procedure for finding extreme values.

Algorithm for Extreme Values

Suppose that $f(x)$ has a derivative at each point of the interval $a \leq x \leq b$. Calculate $f(x)$ at

- the points x in the interval $a \leq x \leq b$ where $f'(x) = 0$
- the end points $x = a$ and $x = b$

The maximum value of $f(x)$ on the interval $a \leq x \leq b$ is the largest of these function values, and the minimum value of $f(x)$ is the smallest of these function values.

In the next example we apply the Algorithm for Extreme Values to a function whose graph we do not know beforehand.

Example 2. Find the maximum value and minimum value of the function

$$f(x) = x^3 - 6x^2 - 4$$

on the interval $-1 \leq x \leq 7$.

Solution. The derivative is

$$f'(x) = 3x^2 - 12x$$

On solving $f'(x) = 0$, we obtain

$$3x(x - 4) = 0,$$

so that

$$x = 0 \quad \text{or} \quad x = 4$$

Note that both values lie in the given interval.

To apply the Algorithm for Extreme Values, we evaluate the function at $x = 0$ and $x = 4$ and at the end points $x = -1$ and $x = 7$:

$$f(-1) = -11, \quad f(0) = -4, \quad f(4) = -36, \quad f(7) = 45$$

Thus the maximum value of $f(x)$ on the interval $-1 \leq x \leq 7$ is $f(7) = 45$, and the minimum value is $f(4) = -36$. ☐

Using the calculated function values and the fact that the tangent line is horizontal only at $x = 0$ and $x = 4$, we can make a rough sketch of the function of Example 2.

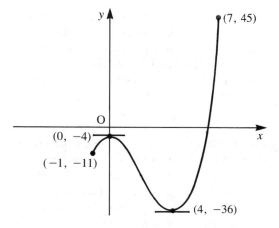

In the next example we use the Algorithm for Extreme Values to solve a maximum problem in an applied setting.

Example 3. A flu epidemic breaks out in Preston. The fraction of the population that is infected at time t (in weeks) is given by the function

$$f(t) = \frac{64t}{(8 + t)^3}$$

What is the largest fraction of the population that is infected during the first 10 weeks? Assume that $t = 0$ when the epidemic starts.

Solution. We have to find the maximum value of the given function on the interval $0 \le t \le 10$. For convenience, we write the function as a product when differentiating:

$$f'(t) = 64 \frac{d}{dt}[t(8 + t)^{-3}]$$
$$= 64[(8 + t)^{-3} - 3t(8 + t)^{-4}]$$
$$= \frac{64(8 + t - 3t)}{(8 + t)^4}$$
$$= \frac{128(4 - t)}{(8 + t)^4}$$

The equation $f'(t) = 0$ has the single solution $t = 4$. This value lies in the given interval. The maximum value will occur either at $t = 4$ or at one of the end points. We thus calculate the function values

$$f(0) = 0, \quad f(4) = \frac{4}{27}, \quad f(10) = \frac{80}{729}$$

It follows that the maximum occurs when $t = 4$. Thus during the first 10 weeks, the largest fraction of the population infected is $\frac{4}{27}$ and occurs after 4 weeks. $\qquad\square$

To end this section, we stress that the Algorithm for Extreme Values only applies to functions that have a derivative (and hence a tangent line) at each point. The algorithm would fail if we tried to find the minimum value of

$$f(x) = |x|$$

on the interval $-1 \le x \le 1$. Note from the diagram that the minimum value occurs at $x = 0$. However, we do not have $f'(0) = 0$, because the derivative of $f(x)$ does not exist at $x = 0$ (see section 1.7). Functions of this type are discussed in section 4.7.

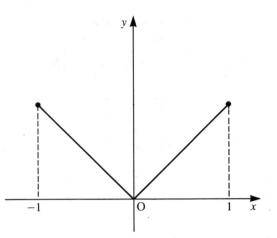

Exercises 3.4

1. Find the maximum and minimum value of each function on the given interval, using the algorithm of this section. Illustrate your results by sketching the graph of each function.

   a. $f(x) = x^2 - 4x + 3, \quad 0 \le x \le 3$
   b. $f(x) = (x - 2)^2, \quad 0 \le x \le 2$
   c. $f(x) = x^3 - 3x^2, \quad -1 \le x \le 3$
   d. $f(x) = x^3 - 3x^2, \quad -2 \le x \le 1$
   e. $f(x) = 2x^3 - 3x^2 - 12x + 1, \quad -2 \le x \le 0$
   f. $f(x) = \frac{1}{3}x^3 - \frac{5}{2}x^2 + 6x, \quad 0 \le x \le 4$

2. Find the maximum and minimum values of each function on the given interval, using the Algorithm for Extreme Values.

   a. $f(x) = \frac{1}{2}\left[\sqrt{x} + \frac{1}{\sqrt{x}}\right], \quad 1 \le x \le 9$

   b. $f(x) = 4\sqrt{x} - x, \quad 2 \le x \le 9$

   c. $f(x) = \frac{1}{x^2 - 2x + 2}, \quad 0 \le x \le 2$

   d. $f(x) = x + \frac{4}{x}, \quad 1 \le x \le 10$

   e. $f(x) = \frac{4x}{x^2 + 1}, \quad -2 \le x \le 4$

   f. $f(x) = \frac{4x}{x^2 + 1}, \quad 2 \le x \le 4$

   g. $f(x) = x - 2\sqrt{x^2 + 12}, \quad 0 \le x \le 6$

   h. $f(x) = \frac{x}{(x + 9)^2}, \quad -1 \le x \le 8$

   i. $f(x) = 5\sqrt{1 + x^2} + 3(4 - x), \quad 0 \le x \le 4$

3. **a.** An object moves in a straight line. Its velocity in m/s at time t is

$$v(t) = \frac{4t^2}{4 + t^3}, \quad t \geq 0$$

Find the maximum and minimum velocities over the time interval $1 \leq t \leq 4$.
   b. Repeat part (a) if

$$v(t) = \frac{4t^2}{1 + t^2}, \quad t \geq 0$$

4. The position function of an object that moves in a straight line is

$$s(t) = 1 + 2t - \frac{8}{t^2 + 1}, \quad 0 \leq t \leq 2$$

Find the maximum and minimum velocities of the object over the given time interval.

5. A swimming pool is treated periodically to control the growth of bacteria. Suppose that t days after a treatment the concentration of bacteria per cubic centimetre is

$$C(t) = 30t^2 - 240t + 500$$

Find the lowest concentration of bacteria during the first week after the treatment.

6. The fuel efficiency E (in litres per hundred kilometres) of a car driven at speed v (in kilometres per hour) is

$$E(v) = \frac{1600v}{v^2 + 6400}$$

   a. If the speed limit is 100 km/h, find the legal speed that will maximize the fuel efficiency.
   b. Repeat part (a) if the speed limit is 50 km/h.

7. The concentration $C(t)$ (in milligrams per cubic centimetre) of a certain medicine in a patient's bloodstream is given by

$$C(t) = \frac{0.1t}{(t + 3)^2}$$

where t is the number of hours after the medicine is taken. Find the maximum and minimum concentrations between the first and sixth hours after the medicine is taken.

8. Suppose that the cost (in dollars) of manufacturing x items is approximated by

$$C(x) = 625 + 15x + 0.01x^2, \quad \text{for } 1 \leq x \leq 500$$

Then the unit cost (the cost of manufacturing one item) is

$$U(x) = \frac{C(x)}{x}$$

How many items should be manufactured in order to ensure that unit cost is minimized?

9. Technicians working for the Ministry of Natural Resources have found that the amount of a pollutant in a certain river can be represented by

$$P(t) = 2t + \frac{1}{(162t + 1)}, \quad 0 \le t \le 1$$

where t is the time (in years) since a clean-up campaign started. At what time was the pollution at its lowest level?

10. A truck travelling at x km/h, where $30 \le x \le 120$, uses gasoline at the rate of $r(x)$ L/km, where

$$r(x) = \frac{1}{400}\left(\frac{4900}{x} + x\right)$$

If fuel costs $0.45/L, what speed will result in the lowest fuel cost for a trip of 200 km? What is the lowest total cost for the trip?

11. In a certain manufacturing process, when the level of production is x units, the cost of production (in dollars) is

$$C(x) = 3000 + 9x + 0.05x^2, \quad 1 \le x \le 300$$

What level of production x will minimize the unit cost $U(x) = \frac{C(x)}{x}$? Keep in mind that the production level must be an integer.

12. Repeat Exercise 11 if the cost of production is

$$C(x) = 6000 + 9x + 0.05x^2, \quad 1 \le x \le 300$$

3.5 Optimization Problems

In this section we shall study applied optimization problems. The first step in solving an optimization problem is to translate the problem into mathematical language. This leads to a function, defined on an interval, to which we can apply the Algorithm for Extreme Values. The final step is to interpret the result in terms of the original problem.

Example 1. A farmer has 600 m of fence, and he wishes to enclose a field beside a straight section of a river on his property. For practical reasons the lengths of the sides of the field should not be less than 50 m. Find the dimensions of the field so that the enclosed area is as large as possible. Keep in mind that fencing is required only on three sides.

Solution. The quantity to be maximized is the enclosed area, which we denote by A. The variables that determine the area are the lengths of the sides of the field, which we denote by x and y, as in the diagram.

The diagram shows three different fields with the same fixed length of fencing but different areas.

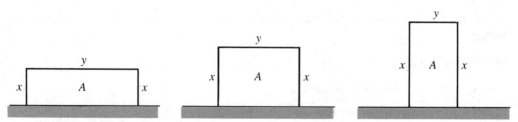

The area of the enclosed region is

$$A = xy$$

Since the total length of fencing is 600 m, the variables x and y are related by

$$2x + y = 600$$

The next step is to use this relation to express A as a function of only one variable, say x. On eliminating y in the equation $A = xy$ we obtain

$$A = x(600 - 2x)$$
$$= 600x - 2x^2.$$

Because each side of the enclosed field must be at least 50 m long, then $x \geq 50$ and $y \geq 50$. Since $y = 600 - 2x$, we have

$$600 - 2x \geq 50$$

which implies that

$$2x \leq 550$$

and hence

$$x \leq 275$$

Therefore the variable x can take on values in the interval $50 \leq x \leq 275$.

We thus have to solve the following mathematical problem: find the maximum value of the function

$$A(x) = 600x - 2x^2$$

on the interval $50 \leq x \leq 275$. In order to apply the Algorithm for Extreme Values we calculate the derivative of $A(x)$,

$$A'(x) = 600 - 4x$$

which exists for all x. Note that $A'(x) = 0$ when $x = 150$, which lies in the interval $50 \leq x \leq 275$. The maximum value of $A(x)$ will occur either at $x = 150$ or at one of the end points of the interval. We thus calculate the function values

$$A(50) = 25\ 000, \quad A(150) = 45\ 000, \quad A(275) = 13\ 750$$

It follows that the maximum area occurs when $x = 150$ and $y = 600 - 2x = 300$.

Therefore the dimensions of the field of largest area are 150 m and 300 m, with the longest side parallel to the river.   □

Before discussing more examples, we shall summarize the method used to solve the previous problem.

Guidelines for Optimization Problems

- Name the quantity to be maximized or minimized.

- Name the other quantities that vary (the variables).

- Write a formula for the quantity to be maximized or minimized.

- If the right side of this formula contains more than one variable, look for other relationships among the variables, so that you can eliminate all but one variable on the right side of the equation (say x).

- Find the restrictions that are imposed on x by the given information; write the restrictions in the form $x_1 \leq x \leq x_2$.

- The problem is now in a standard form: find the maximum or minimum value of a function on the interval $x_1 \leq x \leq x_2$. Solve using the Algorithm for Extreme Values.

Example 2. A piece of wire 8 cm long is cut into two pieces. One piece is bent to form a circle, and the other is bent to form a square. How should the wire be cut if the total enclosed area is to be

a. as large as possible?
b. as small as possible?

Solution. The quantity to be maximized or minimized is the total enclosed area A, that is, the sum of the areas of the circle and the square. Assume that the cut is made at a distance x from one end of the wire and that the piece of length x is formed into the circle. The square will be formed from the piece of wire of length $8 - x$. The resulting dimensions and areas are summarized in the diagram.

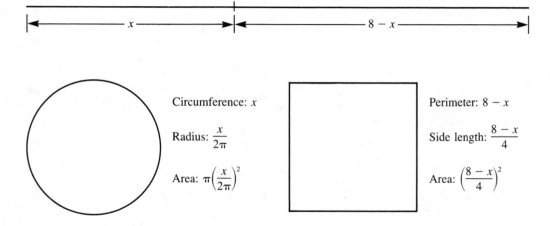

Circumference: x

Radius: $\dfrac{x}{2\pi}$

Area: $\pi\left(\dfrac{x}{2\pi}\right)^2$

Perimeter: $8 - x$

Side length: $\dfrac{8 - x}{4}$

Area: $\left(\dfrac{8 - x}{4}\right)^2$

The total area enclosed is thus given as a function of x by

$$A(x) = \frac{x^2}{4\pi} + \frac{(8-x)^2}{16}$$

where $0 \le x \le 8$. (Do not expand the squared term, because this would lead to a more complicated expression.)

We thus have to solve this mathematical problem: find the maximum value and minimum value of the function $A(x)$ on the interval $0 \le x \le 8$. In order to apply the Algorithm for Extreme Values, we calculate the derivative of $A(x)$. After simplifying, we obtain

$$A'(x) = \frac{x}{2\pi} + \frac{1}{8}x - 1$$

which exists for all x. Now set $A'(x) = 0$ and solve for x to obtain

$$x = \frac{8\pi}{4+\pi}$$

which lies in the interval $0 \le x \le 8$. We thus calculate the function values

$$A(0) = 4, \quad A\left(\frac{8\pi}{4+\pi}\right) = \frac{16}{4+\pi}, \quad A(8) = \frac{16}{\pi}$$

Note that in calculating $A\left(\frac{8\pi}{4+\pi}\right)$ we performed several simplifications, and we suggest that you supply the details of the calculation. (First, simplify $8 - x$ to get $\frac{32}{4+\pi}$. Do not expand the term $(4+\pi)^2$ in the denominator.)

Finally, observe that

$$\frac{16}{4+\pi} < 4 < \frac{16}{\pi}$$

(Convince yourself that these inequalities are valid without using a calculator.)

The conclusion is that the maximum area is $A(8) = \frac{16}{\pi}$ and that the minimum area is $A\left(\frac{8\pi}{4+\pi}\right) = \frac{16}{4+\pi}$. Thus the maximum area occurs when all of the wire is used to form a circle and the minimum area occurs when a piece of length $\frac{8\pi}{(4+\pi)}$ cm is bent into a circle and the remaining piece is used to form the square. $\square$

Example 3. A supermarket is designed to have a rectangular floor area of 3750 m², with three walls made of cement blocks and one wall made of glass. In order to conform to the building code, the length of the glass wall must not exceed 60 m but must not be less than 30 m. The cost per linear metre of constructing a glass wall is twice that of constructing a cement wall. Find the dimensions of the floor area that will minimize the cost of building the walls.

Solution. The quantity to be minimized is the total cost C of the walls. Let x and y be the lengths of the walls, with x being the length of the glass wall.

The first step is to derive an expression for the total cost C. Let the unit cost of building the cement walls be k dollars per linear metre, since a specific value is not given. Then the cost of building the cement walls is

$$(k)(x + 2y) \text{ dollars}$$

Glass wall

The cost of building the glass wall is

$$(2k)(x) \text{ dollars}$$

since the unit cost is $2k$ dollars per linear metre. Thus the total cost is

$$C = k(x + 2y) + 2kx$$

We can eliminate the variable y by using the fact that the floor area has been specified:

$$xy = 3750$$

Substitute $y = \dfrac{3750}{x}$ in the equation for the total cost C and simplify to obtain

$$C(x) = 3k\left(x + \frac{2500}{x}\right)$$

The building regulations require that x lie between 30 and 60.

We thus have to solve this mathematical problem: find the minimum value of the function $C(x)$ on the interval $30 \le x \le 60$. First calculate the derivative of $C(x)$,

$$C'(x) = 3k\left(1 - \frac{2500}{x^2}\right)$$

which exists for all x in the interval. Now set $C'(x) = 0$, which implies that $x^2 = 2500$, or $x = \pm 50$. We retain only $x = 50$, because the interval is $30 \le x \le 60$. The minimum value will occur either at $x = 50$ or at one of the end points. We thus calculate the function values

$$C(30) = 340k, \quad C(50) = 300k, \quad C(60) = 305k$$

It follows that the minimum cost occurs when $x = 50$.

Thus the dimensions of the floor area that will minimize the cost are 50 m by 75 m, with one of the 50 m walls being made of glass.   □

It is of interest that one can solve the problem in Example 3 without knowing the actual cost of the walls. An essential step, however, was to introduce a symbol (we used k) to denote the cost per linear metre of the cement walls. This constant then appeared as an overall factor in the cost function $C(x)$ and hence had no effect when we set $C'(x) = 0$. Also note that the solution is independent of the height of the walls. This is so because we assumed a standard height for the walls, so that the cost of a wall depended only on the length.

Exercises 3.5

You should translate each optimization problem into a mathematical problem of this form: find the maximum (or minimum) value of a function f on an interval $a \le x \le b$. It is essential to specify the interval, because the maximum or minimum value could occur at an end point.

1. A rectangular field along a straight river is to be divided into 3 smaller fields by one fence parallel to the river and 4 fences perpendicular to the river. Find the maximum area that can be enclosed if 1600 m of fencing is available.

2. Find the area of the largest rectangle that can be inscribed inside the ellipse

$$\frac{x^2}{9} + \frac{y^2}{4} = 1$$

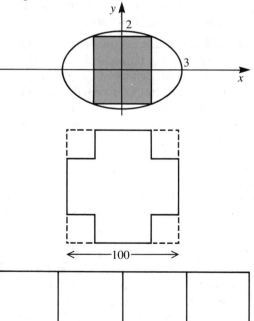

3. A box with an open top is to be made from a square piece of cardboard, of side length 100 cm, by cutting a square from each corner and then folding up the sides. Find the dimensions of the box of largest volume.

4. An experimental farm has 3600 m of fencing with which to enclose and subdivide a rectangular field into 4 equal plots of land.

    a. What is the largest area that can be enclosed?
    b. What is the largest area that can be enclosed if each side of each plot is required to be at least 250 m long?

5. The strength of a rectangular beam is proportional to the product of the width and the square of the depth. Find the dimensions of the strongest beam that can be cut from a circular log with a diameter of 24 cm.

6. A soft drink can in the shape of a right circular cylinder is to have a capacity of 250 mm³. If the diameter of the can must be no less than 4 cm and no greater than 8 cm, find the dimensions of the can that will use the least amount of material (include top, bottom, and side). What is the ratio of height to diameter for this can?

7. If the sum of two non-negative numbers is 10, how should the numbers be chosen so that the sum of their squares is
   a. a maximum? **b.** a minimum?

8. Repeat Example 3 in the text for a supermarket in which the floor area is 7350 m².

9. In microcomputers most of the components are squeezed into a single box-shaped block. If the block has a length equal to twice the width and if the total surface area of the block must be 200 cm² in order to dissipate the heat produced, find the dimensions for the maximum volume of the block.

10. The perimeter of an isosceles triangle is 36 cm. Find the lengths of the sides of the triangle of maximum area.

11. A 400 m track has the shape of two semi-circles at the ends of a rectangle. The straight sections of the track must be at least 100 m in length, and the radius of the semi-circles must be at least 20 m. Find the dimensions of the track that encloses
    a. the maximum area.
    b. the minimum area.

12. A car rental agency has 200 cars. The owner finds that at a price of $36 per day he can rent all the cars. For each $2 increase in price, the demand is less and 5 fewer cars are rented. What price will maximize the total revenue?

13. A piece of wire 180 cm long is cut into 6 sections, 2 of one length and 4 of another length. Each of the two sections having the same length is bent into the form of a circle, and the two circles are then joined by the four remaining sections to make a frame for a model of a right circular cylinder. Find the lengths of the sections that will maximize the volume of the cylinder.

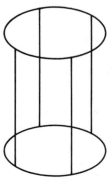

14. The current ticket price at a local theatre is $4, and the theatre attracts an average of 250 customers per show. Every $0.20 increase in ticket price reduces the average attendance by 10 customers, while every $0.20 decrease results in 10 extra customers.

    a. Let x represent the change in ticket price in dollars. Show that the revenue R from ticket sales depends on x according to $R(x) = (4 + x)(250 - 50x)$.

    b. If the seating capacity is 400, show that $-3 \leq x \leq 5$.

    c. Find the ticket price that will maximize revenue.

15. A straight fence is 100 m long. A rectangular area is to be enclosed by using an extra 200 m of fencing and incorporating all of the original 100 m fence in one side. What is the greatest area that can be enclosed in this way?

16. a. Find the point on the curve defined by

$$x^2 - y^2 = 16, \quad 4 \leq x \leq 5$$

    that is closest to the point $P(0, 2)$.

    b. Find the point on the curve that is most distant from P.

    c. Let Q be the point found in part (a). Verify that the line PQ is perpendicular to the tangent to the curve at Q. Can you suggest a geometrical interpretation for this result?

17. Consider the parabolic arc

$$y = kx^2, \quad -\frac{1}{\sqrt{k}} \leq x \leq \frac{1}{\sqrt{k}}.$$

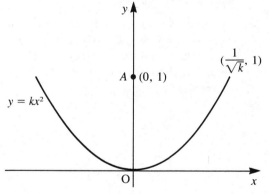

Find the point P on the parabola that is closest to the point $A(0, 1)$, and the point Q on the parabola that is most distant from A. As you might expect, the answer depends on the value of the constant k. Solve the problem when

    a. $k = \dfrac{9}{2}$ **b.** $k = \dfrac{3}{4}$ **c.** $k = \dfrac{1}{4}$

Suggestion: Find the maximum and minimum values of the **square** of the distance. In this way you will avoid messy square roots.

18. A man lives on an island 1 km from the mainland. His favourite pub is 3 km along the shore from the point on the shore closest to the island. The man can paddle his canoe at 3 km/h and can jog at 5 km/h. Determine where he should land so as to reach the pub in the shortest possible time.

19. Repeat Exercise 18, assuming that the pub is only 0.5 km along the shore.

20. A power line is to be constructed from the shore of a lake to an island that is 500 m away. The closest power line ends 4 km along the shore from the point on the shore closest to the island. If it costs 5 times as much to lay the power line under water as along the shore, how should the line be installed to minimize the cost?

Problems 3.5

1. A paper drinking cup in the form of a right circular cone can be made from a circular piece of waxed paper by removing a sector and joining the edges *OA* and *OB*. Show that the maximum capacity of a cup that can be formed from a disc of radius *R* centimetres is

$$V = \frac{2\pi R^3}{9\sqrt{3}} \text{ cm}^3$$

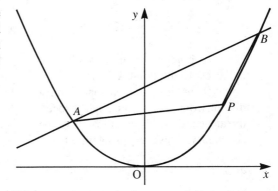

2. Find the area *A* of the largest rectangle that can be inscribed inside the ellipse

$$\frac{x^2}{a^2} + \frac{y^2}{b^2} = 1$$

Show that the ratio of *A* to the area of the ellipse is independent of *a* and *b*.

3. Solve Exercise 17 in this section for an arbitrary value of the positive constant *k*. How many different cases do you have to consider?

4. The line $y = mx + b$ intersects the parabola $x^2 = 4py$ at the points *A* and *B*. Find the coordinates of a point *P* on the arc *AOB* so that the triangle *PAB* has maximum area.

5. A sheet of paper 8 cm by 10 cm is folded as in the diagram. How should the sheet be folded so as to minimize the length *AB* of the fold?

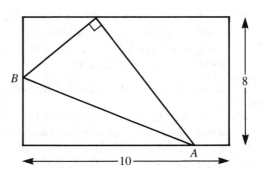

6. A study by the Ministry of Transportation shows that the separation distance L (in metres) between cars travelling in a single lane across the Burlington Skyway is related to their velocity v (in m/s) by

$$L = 4 + 3v + \frac{v^2}{36}$$

It is assumed that all cars move at the same speed.

a. How many cars in a single lane pass a given point in an hour when the traffic speed is v?

b. For what speed is the flow of traffic a maximum? Assume a speed limit of 80 km/h.

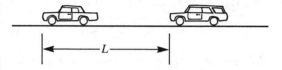

3.6 The Tangent Approximation

When a calculator that is accurate to 10 digits is used to evaluate $\sqrt{2}$, the value

$$1.414\ 213\ 562$$

is displayed. The number $\sqrt{2}$ is a non-terminating, non-repeating decimal. A calculator gives an **approximate value**, correct to the number of digits displayed. You may have wondered how a calculator is programmed. To explain the algorithms that are used to find such approximate values is beyond the scope of this book. However, because aproximations are an important application of mathematics, we shall discuss a simple method of approximating square roots and other functions. The method uses the tangent line to the graph of the function, and is thus called the **tangent approximation**. You will be able to use your calculator to test the accuracy of your approximate values. Although the tangent approximation is not as accurate as a calculator, it is important because of its simplicity and because it forms the basis for more accurate methods of approximation.

Consider the function

$$f(x) = \sqrt{x}$$

The derivative of f is

$$f'(x) = \frac{1}{2}x^{-\frac{1}{2}}$$

$$= \frac{1}{2\sqrt{x}}$$

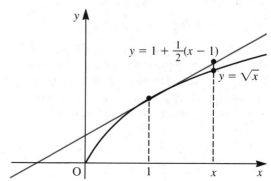

Since

$$f(1) = 1 \quad \text{and} \quad f'(1) = \frac{1}{2}$$

the equation of the tangent line at $x = 1$ is

$$y = 1 + \frac{1}{2}(x - 1)$$

If x is close to 1, we can use the y value on the tangent line to approximate the y value on the graph of $y = \sqrt{x}$. We express this by writing

$$\sqrt{x} \approx 1 + \frac{1}{2}(x - 1), \quad \text{for } x \text{ close to } 1$$

We test this idea by calculating some y values on the tangent line and comparing them to calculator values for $\sqrt{x}$, for values of x close to 1.

x	$1 + \frac{1}{2}(x - 1)$	$\sqrt{x}$	Error
0.9	0.95	0.948 68	0.001 32
0.99	0.995	0.994 99	0.000 01
1.0	1	1	0
1.01	1.005	1.004 99	0.000 01
1.1	1.05	1.048 81	0.001 19
2.0	1.5	1.414 21	0.085 79

As one would expect from the graph, the approximate values are too large and the accuracy decreases as x moves away from 1.

In general, the tangent line to the graph of $y = f(x)$ at $x = a$ has a slope of $m = f'(a)$. The equation of the tangent line can be written in the form

$$y = f(a) + f'(a)(x - a)$$

Since the tangent line is close to the graph, this expression approximates $f(x)$ for x close to a, and we refer to it as the tangent approximation of $f(x)$ at $x = a$. The closer x is to a, the better the approximation is.

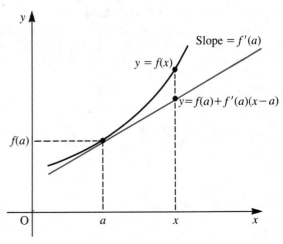

> **The Tangent Approximation**
>
> If x is close to a, then
>
> $$f(x) \approx f(a) + f'(a)(x - a)$$

Example 1.

a. Find the tangent approximation to $f(x) = \sqrt{x}$ at $x = 64$.
b. Using the result of part (a), find an approximate value of $\sqrt{65}$.

Solution.
a. Find the equation of the tangent line at $x = 64$. Since

$$f'(x) = \frac{1}{2\sqrt{x}}$$

the slope of the tangent line is

$$m = f'(64)$$
$$= \frac{1}{2\sqrt{64}}$$
$$= \frac{1}{16}$$

The equation of the tangent line at the point $(64, 8)$ is

$$y = 8 + \frac{1}{16}(x - 64)$$

Thus the tangent approximation is

$$\sqrt{x} \approx 8 + \frac{1}{16}(x - 64)$$

for x close to 64.

b. Choose $x = 65$ in the tangent approximation of part (a), to obtain

$$\sqrt{65} \approx 8 + \frac{1}{16}(1)$$
$$\approx 8.0625$$

Note that the calculator value accurate to 5 decimals is 8.062 26, so that our approximate value is reasonable.

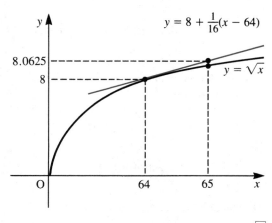

In some applications, it is convenient to approximate the change in the function value directly. For this reason we rewrite the approximation formula as

$$f(x) - f(a) \approx f'(a)(x - a)$$

for x close to a. In terms of the increments

$$\Delta x = x - a$$

and

$$\Delta f = f(x) - f(a)$$

we obtain

$$\Delta f \approx f'(a)\, \Delta x$$

for Δx close to 0.

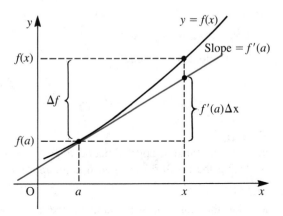

The Tangent Approximation (Increment Form)

If Δx is close to zero, then

$$\Delta f \approx f'(a)\, \Delta x$$

Example 2. A circular metal plate of radius 50 cm expands when heated, so that its radius changes by 0.2 cm. Find an approximate value for the change in area.

Solution. The area A is

$$A = \pi r^2$$

where r is the radius. The derivative of A is

$$A'(r) = 2\pi r$$

and thus the tangent approximation for the change in area is

$$\Delta A \approx 2\pi r\, \Delta r$$

When $r = 50$ and $\Delta r = 0.2$,

$$\Delta A \approx 2\pi(50)(0.2)$$
$$\approx 20\pi$$

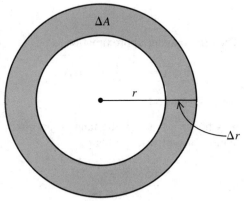

Thus the change in area is approximately 20π cm². $\qquad\square$

In Example 2, the tangent approximation has the following geometric interpretation in terms of the circle: the change in area ΔA (the shaded area) is approximated by the product of the circumference $2\pi r$ of the inner circle and the change Δr in the radius. Can you see from the diagram why this is reasonable?

Exercises 3.6

1. a. Find the tangent approximation to the function

$$f(x) = \sqrt{x}$$

at $x = 100$ and use it to find approximate values for $\sqrt{101}, \sqrt{102} \sqrt{103}$, and $\sqrt{104}$.

b. By sketching the graph and the tangent line determine whether your approximate values are too large or too small.

c. Use a calculator to check the accuracy of your approximate values.

2. By using the square root function $f(x) = \sqrt{x}$ and choosing a suitable point of tangency, find an approximate value for the following.

a. $\sqrt{62}$ **b.** $\sqrt{97}$ **c.** $\sqrt{10\ 168}$ **d.** $\sqrt{147}$

Use a calculator to check the accuracy of your answers.

3. Find the tangent approximation of the function

$$f(x) = \sqrt[3]{x}$$

at $x = 1000$ and use it to find approximate values for $\sqrt[3]{980}, \sqrt[3]{990}, \sqrt[3]{1010}$, and $\sqrt[3]{1020}$. Use a calculator to check the accuracy of your answers.

4. Find an approximate value for $1000^{\frac{1}{10}}$, using the fact that $1024^{\frac{1}{10}} = 2$. Use a calculator to check the accuracy of your approximation.

5. Use the tangent approximation to approximate the following quantities. Check the accuracy of your answers with a calculator.

a. $(16.2)^{\frac{1}{4}}$ **b.** $(31.8)^{\frac{1}{5}}$

c. $(0.97)^{-\frac{4}{9}}$ **d.** $(1.003)^{50}$

6. A sphere of radius 10 cm is painted. If the thickness of the paint is 0.1 cm, find an approximate value for the volume of paint.

7. A right-angled triangle has a base length of 12 cm and a height of 5 cm. If the base is decreased by 0.3 cm, find an approximate value for the change in the length of the hypotenuse.

8. The lateral surface area of a cone of radius r and height 8 cm is

$$S(r) = \pi r \sqrt{r^2 + 64}$$

If the radius increases by 0.02 cm from a value of 6 cm, approximate the change in surface area.

9. Explain the approximation formula

$$\sqrt{1 + x} \approx 1 + \frac{1}{2} x$$

in terms of the tangent approximation. Illustrate with a sketch. For what values of x does this give a reasonable approximation?

Problems 3.6

1. a. You are ready to calculate $\sqrt{6}$ when your calculator battery fails. Your backup calculator does not have a square-root function! You immediately think of the tangent approximation of $f(x) = \sqrt{x}$, but 6 is not close enough to a perfect square (4 or 9) to give a good approximation. Then you notice that $2\sqrt{6} = \sqrt{24}$ and 24 is close to a perfect square. Show that this approach gives an approximate value for $\sqrt{6}$ with an error of less than 0.0006.

    b. Invent a similar method to approximate $\sqrt{11}, \sqrt{12}, \sqrt{13}$, and $\sqrt{14}$. For example, $4\sqrt{14} = \sqrt{224}$, and 224 is close to 15^2.

2. Find an approximation for $(1 + x)^{\frac{1}{n}}$, where n is an integer, that is valid when x is close to zero.

3.7 Newton's Method

Suppose that you have to find the points of intersection of the curve $y = x^3$ and the line $y = 1 - x$. A simple sketch shows that there is only one point of intersection and that its x-coordinate lies between 0 and 1. To find this point of intersection, equate the two expressions for y to obtain the equation

$$x^3 = 1 - x$$

or

$$x^3 + x - 1 = 0$$

which must be solved for x. Lacking a method for finding exact solutions to this and more complicated equations, you wish to develop an algorithm for finding **approximate solutions**. A fundamental and useful procedure for finding approximate solutions to equations is **Newton's method**.

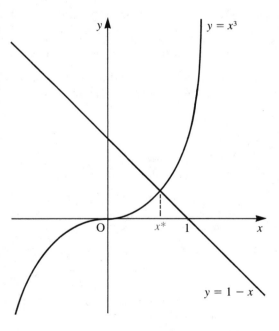

Consider any equation of the form

$$f(x) = 0$$

and let x^* be a solution of this equation, so that $f(x^*) = 0$. We refer to x^* as a **root** of the equation $f(x) = 0$ or a **zero** of the function f. Geometrically, one can think of x^* as the

x-intercept of the curve $y = f(x)$. The first step in Newton's method is to choose a value x_1 and to draw the tangent line to $y = f(x)$ at the point $(x_1, f(x_1))$.

Let x_2 denote the x-intercept of this tangent line, as in the sketch below. Newton's method is based on the observation that, in most cases, if x_1 is chosen to be close to the root x^*, then x_2 is even closer to x^*. Thus x_2 is a better approximation to x^* than x_1 is.

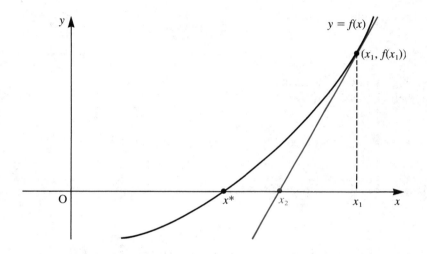

The number x_2 can be calculated in terms of x_1 by using the tangent line. The tangent line at $(x_1, f(x_1))$ has slope $f'(x_1)$. Since the tangent line passes through the points $(x_1, f(x_1))$ and $(x_2, 0)$, its slope can also be expressed in the form

$$\frac{y_1 - y_2}{x_1 - x_2}$$

or

$$\frac{f(x_1) - 0}{x_1 - x_2}$$

Therefore

$$f'(x_1) = \frac{f(x_1) - 0}{x_1 - x_2}$$

This equation can be rearranged to yield

$$x_2 = x_1 - \frac{f(x_1)}{f'(x_1)}$$

This relation shows us how to calculate x_2 once we have chosen x_1.

The above procedure can be repeated, with x_2 taking the place of x_1. The slope of the new tangent line, which passes through the point $(x_3, 0)$ and $(x_2, f(x_2))$ is

$$f'(x_2) = \frac{f(x_2) - 0}{x_2 - x_3}$$

Solving this equation for x_3 results in

$$x_3 = x_2 - \frac{f(x_2)}{f'(x_2)}$$

Compare this equation to the equation for x_2—note their similar form.

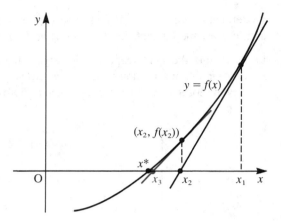

One can repeat this process indefinitely to obtain a sequence of numbers

$$x_1, x_2, x_3, \ldots, x_n, x_{n+1}, \ldots$$

The term x_{n+1} can be determined from the term x_n according to the equation

$$x_{n+1} = x_n - \frac{f(x_n)}{f'(x_n)}, \text{ where } n = 1, 2, \ldots$$

by analogy with the equations for x_1 and x_2. For many functions, as n increases without bound, the numbers x_n will become arbitrarily close to the root x^*. In this case, we say that **the sequence $\{x_n\}$ converges to** x^*, and we can obtain an approximation for x^* of any desired accuracy by performing a sufficient number of steps.

We now discuss some examples. Example 1 is purely illustrative since the answer is known beforehand. The other examples and the exercises show that Newton's method can be used in many different situations.

Example 1. Use Newton's method to approximate $\sqrt{2}$ by considering $\sqrt{2}$ as a solution of the equation $x^2 - 2 = 0$.

Solution. Consider the function

$$f(x) = x^2 - 2$$

and use Newton's method to approximate the solution $x^* = \sqrt{2}$ of the equation $f(x) = 0$. The general formula for an approximation to the root x^* is

$$x_{n+1} = x_n - \frac{f(x_n)}{f'(x_n)}$$

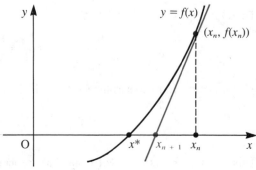

Since in this example $f'(x) = 2x$, we obtain

$$x_{n+1} = x_n - \frac{(x_n^2 - 2)}{2x_n},$$

which can be simplified to give

$$x_{n+1} = \frac{x_n}{2} + \frac{1}{x_n}, \text{ where } n = 1, 2, 3, \ldots \qquad (1)$$

As the initial value, we choose $x_1 = 1$ (which is reasonably close to $\sqrt{2}$). On substituting this in the equation for x_{n+1}, with $n = 1$, we obtain

$$x_2 = \frac{x_1}{2} + \frac{1}{x_1}$$
$$= 1.5$$

With $n = 2$ in equation 1, we get

$$x_3 = \frac{x_2}{2} + \frac{1}{x_2}$$
$$= \frac{1.5}{2} + \frac{1}{1.5}$$
$$= 1.416\ 667$$

We can proceed in this way to use the value of x_3 to find x_4, the value of x_4 to find x_5, etc. The results are

$$x_4 = 1.414\ 216 \quad (n = 3) \qquad x_5 = 1.414\ 214 \quad (n = 4) \qquad x_6 = 1.414\ 214 \quad (n = 5)$$

We conclude that $\quad x^* = \sqrt{2} \approx 1.414\ 214 \quad$ (to 6 decimal places),

as can be verified directly with the square root key on a calculator. $\qquad \square$

A procedure such as Newton's method, in which one successively calculates the terms of a sequence of approximations to the solution of an equation, is an example of an **iterative method**. Such methods are ideally suited to use with a calculator or computer. The equation for x_{n+1}, which relates successive terms in the sequence, is called a **recursion formula**.

Recursion Formula for Newton's Method:

$$x_{n+1} = x_n - \frac{f(x_n)}{f'(x_n)}, \quad n = 1, 2, \ldots,$$

with x_1 suitably chosen.

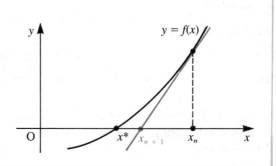

Remember that to use Newton's method you must first guess a value for x_1; then you use the recursion formula to calculate x_2, x_3, ... We recommend that in each application of Newton's method you draw a diagram similar to the one in the box and give a brief derivation of the recursion formula. This will ensure that the geometrical basis for the method is clear to you.

In Example 2 we solve the problem that was discussed at the beginning of this section.

Example 2. Use Newton's method to find the point of intersection (correct to 6 decimal places) of the curve $y = x^3$ and the line $y = 1 - x$.

Solution. To find the x-value of the point of intersection we have to solve the equation

$$x^3 = 1 - x$$

This is equivalent to solving $f(x) = 0$

where $f(x) = x^3 + x - 1$

The recursion formula is

$$x_{n+1} = x_n - \frac{f(x_n)}{f'(x_n)}$$

Since $f'(x) = 3x^2 + 1$, the recursion formula becomes

$$x_{n+1} = x_n - \frac{(x_n^3 + x_n - 1)}{3x_n^2 + 1}$$

which can be simplified to

$$x_{n+1} = \frac{2x_n^3 + 1}{3x_n^2 + 1}$$

From the earlier discussion we know that the root lies between 0 and 1. Hence we take $x_1 = \frac{1}{2}$ as the initial guess. Using the recursion formula and a calculator, we successively obtain

$x_2 = 0.714\ 286$ $(n = 1)$ $x_3 = 0.683\ 180$ $(n = 2)$

$x_4 = 0.682\ 328$ $(n = 3)$ $x_5 = 0.682\ 328$ $(n = 4)$

We conclude that the solution x^* is

$$x^* \approx 0.682\ 328 \quad \text{(to six decimal places)}$$

Since $y = 1 - x$, the point of intersection is approximately $(0.682\ 328, 0.317\ 672)$. $\square$

It is important to make an initial guess x_1 that is sufficiently close to the desired solution x^*. In Example 1, with $f(x) = x^2 - 2 = 0$, the choice $x_1 = 1$ led to the solution $x^* = \sqrt{2}$. On the other hand, the choice $x_1 = -1$ would have led to a different solution, namely $x^* = -\sqrt{2}$.

Another possibility is that the sequence $\{x_n\}$ may not converge, even though there is a solution. Graphing the function can help in making a suitable choice for x_1. Alternatively, the location of the solution can be narrowed down by finding two numbers a and b such that $f(a) < 0$ and $f(b) > 0$. If f is continuous, then $f(x^*) = 0$ for some x^* between a and b; in other words, if the graph is below the x-axis at a and above the x-axis at b, then it must cross the x-axis somewhere between a and b. In Example 2, observe that $f(0) = -1$ and $f(1) = 1$, implying the existence of a solution x^* that satisfies $0 < x^* < 1$.

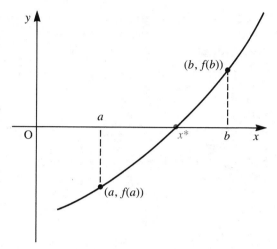

In Example 3, Newton's method is used to find the maximum value and minimum value of a function on an interval. Newton's method is needed to solve the equation $f'(x) = 0$.

Example 3. Find the maximum value and minimum value of the function

$$f(x) = x^2 - \frac{1}{x} + \frac{4}{x^2}$$

on the interval $1 \le x \le 3$.

Solution. The first step is to find the x-values in the interval $1 \le x \le 3$ for which $f'(x) = 0$. The derivative of $f(x)$ is

$$f'(x) = 2x + \frac{1}{x^2} - \frac{8}{x^3}$$

which exists for all x in the interval $1 \le x \le 3$. We now have to solve the equation

$$2x + \frac{1}{x^2} - \frac{8}{x^3} = 0$$

Since we cannot solve this equation exactly, we consider Newton's method. It is desirable to write the equation in as simple a form as possible, and so we multiply both sides by x^3 to obtain

$$2x^4 + x - 8 = 0$$

Define the function $g(x)$ as

$$g(x) = 2x^4 + x - 8$$

and apply Newton's method to this function. It is essential to distinguish $g(x)$ from the given function $f(x)$.

Observe that $g(1) = -5$, and $g(3) = 157$; therefore $g(x)$ has a root x^* in the interval $1 < x < 3$. Since the derivative of $g(x)$

$$g'(x) = 8x^3 + 1$$

is positive on the interval $1 \leq x \leq 3$, the tangent line to the graph of $g(x)$ has a positive slope. This means that the graph of $g(x)$ does not bend down and cut the x-axis again, so that $g(x)$ has only one root in the interval $1 \leq x \leq 3$. We can narrow down the location of the root to the interval $1 \leq x \leq 2$ by noting that $g(2) > 0$. Thus it is reasonable to choose $x_1 = 1.5$ as our initial guess.

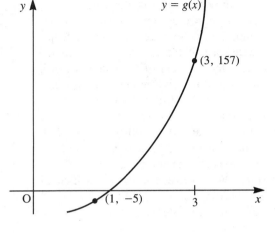

The recursion formula for solving $g(x) = 0$ is

$$x_{n+1} = x_n - \frac{g(x_n)}{g'(x_n)}$$

Using the formulas for $g(x)$ and $g'(x)$, this equation can be simplified to

$$x_{n+1} = \frac{6x_n^4 + 8}{8x_n^3 + 1}$$

With $x_1 = 1.5$, we successively obtain

$$x_2 = 1.370\ 536 \quad (n = 1)$$

$$x_3 = 1.350\ 759 \quad (n = 2)$$

$$x_4 = 1.350\ 338 \quad (n = 3)$$

$$x_5 = 1.350\ 338 \quad (n = 4)$$

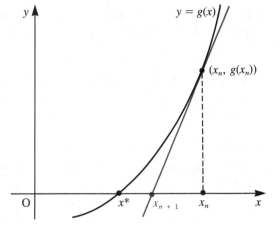

Therefore the solution of the equation $g(x) = 0$, which is also the solution of the equation $f'(x) = 0$, is

$$x^* \approx 1.350\ 338.$$

As a check, note that $f'(x^*) \approx 0.000\ 002$, which is close to 0, as required.

To find the maximum value and minimum value of $f(x)$ on the interval $1 \leq x \leq 3$, we calculate the function values

$$f(1) = 4, \quad f(x^*) \approx 3.276\ 546, \quad f(3) = \frac{82}{9}$$

Thus the maximum value is $f(3)$ and the minimum value is $f(x^*)$.   □

Newton's method has the desirable feature that if the sequence $\{x_n\}$ does converge to x^*, then it converges very rapidly. Typically each iteration doubles the number of significant figures of accuracy, once x_n is close to x^*. How many iterations are performed depends on the accuracy desired. In the examples we continued the process until there was no change in the sixth decimal place. We suggest that you do the same in the exercises.

Exercises 3.7

1. a. By considering the function $f(x) = x^2 - A$, where A is any positive number, show that Newton's recursion formula for $\sqrt{A}$ is

$$x_{n+1} = \frac{1}{2}\left(x_n + \frac{A}{x_n}\right).$$

b. Use part (a) to approximate $\sqrt{3}$ and compare your approximation with the result obtained using a calculator.

2. Consider the function $f(x) = x^4 + x - 25$.

   a. Show that $f(2) < 0$ and $f(3) > 0$ and hence the equation $f(x) = 0$ must have a root r that satisfies $2 < r < 3$.
   b. Use Newton's method to approximate r.
   c. Evaluate $f(r)$ to confirm the accuracy of your result.

3. Use Newton's method to approximate the solution of each equation in the given interval.

   a. $x^5 - 2 = 0, \quad 1 < x < 2$
   b. $x^6 + 7x + 3 = 0, \quad -1 < x < 0$
   c. $2x - \dfrac{4}{x} + \dfrac{1}{x^2} = 0, \quad 0 < x < 1$

   Suggestion: In part (c), simplify the equation first.

4. a. Show graphically that the curve $y = x^4$ and the line $y = x + 1$ have two points of intersection.
   b. Use Newton's method to find the points of intersection.

5. The function $f(x) = x^3 - 3x + 1$ has three distinct real roots. Locate them approximately by calculating $f(-2), f(-1), f(0), f(1)$, and $f(2)$. Use Newton's method to calculate the middle root x^* to five decimal places. Evaluate $f(x^*)$ to test your calculation.

6. Find the maximum value and minimum value of the function

$$f(x) = x^3 - x + \frac{27}{x^3}$$

on the interval $1 \le x \le 3$.

7. Show graphically that the curves $y = \dfrac{1}{x}$ and $y = x^2 + 2$ have only one point of intersection.

Approximate this point using Newton's method.

8. The equation $y^5 + x^2y - 2x^2 = -1$ defines y implicitly as a function of x. Use Newton's method to find y when

   a. $x = 2$.   **b.** $x = 10$.

9. An object moves in a straight line with position function

$$s(t) = 2t - 3t^3 + t^5, \quad t \geq 0.$$

Use Newton's method to find the earliest time at which the object is at rest.

10. a. By considering the function $f(x) = x^m - A$, show that Newton's recursion formula for $\sqrt[m]{A}$, where $A > 0$, is

$$x_{n+1} = \frac{1}{m}\left[(m-1)x_n + \frac{A}{x_n^{m-1}}\right]$$

   (Note that for $m = 2$ this recursion formula agrees with the result of Exercise 1(a) in this section.)

   b. Find an approximate value for $10^{\frac{1}{10}}$ by using the result of part (a).

Review Exercises

1. Find $\dfrac{dy}{dx}$ at the indicated point on the curve.

   a. $2x + y^3 = 6$, at $(2, -1)$ **b.** $xy^2 - x^2y = 12$, at $(3, -1)$
   c. $\sqrt{x} + \sqrt{y} = 10$, at $(4, 64)$ **d.** $(x + y)^3 - x^2y = 5$, at $(2, -1)$

2. The curve

$$x^2 - xy + y^2 = 9$$

is an ellipse with its axes rotated from the standard position.

   a. Find the slopes of the tangent lines to the ellipse at its x-intercepts.
   b. Find the points at which the tangent line is vertical.

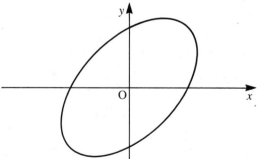

3. The curve

$$(x^2 + y^2)^2 = x^2 - y^2$$

has the shape of a figure eight. Find the points at which the tangent line is horizontal.

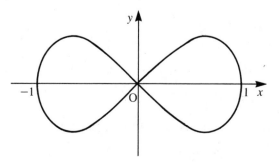

4. Consider the curve $x + xy + 2y^2 = 6$.

    a. Find the equation of the tangent line to the curve at $(2, 1)$.

    b. Find all other points on this curve at which the tangent line is parallel to the tangent line in part (a).

5. Consider a uranium fuel rod in a nuclear reactor, which is a cylinder of height 2 m and diameter 20 cm.

    a. If the radius and height of the cylinder decrease at a constant rate of 1 cm per month after the fuel rod is activated, find a formula for the rate of change of the volume of the fuel rod.

    b. Find the rate of decrease of the volume at the instant when the diameter of the rod is half the original diameter.

    c. Compare the rate of change of volume when $r = 8$ cm to the rate of change when $r = 4$ cm. Explain why the rate is decreasing.

6. One end of a heavy beam is built into a wall, and the other end is supported on a ledge. Away from the ends, the beam sags owing to gravity. At a distance x units from the wall, the deflection of the beam from the horizontal is

$$y = -k(2x^4 - 5Lx^3 + 3L^2x^2)$$

where k is a constant and L is the length of the beam. Determine the maximum deflection for a beam of length 10 m.

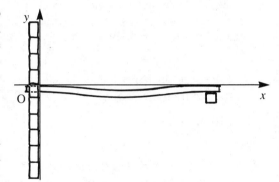

7. If $y^r = x^s$ where r and s are rational numbers, show that

$$\frac{dy}{dx} = \frac{sy}{rx}, \text{ for } x \neq 0$$

8. An ellipse in standard position has axes of lengths 6 and 8. A tangent to the ellipse has slope 1 and meets the coordinate axes at P and Q. Find the length of PQ.

9. A particle moves along the x-axis in such a way that its position s at time t is

$$s(t) = 3t^4 - 16t^3 + 24t^2, \text{ for } -5 \leq t \leq 5$$

    a. Determine the velocity and acceleration of the particle at time t.

    b. At what values of t is the particle at rest?

    c. At what values of t does the particle change direction?

    d. What is the velocity when the acceleration is zero for the first time?

10. The position of an object moving along a straight line is described by the function

$$s(t) = -t^3 + 4t^2 - 10$$

for $t \geq 0$. Is the object moving away from or towards its starting point when $t = 3$?

11. The position function of a particle that moves on the x-axis is shown in the diagram.

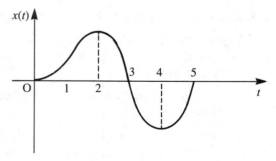
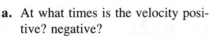

   a. At what times is the velocity positive? negative?

   b. At what times is the particle moving towards the origin?

   c. At what times does the particle reverse its direction?

12. A building is illuminated by a flood light that is 15 m away and at ground level. A man 2 m tall walks away from the light directly towards the building at 2 m/s. Is the length of his shadow on the building increasing or decreasing? Find the rate of change of the length of his shadow when he is 4 m from the light.

13. A boat is being pulled towards a dock by means of a rope and a winch. If the length of the rope is decreasing at $\frac{1}{2}$ m/s, how fast is the boat approaching the dock when it is at the following distances from the dock?

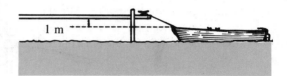

   a. 10 m   b. 2 m

14. Find the area of the largest rectangle (with sides parallel to the coordinate axes) that can be enclosed by the graphs of $f(x) = 18 - x^2$ and $g(x) = 2x^2 - 9$.

15. Consider all enclosed rectangular boxes with square bases that have a volume of 1 m³. Which box requires the least material to make? For practical reasons, assume that all sides are longer than 10 cm.

16. The curve

$$y^2 = x^2(12 - x)$$

is shown in the diagram. Find the maximum length of the vertical chord PQ in the loop of the curve.

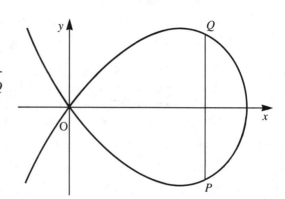

17. A motorist starts braking when she sees a stop sign. After t seconds her distance (in metres) from the sign is $s(t) = 62 - 16t + t^2$.

a. How far was the motorist from the sign when she started braking?
b. Does she go beyond the stop sign before stopping?

18. When the El Rancho Motel charges $25 per room or less, it fills all its 80 rooms every day. For each $1 increase in price, 4 fewer rooms are rented. For each occupied room, it costs $4 for cleaning and other services. Find the room rate that will maximize the daily profit.

19. A truck is being used to raise a heavy load by means of a pulley, as shown. A rope 9 m long is attached to the truck at a point 1 m above ground level. If the rope is taut and the truck moves at $\frac{1}{4}$ m/s, how fast is the load rising when the back of the truck is 3 m from the point directly below the pulley?

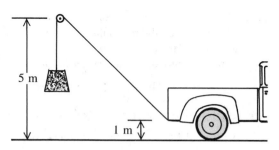

20. A rectangular building is to be constructed with a curtain wall that will be parallel to the front and will divide the building into a sales area of 1500 m² and a storeroom of 500 m². The outside walls at both sides and across the back will cost $100 per linear metre. The curtain wall across the store will cost $45 per linear metre. The front wall (mainly glass) will cost $345 per linear metre. Calculate the dimensions of the rectangular building that will give the required floor areas at the lowest cost for the walls. The front wall should be at least 20 m wide.

21. The operating cost of a truck is $\left(12 + \frac{1}{8}v\right)$ cents per kilometre when it runs at v km/h. The driver earns $10 per hour.

a. Find the most economical speed for a 500 km trip if trucks are required to travel between 50 and 100 km/h.
b. Repeat part (a) if the speed limit is 80 km/h.
c. Does the length of the trip affect the optimum speed?

22. An OPP officer is operating a radar speed trap on a sideroad 100 m from Highway 86, near Listowel. When a car is 200 m from the intersection, its velocity of approach is measured as 70 km/h. Is the car exceeding the speed limit of 80 km/h?

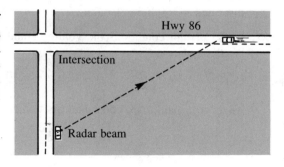

23. In manufacturing processes, the number of defective items that must be rejected tends to increase as the daily output increases. Suppose that the number of rejects r depends on the total daily output x according to

$$r(x) = \frac{40x}{250 - x} \quad \text{for} \quad x \le 200$$

where $x = 200$ represents the maximum possible output. The firm makes a profit of \$300 for each item sold and a loss of \$100 for each reject. What output x will maximize the profit?

24. The flight path of a patrolling plane is represented by the parabola $y = x^2$. We wish to find the point of closest approach of the plane to an aircraft carrier located at $\left(4, -\frac{3}{2}\right)$. The point (a, b) of closest approach is determined by the circle centred at $\left(4, -\frac{3}{2}\right)$ that is tangent to the parabola.

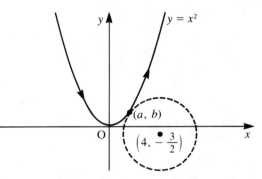

   a. Show that the x-coordinate a of the point of closest approach satisfies the equation

$$a^3 + 2a - 2 = 0.$$

   b. Use Newton's method to solve for a.

25. For a thin lens, the distance s_1 of the object from the lens and the distance s_2 of the image from the lens are related by

$$\frac{1}{s_1} + \frac{1}{s_2} = \frac{1}{f}$$

where f is the (constant) focal length of the lens. Suppose that the object is moving closer to the lens at 2 cm/s. Does the image move closer or further away? Find the rate of change of position of the image when $s_1 = 30$ cm, if the focal length of the lens is 20 cm.

26. What are the dimensions of the right circular cylinder of largest volume that can be inscribed in a sphere of radius R?

27. Under certain conditions the volume v and pressure p of a gas are related by van der Waal's equation

$$\left(p + \frac{a}{v^2}\right)(v - b) = c$$

where a, b, and c are constants. Show that

$$\frac{dp}{dv} = \frac{2a}{v^3} - \frac{c}{(v - b)^2}$$

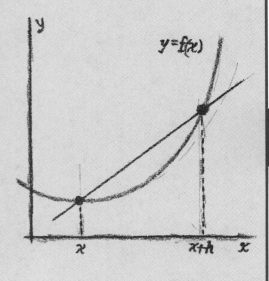

Isaac Newton *(1642–1727), born in Woolsthorpe, England, was one of the greatest geniuses of all time. His achievements, many of which were accomplished during a two-year period beginning when he was twenty-two years old, include the binomial series for negative and fractional exponents, the Differential and Integral Calculus (independently of Leibniz in Germany), the law of universal gravitation and the discovery that sunlight may be resolved into the colours of the rainbow when passed through a prism. In 1687, after eighteen months of total concentration, he published the* Principia, *one of the supreme achievements of the human mind. In this mammoth book he gave the first mathematical treatment of wave motion, deduced Kepler's laws of planetary motion from his law of gravitation, explained the path of comets (Edmund Halley, of Halley's Comet, encouraged Newton to write the* Principia), *calculated the masses of the earth and sun, and founded the theory of tides. Often, the discoveries of this genius became known only through casual conversations, in contrast with Leibniz, the co-founder of the Calculus (and the author of the notation currently used). Gottfried Wilhelm Leibniz (1646–1716), born in Germany, founded the Berlin Academy of Sciences and one of the first scientific journals, to disseminate the knowledge of the day. He himself had an active correspondence with the Bernoullis. Although Newton and Leibniz did correspond, it was Leibniz who freely discussed his methods. This attitude helped to pass the leadership in applications of the Calculus to the European continent for the next 200 years.*

Curve Sketching

Consider the function

$$f(x) = \frac{x}{(x^2 - 5)^2}$$

If we wish to see, at a glance, the essential features of this function, and perhaps to interpret it in terms of a mathematical model, then we will need to make a quick sketch of the graph of $f(x)$. To do this we may be tempted to calculate $f(x)$ for a number of values of x in some interval, plot the points, and then connect the points with a smooth curve. For example, if we choose x-values in the interval $-3 \le x \le 3$, using increments of 0.5, we obtain the following table of values and graph:

x	-3	-2.5	-2	-1.5	-1	-0.5	0	0.5	1	1.5	2	2.5	3
$f(x)$	$-\frac{3}{16}$	$-\frac{8}{5}$	-2	$-\frac{24}{121}$	$-\frac{1}{16}$	$-\frac{8}{361}$	0	$\frac{8}{361}$	$\frac{1}{16}$	$\frac{24}{121}$	2	$\frac{8}{5}$	$\frac{3}{16}$

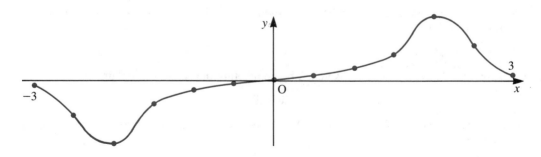

However, the graph is more accurately represented by the following diagram.

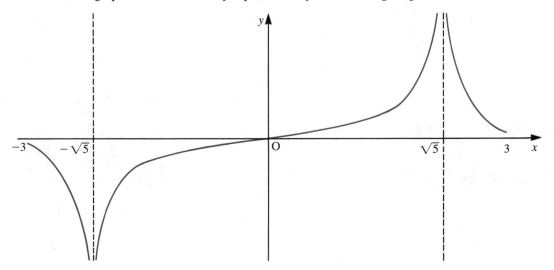

By "plotting points" we would have missed the essential features of the graph! In order to avoid this problem and to eliminate the need to calculate large numbers of function values, in this chapter we shall use the methods of Calculus to sketch graphs. As we shall see, these methods will yield graphs that, although not "exactly to scale," possess all the essential features of the functions. In this way we can obtain a good understanding of the qualitative features of functions.

If we require an accurate graph, we can use a computer to calculate and plot many function values. The sketch provided by the methods of Calculus will suggest a suitable choice of scales for the x-axis and y-axis and will indicate where the x-values used in the program should be closely spaced.

4.1 Local Maxima and Minima

We begin by considering the graphs of polynomial functions. The graph of any quadratic function, for example

$$f(x) = x^2 - 4x + 5$$

is a parabola. This graph can be sketched by completing the square, to obtain

$$f(x) = (x - 2)^2 + 1$$

Observe that the graph of $f(x)$ is simply the parabola $y = x^2$ translated two units to the right and one unit up.

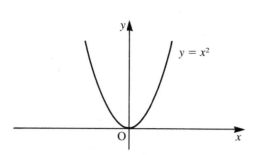
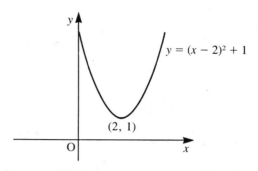

An essential feature of the graph is the vertex $(2, 1)$. By noting that the slope of the tangent line is zero at the vertex, its coordinates can be easily found using the derivative. For the function

$$f(x) = x^2 - 4x + 5$$

the derivative is

$$f'(x) = 2x - 4$$

so that $f'(x) = 0$ when $x = 2$, giving the vertex. Observe also that the slope of the tangent line is negative to the left of the vertex and positive to the right of the vertex:

$$\text{if } x < 2, \text{ then } f'(x) < 0$$

and

$$\text{if } x > 2, \text{ then } f'(x) > 0$$

This means that the derivative changes sign at the vertex.

In general, a point on the graph of a function $f(x)$ at which the derivative equals zero and changes sign is called a **turning point** for the function.

If the derivative changes sign from negative to positive, as at $(c_1, f(c_1))$ in the diagram, then the graph resembles a parabola opening up near the turning point. We say that the function has a **local minimum** at $x = c_1$. If the derivative changes sign from positive to negative, as at $(c_2, f(c_2))$, then the graph resembles a parabola opening down near the turning point. We say that the function has a **local maximum** at $x = c_2$.

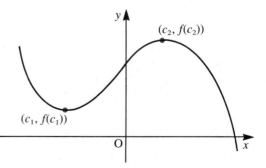

Suppose that you wish to sketch the graph of a polynomial function such as

$$f(x) = x^3 - 3x + 2 \quad \text{or} \quad f(x) = (1 - x^2)^2 - 2$$

By finding all the turning points of the function, you can make a quick sketch of the graph, as is illustrated in Example 1.

Example 1. Find all the turning points of

$$f(x) = x^3 - 3x + 2$$

and hence sketch the graph of the function.

Solution. The derivative of $f(x)$ is

$$f'(x) = 3x^2 - 3$$
$$= 3(x^2 - 1)$$

Solve $f'(x) = 0$ to obtain

$$x^2 - 1 = 0$$

so that

$$x = +1 \quad \text{or} \quad x = -1$$

Now determine the sign of $f'(x)$ on either side of the points $(-1, 4)$ and $(1, 0)$. There are three intervals to consider:

If $x < -1$, then $x^2 > 1$ and $f'(x) > 0$.
If $-1 < x < 1$, then $x^2 < 1$ and $f'(x) < 0$.
If $x > 1$, then $x^2 > 1$ and $f'(x) > 0$.

These results are summarized in the table.

x	$x < -1$	$x = -1$	$-1 < x < 1$	$x = 1$	$x > 1$
$f'(x)$	+	0	−	0	+

It follows that the points $(-1, 4)$ and $(1, 0)$ are turning points. Since the sign of the derivative changes from positive to negative at $x = -1$, the function has a local maximum at $x = -1$, and the graph is like a parabola opening down near $x = -1$. Since the sign of the derivative changes from negative to positive at $x = 1$, the function has a local minimum at $x = 1$, and the graph is like a parabola opening up near $x = 1$. Now that we have found all the turning points, we can sketch the graph, as shown in the diagram.

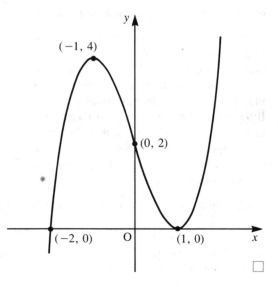

The graph can be confirmed by using other information—for example, the points (0, 2) and (−2, 0). In addition, when x becomes large and positive, the x^3 term in $f(x)$ is much larger than the quantity $-3x + 2$, and thus $f(x)$ becomes large and **positive**, as it does in the graph. Similarly, when x becomes large and negative, the x^3 term, and hence $f(x)$, becomes large and **negative**. Since x^3 determines the behaviour of the polynomial $f(x) = x^3 - 3x + 2$ for large values of x, it is called the **dominant term**.

The following summary shows the procedure that was used in Example 1 for testing whether a turning point is a local maximum or local minimum.

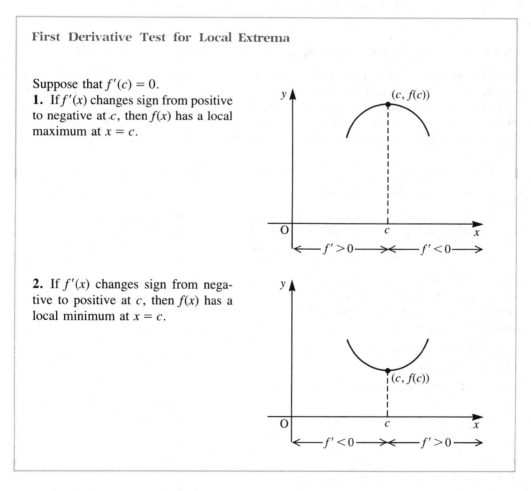

First Derivative Test for Local Extrema

Suppose that $f'(c) = 0$.
1. If $f'(x)$ changes sign from positive to negative at c, then $f(x)$ has a local maximum at $x = c$.

$(c, f(c))$

$\longleftarrow f' > 0 \longrightarrow \longleftarrow f' < 0 \longrightarrow$

2. If $f'(x)$ changes sign from negative to positive at c, then $f(x)$ has a local minimum at $x = c$.

$(c, f(c))$

$\longleftarrow f' < 0 \longrightarrow \longleftarrow f' > 0 \longrightarrow$

Keep in mind that when $f'(x) > 0$, the function is **increasing** and that when $f'(x) < 0$ the function is **decreasing**. Thus, at a local maximum, the function changes from increasing to decreasing, and at a local minimum, the function changes from decreasing to increasing.

In Example 2 the first derivative test is used to sketch the graph of a polynomial of degree 4.

Example 2. Find all turning points of

$$f(x) = (1 - x^2)^2 - 2$$

and use them to sketch the graph of the function.

Solution. The derivative of $f(x)$ is

$$\begin{aligned} f'(x) &= 2(1 - x^2)(-2x) \\ &= 4x(x - 1)(x + 1) \end{aligned}$$

The equation $f'(x) = 0$ has the solutions

$$x = -1, \quad x = 0, \quad \text{and } x = 1$$

Therefore there are three possible turning points: $(-1, -2)$, $(0, -1)$, and $(1, -2)$.

Now determine the sign of $f'(x)$ in the intervals $x < -1$, $-1 < x < 0$, $0 < x < 1$, and $x > 1$, in order to find out whether the derivative changes sign at $x = -1$, $x = 0$, and $x = 1$. The sign of $f'(x)$ is determined by the signs of the factors x, $x - 1$, and $x + 1$. If $-1 < x < 0$, then x and $x - 1$ are negative, but $x + 1$ is positive, so that $f'(x)$ is positive. Continuing in this way and applying the first derivative test, we obtain the results in the table.

x	$x < -1$	$x = -1$	$-1 < x < 0$	$x = 0$	$0 < x < 1$	$x = 1$	$x > 1$
$f'(x)$	$-$	0	$+$	0	$-$	0	$+$
$f(x)$	decreasing	local minimum	increasing	local maximum	decreasing	local minimum	increasing

Thus, near the points $(-1, -2)$ and $(1, -2)$ the graph is like a parabola opening up, and near the point $(0, -1)$ the graph is like a parabola opening down.

By solving the equation $f(x) = 0$, we find that the x-intercepts are $\pm\sqrt{1 + \sqrt{2}} \approx \pm 1.55$, which helps to confirm the graph.

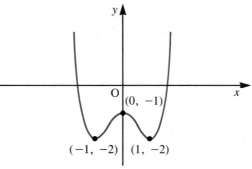

When expanded, the function in Example 2 is

$$f(x) = x^4 - 2x^2 - 1$$

When x becomes large, positively or negatively, the dominant term in $f(x)$ is x^4. Since x^4 is an even power of x, it follows that $f(x)$ is large and **positive** for large positive or large negative values of x, confirming the graph. It is always useful to analyze the term of highest degree (the dominant term) in a polynomial function when one is sketching the graph of the function, and it helps to confirm the results obtained by finding the turning points.

You may be wondering what happens if the derivative does not change sign when $f'(c) = 0$. The simplest example of this situation is the function

$$f(x) = x^3$$

The derivative of $f(x)$ is

$$f'(x) = 3x^2$$

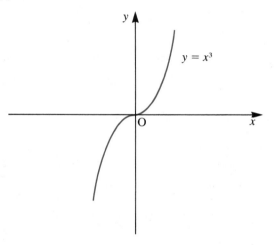

It follows that $f'(0) = 0$ but that $f'(x) > 0$ for $x \neq 0$. Since $f'(x)$ does not change sign at $x = 0$, $(0, 0)$ is not a turning point. The function is increasing for $x < 0$, the tangent line is horizontal at $x = 0$, and the function is again increasing for $x > 0$.

This example should be kept in mind when one is finding the local maxima and minima (turning points) of a function. The point is that **solutions of $f'(x) = 0$ do not necessarily yield turning points**.

In Chapter 3, when optimization problems were being solved the maximum (or minimum) value of a function was found **over a finite interval** by means of the extreme-value algorithm. In order to relate this to local maxima and minima, consider the problem of finding the maximum value and minimum value of the function in Example 1,

$$f(x) = x^3 - 3x + 2$$

on the interval $-\frac{5}{2} \leq x \leq \frac{3}{2}$. Restrict the graph in Example 1 to this interval and calculate the function values at the end points:

$$f\left(-\frac{5}{2}\right) = -\frac{49}{8}, \quad \text{and} \quad f\left(\frac{3}{2}\right) = \frac{7}{8}.$$

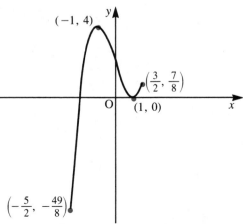

The maximum value on the interval is $f(-1) = 4$, and the minimum value is $f\left(-\frac{5}{2}\right) = -\frac{49}{8}$. In this example the local maximum at $x = -1$ is also the maximum value on the interval $-\frac{5}{2} \leq x \leq \frac{3}{2}$, but the local minimum at $x = 1$ is not the minimum value on the interval, since

$$f\left(-\frac{5}{2}\right) < f(1)$$

Exercises 4.1

1. Find the turning points of the following polynomial functions, and hence sketch their graphs.

   a. $f(x) = x^2 - 4x - 3$

   c. $f(x) = x^3 - 12x$

   e. $f(x) = \dfrac{x^3}{2} - 4$

   g. $f(x) = -4x^3 + 18x^2 + 3$

   i. $f(x) = -3x^4 + 4$

   k. $f(x) = 3x^4 - 4x^3$

   m. $f(x) = -2x^5 + 5$

   b. $f(x) = -2x^2 + 6x + 13$

   d. $f(x) = 2x^3 + 9x^2 + 12x$

   f. $f(x) = x^3 + 3x^2 + 3x$

   h. $f(x) = -3x^3 - 5x$

   j. $f(x) = x^4 - 4x^3 - 8x^2 + 48x$

   l. $f(x) = x^4 + 4x^3 - 8x^2$

   n. $f(x) = 3x^5 - 5x^3 - 30x$

2. For large values of x, the graph of a polynomial resembles the graph of the term of highest degree (the dominant term).

   a. Make an accurate sketch of the graphs of $y = x^2, y = x^3, y = x^4$, and $y = x^5$, for $-3 \leq x \leq 3$.

   b. Sketch the graph of the function

   $$f(x) = x^3 - 12x + 4$$

   Sketch the graph of its dominant term x^3 in the same diagram.

   c. Sketch the graph of the function

   $$f(x) = x^4 - 8x^2 + 8$$

   Sketch the graph of its dominant term x^4 in the same diagram.

3. The graph of the function

   $$f(x) = \tfrac{1}{4}x^4 - x^3 - 2x^2 + 12x + 5$$

   is shown in the diagram. Find the values of a, b, and c.

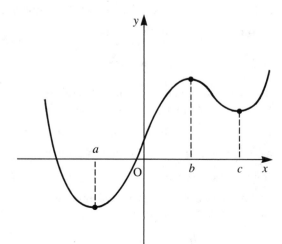

4. Find all local maxima and minima of $f(x)$, and hence find the maximum value and minimum value of $f(x)$ on the given interval. Illustrate your answer with a sketch.

a. $f(x) = 2x^3 + 3x^2 - 12x, \quad 0 \le x \le 3$
b. $f(x) = 4x^3 - 27x + 10, \quad -4 \le x \le 4$
c. $f(x) = 2x^4 - 8x^3 + 9x^2, \quad -1 \le x \le 2$

5. A cable is stretched across a river. The shape of the cable is approximated by

$$y = 50 - \frac{9}{10}x + \frac{x^2}{80} - \frac{x^3}{25\ 000}, \quad 0 \le x \le 100$$

Determine the coordinates of the lowest point on the cable and illustrate your answer with a sketch.

6. Each of the given graphs represents the derivative $f'(x)$ of a function $f(x)$. Answer parts (i), (ii), and (iii) for each graph.
(i) On what intervals is $f(x)$ increasing, and on what intervals is $f(x)$ decreasing?
(ii) Find the x-values of all local maxima and minima of $f(x)$.
(iii) Hence make a rough sketch of the graph of $f(x)$, assuming that $f(0) = 1$.

a.

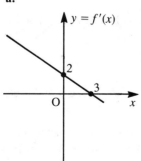

b.

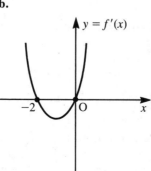

c.

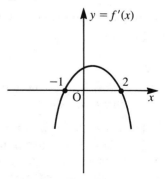

7. Sketch the graph of a function $f(x)$ that satisfies

$$f'(x) > 0 \quad \text{on the intervals} \quad x < -2 \text{ and } x > 3$$

and

$$f'(x) < 0 \quad \text{on the interval} \quad -2 < x < 3.$$

8. Sketch the graph of a function $f(x)$ that satisfies

$$f'(x) > 0 \quad \text{on the intervals} \quad -3 < x < -2 \text{ and } x > 2$$

and

$$f'(x) < 0 \quad \text{on the intervals} \quad x < -3 \text{ and } -2 < x < 2.$$

9. Suppose that

$$f'(x) > 0 \quad \text{on the interval} \quad 1 < x < 4$$

and

$$f'(x) < 0 \quad \text{on the intervals} \quad x < 1 \text{ and } x > 4.$$

For each of the following pairs of function values, state which is greater, where possible.

a. $f(2), f(3)$ **b.** $f(2), f(5)$ **c.** $f(-10), f(0)$
d. $f(0), f(2)$ **e.** $f(5), f(10)$ **f.** $f(0), f(10)$

10. In each case you are given the derivative $f'(x)$ of a function $f(x)$. Find the intervals on which $f(x)$ is increasing and the intervals on which $f(x)$ is decreasing. Use your results to make a rough sketch of the graph of $f(x)$, assuming that $f(0) = 0$.

a. $f'(x) = 2x - 1$ **b.** $f'(x) = (x - 2)(x + 1)$
c. $f'(x) = (3x - 5)^2$ **d.** $f'(x) = x(x - 1)(x - 2)$
e. $f'(x) = x^2(x - 1)(x - 2)$ **f.** $f'(x) = (x^2 - 1)^2$

11. The function

$$f(x) = x^3 + ax^2 + b$$

has a turning point at $(-2, 6)$. Find the constants a and b and sketch the graph of $f(x)$.

12. The function

$$f(x) = ax^3 + bx^2 + cx + d$$

has turning points at $(0, 2)$ and $(2, -4)$. Find the constants a, b, c, and d and sketch the graph of $f(x)$.

13. For each graph of the function $f(x)$, make a rough sketch of the graph of the derivative $f'(x)$. By comparing the graphs of $f(x)$ and $f'(x)$, show that the intervals on which $f(x)$ is increasing and decreasing correspond respectively to the intervals on which $f'(x)$ is positive and negative.

a.   **b.**   **c.**

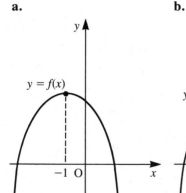 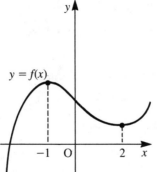 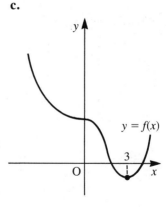

Problems 4.1

1. Three possible shapes of cubic graphs are shown below.

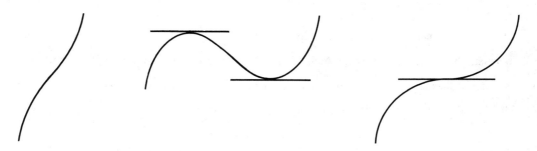

For what values of a and b will the graph of the function

$$f(x) = x^3 + ax^2 + bx$$

resemble each of these three shapes?

2. If $f'(x) > g'(x)$ for all x, determine the possible number of points of intersection of the continuous curves $y = f(x)$ and $y = g(x)$. How many different cases are there?

3. Suppose that $f(x)$ and $g(x)$ are positive functions such that $f(x)$ has a local maximum and $g(x)$ has a local minimum at $x = c$. Prove that

$$h(x) = \frac{f(x)}{g(x)}$$

has a local maximum at $x = c$.

4. Consider the function

$$f(x) = x^4 + 4x^2 - 16x$$

a. Show that the equation $f'(x) = 0$ has exactly one solution, and find an approximation to the solution, using Newton's method.

b. Sketch the graph of $f(x)$.

4.2 Vertical Asymptotes

In this section we shall explain how to sketch the graphs of rational functions, such as

$$f(x) = \frac{x + 1}{(x - 1)(x + 2)}$$

Rational functions are undefined at values of x for which the denominator is zero ($x = +1$ or $x = -2$ in the example). In order to sketch the graph of a rational function, it is necessary to determine what happens to $f(x)$ as x gets close to the values at which $f(x)$ is undefined.

Consider the function

$$f(x) = \frac{1}{x}$$

which is undefined when $x = 0$. As x approaches 0 from the right, $\frac{1}{x}$ is positive and becomes increasingly large, since it is the reciprocal of a small positive number. On the other hand, as x approaches zero from the left, $\frac{1}{x}$ is negative and becomes increasingly large in magnitude. This is illustrated in the table and the accompanying graph.

x	1	$\frac{1}{10}$	$\frac{1}{100}$	$\frac{1}{1000}$	...
$f(x) = \frac{1}{x}$	1	10	100	1000	...
x	-1	$-\frac{1}{10}$	$-\frac{1}{100}$	$-\frac{1}{1000}$	...
$f(x) = \frac{1}{x}$	-1	-10	-100	-1000	...

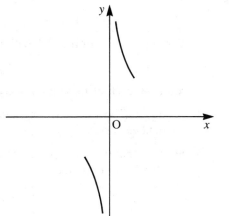

The line $x = 0$ is called a **vertical asymptote** of the graph of $f(x) = \frac{1}{x}$.

The notation for this type of behaviour is

$$\lim_{x \to 0^+} \frac{1}{x} = +\infty \tag{1}$$

and

$$\lim_{x \to 0^-} \frac{1}{x} = -\infty \tag{2}$$

As in Chapter 1, the notation $x \to 0^+$ means that x approaches 0 from the right (so that $x > 0$) and $x \to 0^-$ means that x approaches 0 from the left (so that $x < 0$). It is essential to note that **the symbol ''$+\infty$,''** read ''positive infinity,'' **is not a number**. You should think of ''$= +\infty$'' as shorthand for ''becomes arbitrarily large and positive.'' Similarly, ''$= -\infty$'' is shorthand for ''becomes arbitrarily large and negative.'' Thus the limits

$$\lim_{x \to 0^+} \frac{1}{x} \quad \text{and} \quad \lim_{x \to 0^-} \frac{1}{x}$$

do not exist. The statements (1) and (2) are useful, however, because they describe the behaviour of $f(x) = \dfrac{1}{x}$ near the point $x = 0$ at which $f(x)$ is undefined.

Example 1. Consider the function

$$f(x) = \frac{3 - 2x}{x - 3}.$$

Express $\lim\limits_{x \to 3^+} f(x)$ and $\lim\limits_{x \to 3^-} f(x)$ using the symbol ∞. Sketch the graph of $f(x)$ for x near 3.

Solution. As $x \to 3^+$, $3 - 2x$ is negative and approaches -3, and $x - 3$ is positive and approaches 0. Thus as $x \to 3^+$, $f(x)$ is negative and becomes larger and larger in magnitude. We write

$$\lim_{x \to 3^+} \frac{3 - 2x}{x - 3} = -\infty$$

As $x \to 3^-$, $3 - 2x$ is negative and approaches -3, and $x - 3$ is negative and approaches 0. It follows that $f(x)$ is positive and becomes larger and larger as $x \to 3^-$, and so we write

$$\lim_{x \to 3^-} \frac{3 - 2x}{x - 3} = +\infty$$

The line $x = 3$ is thus a vertical asymptote of the graph, and for x near 3 the graph is as shown.

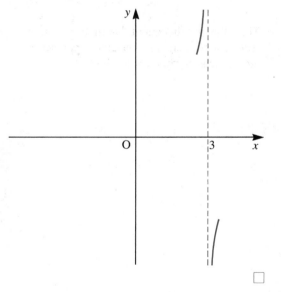

In Example 1, a vertical asymptote occurs at $x = 3$ because the denominator of $f(x)$ is zero and the numerator is non-zero at $x = 3$. Whether the graph moves upward or downward when approaching the asymptote is determined by the sign of $f(x)$ on either side of $x = 3$:

If $x > 3$, then $f(x) < 0$, and so the graph of $f(x)$ moves downward when approaching the asymptote from the right.

If $x < 3$, then $f(x) > 0$, and so the graph of $f(x)$ moves upward when approaching the asymptote from the left.

In Example 2, a function that has two vertical asymptotes is considered.

Example 2. Sketch the graph of the function

$$f(x) = \frac{2(x^2 + 1)}{(x - 1)(x + 2)}$$

near its vertical asymptotes.

Solution. Observe that the function has the vertical asymptotes $x = 1$ and $x = -2$. In order to determine whether the graph moves upward or downward near an asymptote, determine the sign of $f(x)$. Since $x^2 + 1$ is always positive, the sign of $f(x)$ will change when the factors $x - 1$ and $x + 2$ change sign. If $x > 1$, then $x - 1$ and $x + 2$ are positive, and so is $f(x)$. Continue in this way to obtain the following table:

	$x < -2$	$-2 < x < 1$	$x > 1$
$f(x)$	+	−	+

Thus the graph cannot lie in the shaded regions in the diagram. The graph approaches the vertical asymptotes as shown.

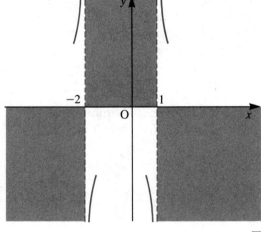

The corresponding limit statements are:

$$\lim_{x \to -2^-} f(x) = +\infty, \quad \lim_{x \to -2^+} f(x) = -\infty, \quad \lim_{x \to 1^-} f(x) = -\infty, \quad \lim_{x \to 1^+} f(x) = +\infty$$

The graph is starting to take shape. Before we can complete it we have to analyze how $f(x)$ behaves when x becomes large and positive ($x \to +\infty$), and large and negative ($x \to -\infty$). This is the topic of the next section.

We now summarize the situation as regards vertical asymptotes.

Vertical Asymptotes

The graph of $f(x)$ has a vertical asymptote $x = a$ if one of the following limit statements holds:

$$\lim_{x \to a^+} f(x) = +\infty, \quad \lim_{x \to a^+} f(x) = -\infty, \quad \lim_{x \to a^-} f(x) = +\infty, \quad \lim_{x \to a^-} f(x) = -\infty$$

The graphs corresponding to the limit statements are:

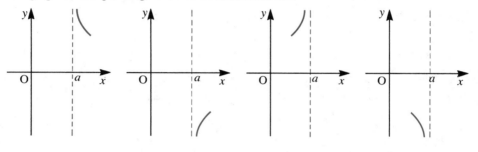

To find the vertical asymptotes of a rational function

$$f(x) = \frac{p(x)}{q(x)}$$

find the x-values where the denominator is zero. If $q(a) = 0$ and $p(a) \neq 0$, then $x = a$ is a vertical asymptote. Whether the asymptote is approached in an upward or downward direction is determined by the sign of $f(x)$ on either side of $x = a$.

As an application of the ideas of this section, consider a simple electrical circuit consisting of a variable resistor R (in ohms) connected across a 12 volt battery. According to Ohm's law, the current (in amperes) that flows in the circuit is

$$I = \frac{12}{R}$$

As R tends to zero, the current increases without bound, since

$$\lim_{R \to 0^+} \frac{12}{R} = +\infty$$

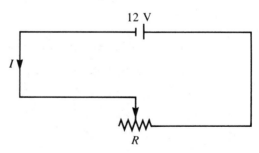

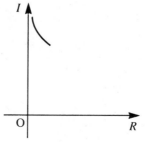

In practical terms, R's tending to zero can be thought of as a short circuit, and the resulting large current would either cause the battery to fail or would break the circuit. Our simple mathematical model fails to describe the physical situation when the current is large.

In an applied situation, the occurrence of a vertical asymptote, for example

$$\lim_{x \to a^+} f(x) = +\infty$$

usually means that the mathematical model has a flaw or that an unreasonable demand is being placed on it.

Exercises 4.2

1. Evaluate each limit statement, using the symbol "∞" where appropriate.

   a. $\lim\limits_{x \to 4^+} \dfrac{1}{x - 4}$

   b. $\lim\limits_{x \to 4^-} \dfrac{1}{x - 4}$

   c. $\lim\limits_{x \to 3^+} \dfrac{2x + 1}{x - 3}$

   d. $\lim\limits_{x \to 3^-} \dfrac{2x + 1}{x - 3}$

   e. $\lim\limits_{x \to 2^+} \dfrac{x}{(x - 2)^2}$

   f. $\lim\limits_{x \to 2^-} \dfrac{x}{(x - 2)^2}$

   g. $\lim\limits_{x \to -4^+} \dfrac{x}{x + 4}$

   h. $\lim\limits_{x \to -4^-} \dfrac{x}{x + 4}$

   i. $\lim\limits_{x \to -2^+} \dfrac{x}{(x + 2)(x - 3)}$

   j. $\lim\limits_{x \to -2^-} \dfrac{x}{(x + 2)(x - 3)}$

   k. $\lim\limits_{x \to \sqrt{3}^+} \dfrac{x - 2}{x^2 - 3}$

   l. $\lim\limits_{x \to \sqrt{3}^-} \dfrac{x - 2}{x^2 - 3}$

2. For each vertical asymptote $x = a$ of the given function, write statements for $\lim\limits_{x \to a^+} f(x)$ and $\lim\limits_{x \to a^-} f(x)$. Sketch the graph near the asymptotes.

   a. $f(x) = \dfrac{3}{x}$

   b. $f(x) = \dfrac{3}{x^2}$

   c. $f(x) = -\dfrac{2}{x}$

   d. $f(x) = -\dfrac{2}{x^3}$

   e. $f(x) = \dfrac{1}{x - 3}$

   f. $f(x) = \dfrac{1}{(x - 3)^2}$

   g. $f(x) = \dfrac{x - 2}{x + 3}$

   h. $f(x) = \dfrac{x - 4}{(x - 3)^2}$

   i. $f(x) = \dfrac{x}{(x - 2)(x + 1)}$

   j. $f(x) = \dfrac{3(x + 1)^2}{9x^2 - 4}$

   k. $f(x) = \dfrac{3(x + 2)(x - 1)}{x^2 - 2x}$

   l. $f(x) = \dfrac{x - 2}{(x - 1)^2 x}$

3. a. Sketch the graph of $f(x)$ near its asymptote.

$$\text{(i) } f(x) = \frac{1}{x-2} \qquad \text{(ii) } f(x) = \frac{1}{(x-2)^2} \qquad \text{(iii) } f(x) = \frac{1}{(x-2)^3}$$

b. Do you see a pattern? Can you extend the results of part (a) to higher powers?

4. Try to complete the graph of the function in Example 2. Some essential features are still missing!

Problems 4.2

1. When a periodic voltage of frequency ω is applied to a certain electric circuit, the current I (in amperes) that results is given by

$$I = \frac{\omega(\omega^2 - 1)}{\omega^4 - 3\omega^2 + 1}$$

Sketch the graph of I vs ω for $\omega > 0$.

2. This problem shows that one cannot work with the symbol ''∞'' as though it were a real number. Consider the functions

$$f(x) = \frac{1}{x-2} \quad \text{and} \quad g(x) = \frac{2x-3}{x-2}$$

a. Show that

$$\lim_{x \to 2^+} f(x) = +\infty \quad \text{and} \quad \lim_{x \to 2^+} g(x) = +\infty.$$

b. Evaluate $\lim_{x \to 2^+} [f(x) - g(x)]$ and show that the limit is not zero.

3. Let $f(x) = \dfrac{p(x)}{(x-a)^n}$, where n is a positive integer. Write statements for $\lim_{x \to a^+} f(x)$ and $\lim_{x \to a^-} f(x)$, in each case, and sketch the graph near $x = a$.

a. $p(a) > 0$, n is even   **b.** $p(a) < 0$, n is even
c. $p(a) > 0$, n is odd   **d.** $p(a) < 0$, n is odd

4. Find the domain of the function $y = \dfrac{2x}{\sqrt{x^2 - 5x + 6}}$ and sketch the graph near the vertical asymptotes.

4.3 Horizontal Asymptotes

In this section we shall study the behaviour of rational functions as x increases without bound, both positively and negatively. The notations

$$\lim_{x \to +\infty} f(x) \quad \text{and} \quad \lim_{x \to -\infty} f(x)$$

are used to describe this behaviour. The notation "$x \to +\infty$," read "x tends to positive infinity," is shorthand for "x increases without bound in the positive sense." The notation "$x \to -\infty$," read "x tends to minus infinity," means "x increases without bound in the negative sense." For example, we write

$$\lim_{x \to +\infty} \frac{1}{x} = 0 \tag{1}$$

and

$$\lim_{x \to -\infty} \frac{1}{x} = 0 \tag{2}$$

since the reciprocal of a large number (positive or negative) has a value close to zero.

The limits (1) and (2) imply that the graph of $f(x) = \dfrac{1}{x}$ gets close to the line $y = 0$ as x increases without bound. Since $\dfrac{1}{x} > 0$ if $x > 0$, and $\dfrac{1}{x} < 0$ if $x < 0$, we obtain the partial graph, as shown.

We say that the line $y = 0$ is a **horizontal asymptote** of $y = \dfrac{1}{x}$.

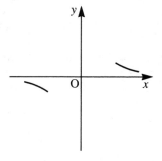

By incorporating the vertical asymptote that we found in section 4.2, we can complete the graph of $f(x) = \dfrac{1}{x}$, as shown.

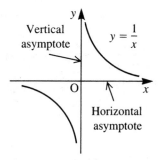

The fundamental limits (1) and (2) can be used to evaluate limits of rational functions as x tends to infinity, as we now show, using the function in Example 1 of section 4.2.

Example 1. Consider the function

$$f(x) = \frac{3 - 2x}{x - 3}$$

Evaluate $\lim_{x \to +\infty} f(x)$ and $\lim_{x \to -\infty} f(x)$ and show that the graph of $f(x)$ has a horizontal asymptote.

Solution. The idea is to express $f(x)$ in terms of $\dfrac{1}{x}$. The function $f(x)$ can be expressed as

$$f(x) = \frac{x\left(\dfrac{3}{x} - 2\right)}{x\left(1 - \dfrac{3}{x}\right)}$$

$$= \frac{-2 + \dfrac{3}{x}}{1 - \dfrac{3}{x}}$$

Thus

$$\lim_{x \to +\infty} f(x) = \frac{-2 + 3\left[\displaystyle\lim_{x \to +\infty} \frac{1}{x}\right]}{1 - 3\left[\displaystyle\lim_{x \to +\infty} \frac{1}{x}\right]}$$

$$= \frac{-2 + 0}{1 - 0}$$

$$= -2$$

and

$$\lim_{x \to -\infty} f(x) = \frac{-2 + 3\left[\displaystyle\lim_{x \to -\infty} \frac{1}{x}\right]}{1 - 3\left[\displaystyle\lim_{x \to -\infty} \frac{1}{x}\right]}$$

$$= \frac{-2 + 0}{1 - 0}$$

$$= -2$$

It follows that $y = -2$ is a horizontal asymptote. In order to determine whether the asymptote is approached from above or below, consider the quantity

$$f(x) - (-2) = \frac{3 - 2x}{x - 3} + 2$$

$$= \frac{-3}{x - 3}$$

This quantity is negative when x is large and positive, and positive when x is large and negative.

It follows that,

as $x \to +\infty$, $f(x) < -2$ and the graph is below the asymptote $y = -2$;
as $x \to -\infty$, $f(x) > -2$ and the graph is above the asymptote $y = -2$.

This leads to the graph below on the left. By incorporating the vertical asymptote that we found in Example 1 of section 4.2, we can complete the graph shown on the right. ☐

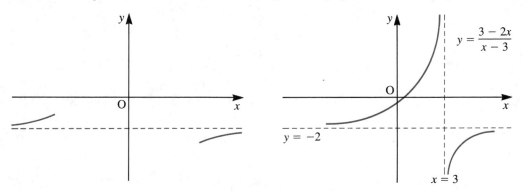

We now give a summary of the concepts of limits at infinity and horizontal asymptotes. The statement $\lim\limits_{x \to +\infty} f(x) = L$ means that $f(x)$ approaches L as x becomes large and positive. Similarly $\lim\limits_{x \to -\infty} f(x) = L$ means that $f(x)$ approaches L as x becomes large and negative.

Horizontal Asymptotes

If $\lim\limits_{x \to +\infty} f(x) = L$ or $\lim\limits_{x \to -\infty} f(x) = L$, we say that the line $y = L$ is a horizontal asymptote of the graph of $f(x)$.

Four typical situations are illustrated:

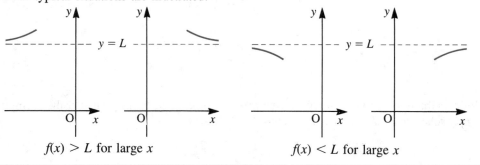

We now apply these concepts to complete the graph in Example 2 of section 4.2.

Example 2. Consider the function $f(x) = \dfrac{2(x^2 + 1)}{(x - 1)(x + 2)}$. Evaluate $\lim\limits_{x \to +\infty} f(x)$ and $\lim\limits_{x \to -\infty} f(x)$, and sketch the graph for large x. Complete the graph using the results from Example 2 of section 4.2.

Solution. The function $f(x)$ can be expressed as

$$f(x) = \frac{2x^2\left(1 + \dfrac{1}{x^2}\right)}{x^2\left(1 - \dfrac{1}{x}\right)\left(1 + \dfrac{2}{x}\right)}$$

$$= \frac{2\left(1 + \dfrac{1}{x^2}\right)}{\left(1 - \dfrac{1}{x}\right)\left(1 + \dfrac{2}{x}\right)}$$

Since $\lim\limits_{x \to +\infty} \dfrac{1}{x} = 0$, and $\lim\limits_{x \to -\infty} \dfrac{1}{x} = 0$, it follows that

$$\lim_{x \to +\infty} f(x) = \frac{2(1 + 0)}{(1 - 0)(1 + 0)}$$
$$= 2$$

and that

$$\lim_{x \to -\infty} f(x) = 2.$$

Thus, $y = 2$ is a horizontal asymptote. In order to determine whether the graph approaches the asymptote from above or below, consider the expression

$$f(x) - 2 = \frac{2(x^2 + 1)}{(x - 1)(x + 2)} - 2$$
$$= \frac{-2x + 6}{(x - 1)(x + 2)}$$

If x is large and positive, it follows that $f(x) - 2 < 0$ so that $f(x) < 2$. If x is large and negative, it follows that $f(x) - 2 > 0$ and that $f(x) > 2$. This justifies the first graph.

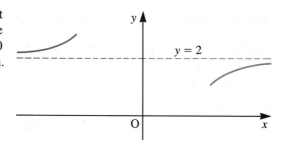

We now combine the present diagram, which shows the horizontal asymptotes, with the diagram in Example 2 of section 4.2, which shows the vertical asymptotes, and by joining the pieces together smoothly we obtain the second graph.

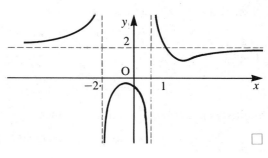

The second graph in Example 2 suggests that the function has two turning points, a local maximum somewhere between $x = -2$ and $x = 1$, and a local minimum with $x > 1$. In the exercises, you are asked to verify these features of the graph.

A polynomial function $f(x)$ increases without bound, positively or negatively, as $x \to +\infty$. In this case $\lim_{x \to +\infty} f(x)$ does not exist. We describe this situation by writing

$$\lim_{x \to +\infty} f(x) = +\infty \quad \text{or} \quad \lim_{x \to +\infty} f(x) = -\infty$$

depending on whether $f(x)$ becomes large and positive or large and negative. The same notation is used to describe the situation as $x \to -\infty$. For example

$$\lim_{x \to +\infty} (1 - x^3) = -\infty, \quad \lim_{x \to -\infty} (1 - x^3) = +\infty$$

This type of behaviour can also occur for a rational function, as is illustrated in Example 3.

Example 3. Consider the function

$$f(x) = \frac{2x^4 + 3x^3 + 1}{-x + 1}$$

Write a statement for $\lim_{x \to +\infty} f(x)$ and $\lim_{x \to -\infty} f(x)$. Then sketch the graph of $f(x)$ for large x.

Solution. The function $f(x)$ can be expressed as

$$f(x) = \frac{x^4 \left(2 + \dfrac{3}{x} + \dfrac{1}{x^4}\right)}{x \left(-1 + \dfrac{1}{x}\right)} = (x^3) \left(\frac{2 + \dfrac{3}{x} + \dfrac{1}{x^4}}{-1 + \dfrac{1}{x}}\right)$$

Observe that, if x is large and positive, then

$$f(x) = [\text{large and positive}] \times [\text{finite and negative}].$$

Hence,

$$\lim_{x \to +\infty} f(x) = -\infty$$

Similarly, if x is large and negative, then

$$f(x) = [\text{large and negative}] \times [\text{finite and negative}].$$

Hence,

$$\lim_{x \to -\infty} f(x) = +\infty$$

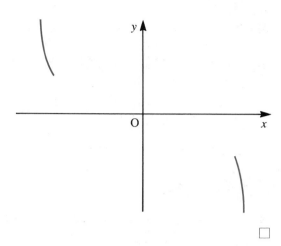

In Example 3, we could have discovered the behaviour of the function for large x by retaining only the dominant term in the numerator and denominator. For large x, the function

$$f(x) = \frac{2x^4 + 3x^3 + 1}{-x + 1}$$

behaves like

$$\frac{2x^4}{-x} = -2x^3$$

so that

$$\lim_{x \to +\infty} f(x) = -\infty, \quad \text{and} \quad \lim_{x \to -\infty} f(x) = +\infty.$$

Finally, consider the following application of limits. Suppose that the number of houses in a new subdivision after t months of development is modelled by the function

$$N(t) = \frac{1000t^3}{100 + t^3}, \quad t \geq 0$$

Using the techniques of this section, it can be shown that

$$\lim_{t \to +\infty} N(t) = 1000$$

This value represents the number of houses in the subdivision when the development is complete. In an applied situation $t \to +\infty$ means "after a sufficiently long time." In this example, after 5 years ($t = 60$), we have

$$N(60) \approx 999.53$$

and the nearest integer value is 1000. This means that the subdivision is fully developed after 5 years.

Exercises 4.3

1. Find the horizontal asymptote for the graph of each function. Determine whether the graph approaches the asymptote from above or below, and sketch the graph for large x.

a. $f(x) = -\dfrac{2}{x}$　　　　　　　　　　**b.** $f(x) = \dfrac{3}{x^2}$

c. $f(x) = \dfrac{1}{x+1}$　　　　　　　　　**d.** $f(x) = \dfrac{2}{3-x}$

e. $f(x) = \dfrac{5}{x^2+1}$　　　　　　　　**f.** $f(x) = \dfrac{2x}{x-1}$

g. $f(x) = \dfrac{5x}{1-2x}$　　　　　　　　**h.** $f(x) = \dfrac{-3x^2+1}{2x^2+x}$

2. Sketch the graph of each function by translating the graph of $f(x) = \dfrac{1}{x}$. Label all horizontal and vertical asymptotes.

a. $f(x) = \dfrac{1}{x-1}$　　　　　　　　　**b.** $f(x) = \dfrac{1}{x+2}$

c. $f(x) = \dfrac{1}{x-3} + 2$　　　　　　　**d.** $f(x) = \dfrac{4}{4x-3} + 1$

3. Evaluate $\lim\limits_{x \to +\infty} f(x)$ and $\lim\limits_{x \to -\infty} f(x)$, using the symbol "$\infty$" where appropriate. Verify your results by retaining only the dominant terms in the numerator and denominator.

a. $f(x) = \dfrac{-2x^2+3x}{x-1}$　　　　　　**b.** $f(x) = \dfrac{3x^3-2}{x^2+1}$

c. $f(x) = \dfrac{-3x^2+7x}{4x^2-5}$　　　　　**d.** $f(x) = \dfrac{-2x^4+3x^2}{3x^2+2}$

e. $f(x) = \dfrac{3x^3-2}{x^3+1}$　　　　　　**f.** $f(x) = \dfrac{3x^5-2x^2+1}{2x^4+x-2}$

g. $f(x) = \dfrac{3x^2+2}{-2x^4+3x^2}$　　　　**h.** $f(x) = -3x^2+2x$

i. $f(x) = -4x^3+6x^2+1$　　　　　　**j.** $f(x) = \dfrac{7x^3}{(2x-1)^3}$

4. By finding all vertical and horizontal asymptotes, make a preliminary sketch of each graph.

a. $f(x) = \dfrac{1}{x^2-1}$　　　　　　　　**b.** $f(x) = \dfrac{x}{x^2-1}$

c. $f(x) = \dfrac{x^2}{x^2-1}$　　　　　　　**d.** $f(x) = \dfrac{3x-1}{x+1}$

e. $f(x) = \dfrac{2-x}{3x+6}$　　　　　　　**f.** $f(x) = \dfrac{(2-x)(3x+2)}{x^2}$

g. $f(x) = \dfrac{(x+2)^2}{2x^2}$　　　　　　**h.** $f(x) = \dfrac{(2-x)(3x+2)}{(x-1)^2}$

i. $f(x) = \dfrac{2x(x-2)}{(x-1)(x+1)}$　　　　**j.** $f(x) = \dfrac{x^2-x-2}{x^2+x}$

5. a. Show that the function in Example 2 of this section,

$$f(x) = \frac{2(x^2 + 1)}{(x - 1)(x + 2)}$$

has one local maximum and one local minimum, as predicted by the rough graph.

b. Show that the graph of this function intersects its horizontal asymptote at one point.

6. Find where the graphs intersect their horizontal asymptotes.

a. $y = \dfrac{(2 - x)(3x + 2)}{x^2}$ **b.** $y = \dfrac{2x(x - 2)}{(x - 1)(x + 1)}$

(Refer to parts (f) and (i) of Exercise 4.)

7. Find the horizontal asymptote of the graph

$$y = \frac{ax + b}{cx + d}$$

where a, b, c, and d are constants, $a \neq 0$, and $c \neq 0$.

Problems 4.3

1. This is an example to illustrate that one cannot work with the symbol ''∞'' as though it were a real number. Consider the functions

$$f(x) = \frac{x^2 + 1}{x + 1} \quad \text{and} \quad g(x) = \frac{x^2 + 3x + 1}{x + 1}$$

a. Show that

$$\lim_{x \to +\infty} f(x) = +\infty \quad \text{and} \quad \lim_{x \to +\infty} g(x) = +\infty$$

b. Evaluate $\lim_{x \to +\infty} [f(x) - g(x)]$ and show that the limit is not zero.

2. Functions other than rational functions can have two different horizontal asymptotes; that is, it is possible that

$$\lim_{x \to +\infty} f(x) = L_1 \quad \text{and} \quad \lim_{x \to -\infty} f(x) = L_2$$

where $L_1 \neq L_2$. Find L_1 and L_2 for each function.

a. $f(x) = \dfrac{x}{\sqrt{x^2 + 1}}$ **b.** $f(x) = \dfrac{x\sqrt{4x^2 + 1}}{1 - 3x^2}$

c. $f(x) = \sqrt{x^2 + 4x} - \sqrt{x^2 + x}$

3. A graph can have an asymptote that is neither horizontal nor vertical. The line $y = mx + c$ is said to be an inclined asymptote of the graph $y = f(x)$ if

$$\lim_{x \to +\infty} d = 0 \quad \text{or} \quad \lim_{x \to -\infty} d = 0$$

where

$$d = f(x) - (mx + c)$$

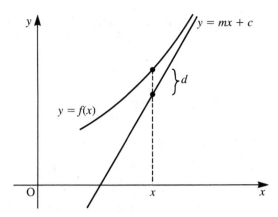

a. Show that $y = x + 2$ is an inclined asymptote of the graph of $y = \dfrac{x^3 + 2x^2}{x^2 - 1}$. Sketch the graph, using the techniques that we have developed so far.

b. Show that $y = x + \dfrac{1}{2}$ is an inclined asymptote of the graph of $y = \sqrt{x^2 + x}$.

4.4 An Overview of Curve Sketching

We have now developed techniques that enable us to sketch a wide variety of graphs without making a table of values. For polynomial functions we can obtain a rough graph simply by finding the turning points, as in section 4.1. We can also predict the form of the graph for large x by noting the dominant term in $f(x)$ as $x \to \pm\infty$. In addition, finding intercepts enables us to identify specific points on the graph. For rational functions we can obtain a rough graph simply by finding the vertical and horizontal asymptotes, and the intercepts, as in sections 4.2 and 4.3. If there are no horizontal asymptotes ($f(x) \to \pm\infty$ as $x \to \pm\infty$) one can obtain the form of the graph for large x by finding the dominant term in $f(x)$ as $x \to \pm\infty$. Further detail may be obtained by finding the turning points. Often, however, the rough graph will suggest the approximate location of the turning points.

We illustrate these ideas by completing the graph in Example 2 of section 4.3.

Example 1. Sketch the graph of the function

$$f(x) = \frac{2(x^2 + 1)}{(x - 1)(x + 2)}$$

Solution. In Example 2 of section 4.3 a preliminary sketch of the graph was obtained, showing the vertical and horizontal asymptotes. If we join the separate parts smoothly, we obtain a graph with a local maximum between $x = -2$ and $x = 1$, and a local minimum in the interval $x > 1$. In order to verify that there are no others, calculate the derivative of $f(x)$.

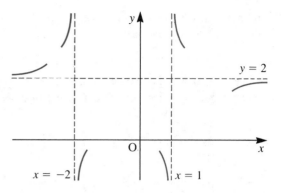

To simplify the differentiation, express $f(x)$ as

$$f(x) = \frac{2(x^2 + 1)}{x^2 + x - 2}$$

By the quotient rule,

$$f'(x) = 2\frac{[(x^2 + x - 2)(2x) - (x^2 + 1)(2x + 1)]}{(x^2 + x - 2)^2}$$
$$= \frac{2(x^2 - 6x - 1)}{(x^2 + x - 2)^2}$$

Now set $f'(x) = 0$; then

$$x^2 - 6x - 1 = 0$$

and, by the quadratic formula,

$$x = 3 \pm \sqrt{10}$$

It follows that the local maximum occurs at $x = 3 - \sqrt{10} \approx -0.16$ and that the local minimum occurs at $x = 3 + \sqrt{10} \approx 6.16$. There are no other turning points. The final graph is shown below.

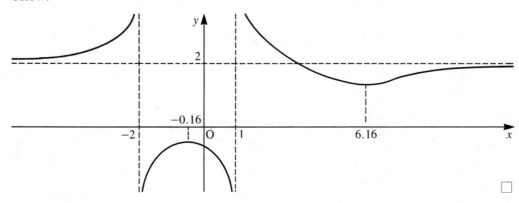

It should also be kept in mind that simple graphs can often be sketched by elementary means. For example, if one knows the graph of $f(x)$, one can sketch the graphs of

$$-f(x), \quad |f(x)|, \quad f(x - a) \quad \text{and} \quad f(x) + b$$

where a and b are constants, without detailed analysis. As an illustration, if $f(x) = x^2 - 1$, (shown dotted in each of the diagrams) then we have:

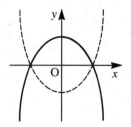   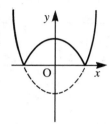   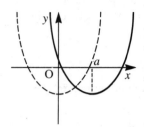   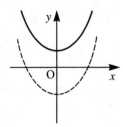

$\quad\;\; y = -(x^2 - 1) \qquad\qquad y = |x^2 - 1| \qquad\qquad y = (x - a)^2 - 1 \qquad\qquad y = x^2 - 1 + b$

It is also possible to sketch the graphs of the reciprocal $\dfrac{1}{f(x)}$ and of a sum $f(x) + g(x)$ or difference $f(x) - g(x)$ of known functions.

In addition, **symmetry properties** can facilitate curve sketching. If $f(-x) = f(x)$ for all x, then $y = f(x)$ is symmetric under reflection in the y-axis. Such functions are called **even functions**.

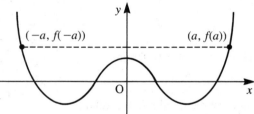

If $f(-x) = -f(x)$ for all x, then $y = f(x)$ is symmetric under reflection through the origin. Such functions are called **odd functions**.

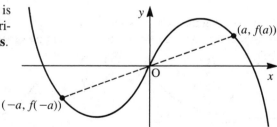

For example,

$$f(x) = \frac{1}{x^2}$$

is an even function, since

$$f(-x) = \frac{1}{(-x)^2} = \frac{1}{x^2} = f(x)$$

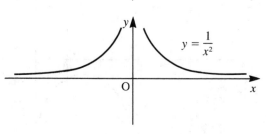

On the other hand,

$$f(x) = \frac{1}{x}$$

is an odd function, since

$$f(-x) = \frac{1}{-x} = -\frac{1}{x} = -f(x)$$

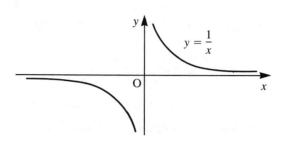

For a function that is even or odd, one only has to draw the graph for $x > 0$. The rest of the graph can be obtained by a reflection.

Examples 2 and 3 illustrate the use of these ideas.

Example 2. Sketch the graph of

$$f(x) = \frac{1}{1 + x^2}$$

Solution. Note the following points:

1. There are no x-intercepts and $f(x) > 0$ for all x.

2. The y-intercept is 1.

3. The horizontal asymptote is $y = 0$, since $\lim\limits_{x \to +\infty} f(x) = 0$ and $\lim\limits_{x \to -\infty} f(x) = 0$.

4. There is no vertical asymptote.

5. The function f is even, because $f(-x) = \dfrac{1}{1 + (-x)^2} = \dfrac{1}{1 + x^2} = f(x)$.

The last property implies that the graph is symmetric under reflection in the y-axis. Because of this symmetry, one might guess that the tangent line is horizontal at $x = 0$; this can be verified by calculating $f'(x)$ and showing that $f'(0) = 0$. (Also see Problem **6**).

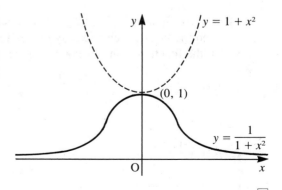

□

Example 3. Sketch the graph of the function

$$f(x) = x + \frac{1}{x}$$

Solution. The graph can be obtained by summing the functions $y = x$ and $y = \frac{1}{x}$. The graph has the vertical asymptote $x = 0$ but no intercepts. Since

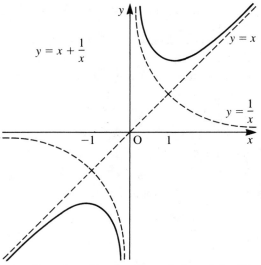

$$f(-x) = -x + \frac{1}{(-x)}$$

$$= -\left(x + \frac{1}{x}\right)$$

$$= -f(x)$$

the function is odd and hence the graph is symmetric under reflection through the origin. The only uncertainty is the exact position of the local extrema. Since

$$f'(x) = 1 - \frac{1}{x^2}$$

$f'(x) = 0$ when $x = \pm 1$. Thus, it follows from the graph that there is a local minimum when $x = 1$ and a local maximum when $x = -1$.

It should be noted that x is the dominant term when x is large and that $\frac{1}{x}$ is dominant when x is close to zero. Hence the graph behaves like $y = x$ for large x and like $y = \frac{1}{x}$ for x close to zero. □

Exercises 4.4

1. Make a rough sketch of each graph without using the derivative. Confirm your results and find the local extrema exactly by analyzing the derivatives. Indicate the intervals in which the function is increasing and decreasing.

a. $f(x) = \frac{1}{3}x + \frac{1}{x}$

b. $f(x) = \frac{1}{3}x - \frac{1}{x}$

c. $f(x) = 2x - \frac{1}{x^2}$

d. $f(x) = \frac{1}{x} - \frac{1}{x^3}$

e. $f(x) = \frac{1}{x} - \frac{1}{x^2}$

f. $f(x) = \frac{x^2 + 3x}{x - 1}$

g. $f(x) = \frac{16x}{(x + 4)^2}$

h. $f(x) = \frac{x^3}{x + 2}$

2. For each function in Exercise 1, identify the term that is dominant for large x and obtain an approximating function. Sketch the graphs of the approximating function in the corresponding diagrams of Exercise 1.

3. Sketch the graphs of each function, using the techniques that are most suitable.

   a. $f(x) = \dfrac{x}{8 + x^3}$

   b. $f(x) = \dfrac{x^3}{x^2 - 1}$

   c. $f(x) = \dfrac{x^2 - 1}{x^2 - 4}$

   d. $f(x) = (x - 1)^3 + 1$

   e. $f(x) = 3x^4 - 4x^3 - 12x^2 + 3$

   f. $f(x) = \dfrac{6}{(1 - x)^2} - 2$

   g. $f(x) = \dfrac{x + 1}{x}$

   h. $f(x) = \left(\dfrac{x + 1}{x}\right)^2$

   i. $f(x) = x^2 + \dfrac{8}{x}$

   j. $f(x) = x^2 + \dfrac{16}{x^2} - 8$

4. Referring to Exercise 3, state which functions are even and which are odd. Be sure that your graphs have the correct symmetry properties.

5. Sketch the graph of the function

$$f(x) = \frac{k - x}{k^2 + x^2}$$

   where k is any positive constant.

6. Squaring a factor will significantly influence the graph of a rational function. To illustrate this, sketch each pair of functions.

   a. $f(x) = \dfrac{x - 1}{x + 2}$ and $g(x) = \dfrac{x - 1}{(x + 2)^2}$

   b. $f(x) = \dfrac{(x + 1)(x - 2)}{x}$ and $g(x) = \dfrac{(x + 1)^2(x - 2)}{x}$

   Do you see any pattern in what happens when a factor is squared?

7. Invent a rational function $f(x)$ that satisfies the given conditions and sketch the graph of your function.

   a. $y = 2$ is a horizontal asymptote and $x = 0$ is a vertical asymptote
   b. $y = 0$ is a horizontal asymptote and $x = 1$ is a vertical asymptote
   c. $y = 1$ is a horizontal asymptote and $x = -1$ and $x = 2$ are vertical asymptotes
   d. $f(x)$ behaves like $2x$ for large x, and $x = 0$ is a vertical asymptote

Problems 4.4

1. Let a, b, and c be three numbers such that $a < 0 < b < c$, and let
$$f(x) = (x - a)(x - b)(x - c).$$
Sketch the graph of each function.

   a. $f(x)$
   b. $|f(x)|$
   c. $\dfrac{1}{f(x)}$

2. Referring to Problem 1, show that if
$$\frac{1}{a} + \frac{1}{b} + \frac{1}{c} = 0$$
the tangent line to the graph of $f(x)$ is horizontal when $x = 0$.

3. A mechanical device oscillates with an amplitude A under the influence of a periodic force of frequency ω. The square of the amplitude satisfies the equation
$$A^2 = \frac{1}{(\omega^2 - 1)^2 + k\omega^2}$$
where k is a constant.

   a. Sketch the graph of A^2 as a function of ω on the interval $0 \le \omega \le 3$, for the cases $k = 0.1$, $k = 1$, and $k = 10$. In each case determine the maximum amplitude and the frequency at which it occurs.
   b. For which values of k will there be no turning point in the interval $0 < \omega < 3$?

4. By sketching the graph of $y = x + \dfrac{3}{x}$, prove that
$$x + \frac{3}{x} \ge 2\sqrt{3}$$
for all $x > 0$.

5. Sketch the curve $y^2(x + 3) = 9x$.

6. If $f(x)$ is an even function (whose derivative exists), prove that
$$f'(0) = 0$$
Hint: Differentiate the equation $f(-x) = f(x)$ with respect to x.

4.5 The Second Derivative and Points of Inflection

Consider the graph of the function

$$f(x) = x^3$$

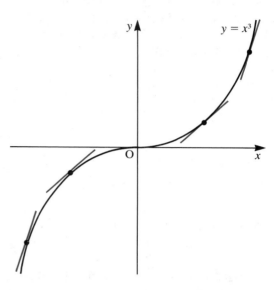

Since $f'(x) = 3x^2$, the slope of the tangent line is positive for $x \neq 0$. There is, however, an interesting difference in the graph when $x > 0$ and when $x < 0$. In the interval $x > 0$, the graph "bends upward", so that it lies above the tangent line at each point. On the other hand, in the interval $x < 0$ the graph "bends downward" so that it lies below the tangent line at each point. How can we describe this difference mathematically? Consider the values of the derivative (the slope of the tangent line) in the table below.

x	-3	-2	-1	0	1	2	3
$f'(x)$	27	12	3	0	3	12	27

Note that when $x < 0$, the derivative (slope of the tangent line) is decreasing, whereas for $x > 0$ it is increasing. This suggests that we should calculate the rate of change of the derivative, and so we differentiate the derivative $f'(x)$. The derivative of $f'(x)$ is called **the second derivative of** $f(x)$ and is denoted by $f''(x)$.

The Second Derivative of $f(x)$

$$f''(x) = \frac{d}{dx}(f'(x))$$

Geometrically, the second derivative $f''(x)$ of $f(x)$ equals the rate of change of the slope of the tangent line to the graph of $f(x)$.

For the function $f(x) = x^3$, we have $f'(x) = 3x^2$ and hence

$$f''(x) = \frac{d}{dx}(3x^2)$$
$$= 6x$$

If $x<0$, then $f''(x)<0$. The slope is decreasing, and the graph lies **below** the tangent line. We say that the graph is **concave down**. If $x>0$, then $f''(x)>0$. In this case the slope is increasing and the graph lies **above** the tangent line. We say that the graph is **concave up**.

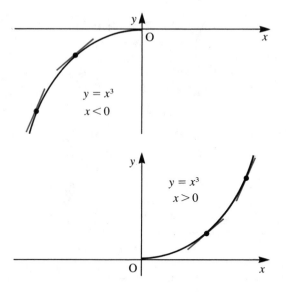

$y = x^3$
$x < 0$

$y = x^3$
$x > 0$

We now apply these ideas to an example.

Example 1. Consider the function $f(x) = x^3 - 3x^2 + 4x$. Determine the interval(s) on which the graph is concave up and the interval(s) on which it is concave down. Use the results to sketch the graph.

Solution. The derivative of $f(x)$ is

$$f'(x) = 3x^2 - 6x + 4$$

and its second derivative is

$$f''(x) = \frac{d}{dx}(3x^2 - 6x + 4)$$
$$= 6x - 6$$
$$= 6(x - 1)$$

It follows that if $x>1$, then $f''(x)>0$. This implies that the slope is increasing (the rate of change is positive). The graph bends upwards and lies above the tangent line (concave up). Similarly if $x<1$, then $f''(x)<0$. In this case the slope is decreasing. The graph bends downwards and lies below the tangent line (concave down). The results are summarized in the table.

	$x<1$	$x = 1$	$x>1$
$f''(x)$	−	0	+
graph of $f(x)$	concave down		concave up

The function has no turning points, since $f'(x) = 0$ gives

$$3x^2 - 6x + 4 = 0$$

which has no real solutions. For large x, positive or negative, the dominant term is x^3. Thus the graph is as shown.

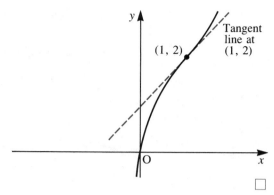

Graphs That Are Concave Up

The graph of $f(x)$ is said to be concave up on the interval $a < x < b$ if

$$f''(x) > 0 \quad \text{for} \quad a < x < b.$$

This means that the graph lies above the tangent line at each point in the interval.

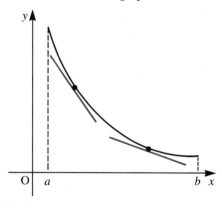   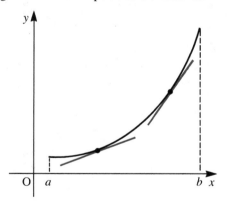

The simplest graph that is concave up throughout its domain is the parabola

$$f(x) = x^2$$

Since $f''(x) = 2$, then $f''(x) > 0$ for all $x \in R$. It is often convenient to think of this parabola when picturing a graph that is concave up.

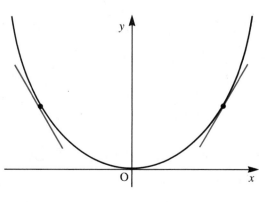

Graphs That Are Concave Down

The graph of $f(x)$ is said to be concave down on the interval $a < x < b$ if

$$f''(x) < 0 \quad \text{for} \quad a < x < b.$$

This means that the graph lies below the tangent line at each point in the interval.

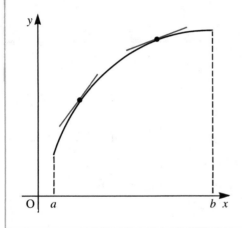 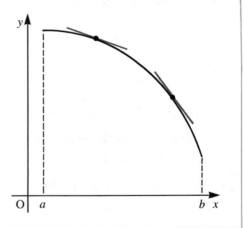

To picture a graph that is concave down, think of the parabola

$$f(x) = -x^2$$

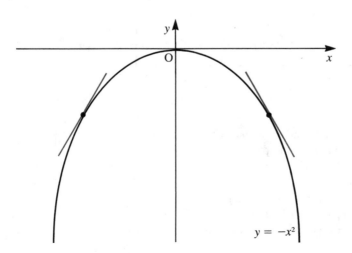

Since $f''(x) = -2$, it follows that $f''(x) < 0$ for all x.

Points where the concavity changes are important in curve sketching.

Consider the graph of $f(x) = x^3$. At the point (0, 0), the graph changes from being concave down to concave up. This means that the second derivative $f''(x) = 6x$ changes sign at $x = 0$. Such points are called **points of inflection** of the graph. In Example 1, the point (1, 2) is a point of inflection.

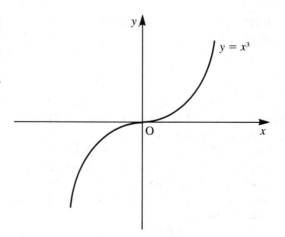

Points of Inflection

A point $(c, f(c))$ on the graph of $f(x)$ is said to be a point of inflection if the graph has a tangent line at $x = c$ and if $f''(x)$ changes sign at $x = c$.
Typical points of inflection are shown below:

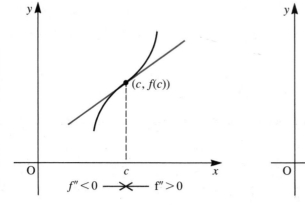

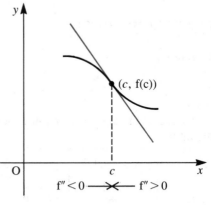

Note that the second derivative is equal to zero at a point of inflection,

$$f''(c) = 0$$

(provided that the second derivative exists). Also note that at a point of inflection the graph crosses the tangent line.

We now find the points of inflection of the graph that was sketched in Example 2 of section 4.4.

Example 2. Find the points of inflection of the graph of

$$f(x) = \frac{1}{1 + x^2}$$

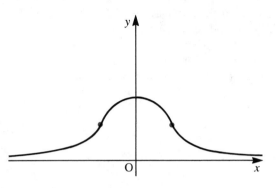

Solution. From Example 2 of section 4.4, we have a rough graph of the function. The graph is concave down when $x = 0$ and because of the horizontal asymptote, the graph must be concave up when x is large, positively or negatively. Therefore, two points of inflection are expected as indicated in the diagram.

The derivative of $f(x)$ is

$$f'(x) = \frac{-2x}{(1 + x^2)^2}$$

and the second derivative is

$$
\begin{aligned}
f''(x) &= \frac{d}{dx}[-2x(1 + x^2)^{-2}] \\
&= -2[(1 + x^2)^{-2} + x(-2)(1 + x^2)^{-3}(2x)] \\
&= -2\frac{(1 - 3x^2)}{(1 + x^2)^3}
\end{aligned}
$$

The equation $f''(x) = 0$ leads to

$$1 - 3x^2 = 0$$

with solutions

$$x = -\frac{1}{\sqrt{3}} \quad \text{and} \quad x = \frac{1}{\sqrt{3}}$$

Now determine the sign of $f''(x)$ on either side of these points. The results are summarized in the table.

	$x < -\frac{1}{\sqrt{3}}$	$x = -\frac{1}{\sqrt{3}}$	$-\frac{1}{\sqrt{3}} < x < \frac{1}{\sqrt{3}}$	$x = \frac{1}{\sqrt{3}}$	$x > \frac{1}{\sqrt{3}}$
$f''(x)$	$+$	0	$-$	0	$+$
graph of $f(x)$	concave up	point of inflection	concave down	point of inflection	concave up

The sign changes show that $\left(-\frac{1}{\sqrt{3}}, \frac{3}{4}\right)$ and $\left(\frac{1}{\sqrt{3}}, \frac{3}{4}\right)$ are points of inflection of the graph.

□

In general, to find the points of inflection of a graph, begin by finding all x-values for which $f''(x) = 0$. It is essential to note that these x-values do not necessarily correspond to points of inflection. **You must also verify that the second derivative changes sign.** To test whether the sign changes, you should make a table showing the zeros and sign of the second derivative, as in Example 2.

To illustrate the need to verify that the second derivative changes sign to establish an inflection point, consider the function $f(x) = x^4$. The first and second derivatives of $f(x)$ are

$$f'(x) = 4x^3 \quad \text{and} \quad f''(x) = 12x^2$$

It follows that $f''(0) = 0$, but, as can be seen from the graph, **the point $(0, 0)$ is not a point of inflection**. The reason is that $f''(x) > 0$ for $x \neq 0$, and hence $f''(x)$ does not change sign at $x = 0$, as shown in the table. This example should be kept in mind when one is finding points of inflection. It illustrates that the condition $f''(c) = 0$ does not guarantee a point of inflection at $x = c$.

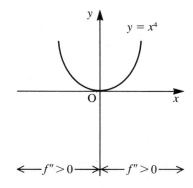

	$x < 0$	$x = 0$	$x > 0$
$f''(x)$	$+$	0	$+$

On the other hand, a graph can change in concavity without having a point of inflection. Consider the graph of $f(x) = \dfrac{1}{x}$. The second derivative is

$$f''(x) = \frac{2}{x^3}$$

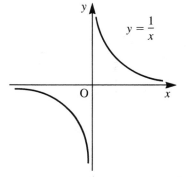

which **does** change sign at $x = 0$. Nevertheless, $x = 0$ does not correspond to a point of inflection, since $f(0)$ is undefined.

Finally, we can also express second derivatives in Leibniz notation. The second derivative of $y = f(x)$ is denoted by $\dfrac{d^2y}{dx^2}$:

$$\frac{d^2y}{dx^2} = \frac{d}{dx}\left(\frac{dy}{dx}\right)$$

For example, if $y = \dfrac{1}{x^2}$, then $\dfrac{dy}{dx} = -\dfrac{2}{x^3}$, and the second derivative of y is

$$\frac{d^2y}{dx^2} = \frac{d}{dx}\left(-\frac{2}{x^3}\right)$$
$$= \frac{6}{x^4}$$

Other variables can be used. For example, if $u = g(v)$, the second derivative of u is denoted by $\dfrac{d^2u}{dv^2}$. In addition, for a problem of motion, the acceleration is

$$a = \frac{dv}{dt}$$
$$= \frac{d}{dt}\left(\frac{ds}{dt}\right)$$
$$= \frac{d^2s}{dt^2}$$

In words, the acceleration function is the second derivative of the position function.

Exercises 4.5

1. Calculate the second derivative $f''(x)$ in each case.

a. $f(x) = \frac{1}{4}x^5$

b. $f(x) = 3x^2 + 5x - 7$

c. $f(x) = 3x^5 + 5x^3 + 13$

d. $f(x) = -3x + 2$

e. $f(x) = x^{\frac{3}{2}} + x^{\frac{1}{2}}$

f. $f(x) = 2x + \frac{3}{x}$

g. $f(x) = \sqrt{4 - 3x}$

h. $f(x) = \frac{2x}{1 - 3x}$

i. $f(x) = \frac{1}{x^2 + 4}$

j. $f(x) = \frac{x - 3}{x^4}$

2. Calculate the second derivative of each function, using Leibniz notation.

a. $y = \frac{1}{5}x^6$

b. $y = 2t^{\frac{5}{3}}$

c. $y = (2x - 6)^{10}$

d. $x = \frac{1}{(3t - 2)^2}$

e. $s = (t^2 + \pi^2)^4$

f. $u = \frac{1}{\sqrt{5 - 2v}}$

g. $s = t^2 - \frac{1}{10 - t}$

h. $w = \sqrt{4 - u^2}$

3. Evaluate $f''(x)$ at the indicated value, and state whether the graph lies above or below the tangent at that point.

a. $f(x) = 2x^3 - 10x + 3, \quad x = 2$

b. $f(x) = (3x + 5)^5, \quad x = -\frac{4}{3}$

c. $f(x) = x^2 - \frac{2}{x}, \quad x = -2$

d. $f(x) = \frac{1}{2x^2 + 1}, \quad x = -1$

4. The following functions were graphed in Exercise 1 of section 4.1 by finding the turning points. In each case, find the intervals on which the graph of $f(x)$ is concave up and the intervals on which the graph is concave down. Find all points of inflection and show them on the graph.

a. $f(x) = x^2 - 4x - 3$ **b.** $f(x) = -2x^2 + 6x + 13$

c. $f(x) = x^3 - 12x$ **d.** $f(x) = 2x^3 + 9x^2 + 12x$

e. $f(x) = \dfrac{x^3}{2} - 4$ **f.** $f(x) = x^3 + 3x^2 + 3x$

g. $f(x) = -4x^3 + 18x^2 + 3$ **h.** $f(x) = -3x^4 + 4$

i. $f(x) = 3x^4 - 4x^3$ **j.** $f(x) = -2x^5 + 5$

5. For the following functions, sketch the graph by finding asymptotes and the turning points. Using your graph, predict the number of points of inflection. Using $f''(x)$, check your prediction by finding the points of inflection.

a. $f(x) = x^3 - 4x^2 + 3$ **b.** $f(x) = x^4 - 4x^3 - 5$

c. $f(x) = x^2 - \dfrac{1}{x - 1}$ **d.** $f(x) = \dfrac{x}{1 + x^4}$

e. $f(x) = \dfrac{1}{x^2 + x}$ **f.** $f(x) = \dfrac{x}{1 + x^3}$

6. Each of the graphs below represents the second derivative $f''(x)$ of a function $f(x)$.

a.

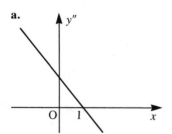

b.

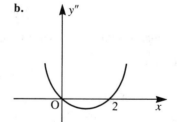

c.

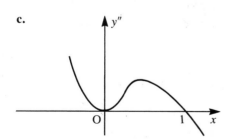

d.

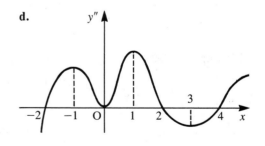

(i) On what intervals is the graph of $f(x)$ concave up, and on what intervals is the graph concave down?

(ii) List the x-coordinates of all points of inflection.

(iii) Make a rough sketch of a possible graph of $f(x)$, assuming that $f(0) = 1$.

7. Sketch the graph of a function that satisfies the conditions

$$f''(x) > 0 \quad \text{on the interval} \quad x < 2$$
$$f''(x) < 0 \quad \text{on the interval} \quad x > 2$$
$$\text{and } f(2) = 1.$$

8. Sketch the graph of a function that satisfies the conditions

$$f''(x) > 0 \quad \text{on the interval} \quad -4 < x < 1$$
$$f''(x) < 0 \quad \text{on the intervals} \quad x < -4 \text{ and } x > 1$$
$$\text{and } f(-4) = 3, \quad f(1) = -1.$$

9. Let $f(x) = x^3 + ax^2 + b$. For what values of a and b is $(-1, 3)$ a point of inflection on the graph of $f(x)$?

10. Find the value of the constant b so that the function

$$f(x) = \sqrt{x + 1} + \frac{b}{x}$$

has a point of inflection at $x = 3$.

11. Show that the graph of a quadratic function

$$f(x) = ax^2 + bx + c$$

has no points of inflection. Under what conditions is the graph

a. concave up?   b. concave down?

12. Given the second derivative of $f(x)$, find all points of inflection of the graph of $f(x)$. Make a rough sketch of a possible graph of $f(x)$.

a. $f''(x) = 4x^2 + 12x$ b. $f''(x) = 3x^3 - 15x$
c. $f''(x) = 3x^3 + 2x^2$ d. $f''(x) = (x + 3)(x^2 - 4)$

13. Suppose that

$$f''(x) > 0 \quad \text{on the interval} \quad -2 < x < 3$$

and

$$f''(x) < 0 \quad \text{on the intervals} \quad x < -2 \text{ and } x > 3$$

For each pair of slopes (that is, values of the derivative), state, where possible, which is greater.

a. $f'(0), \quad f'(2)$ b. $f'(-1), \quad f'(1)$ c. $f'(3), \quad f'(10)$
d. $f'(-3), \quad f'(1)$ e. $f'(-7), \quad f'(-3)$ f. $f'(-2), \quad f'(4)$

14. Sketch the graph of the function

$$f(x) = 4 - \frac{8}{2 + x^2}, \quad 0 \le x \le 4$$

Determine the point at which the slope is greatest and interpret the result geometrically.

Problems 4.5

1. Determine the constants a, b, c, and d so that the curve

$$y = ax^3 + bx^2 + cx + d$$

has a point of inflection at the origin and a local maximum at the point $(2, 4)$. Sketch the curve.

2. Find an expression for $\dfrac{d^2}{dx^2} [p(x)q(x)]$ in terms of $p(x)$ and $q(x)$ and their derivatives.

3. Let $y = f(x^2)$. Find $\dfrac{d^2y}{dx^2}$ when $x = 2$, given that $f'(4) = 3$ and $f''(4) = -1$.

4. Show that the graph of

$$f(x) = ax^4 + bx^3$$

has two points of inflection. Show that the x-coordinate of one of these points lies midway between the x-intercepts.

5. Suppose that the cubic polynomial

$$h(x) = x^3 - 3bx^2 + 3cx + d$$

has a local maximum at $A(x_1, y_1)$ and a local minimum at $B(x_2, y_2)$. Prove that the point of inflection of $h(x)$ is at the midpoint of the line segment AB.

6. Let $f(x) = x^4 + ax^3 + bx^2 + cx + d$. Show that the graph of $f(x)$ has either two points of inflection or none. What conditions on the coefficients distinguish the two cases?

7. a. Show that for any cubic function

$$f(x) = ax^3 + bx^2 + cx + d$$

the graph of $f(x)$ has one point of inflection, and show that the slope at that point equals $c - \dfrac{b^2}{3a}$.

b. Show that the general cubic function in part (a) has six possible shapes, depending on whether

$$3ac < b^2, \quad 3ac = b^2, \quad \text{or } 3ac > b^2$$

and also depending on the sign of a. Sketch the six possible shapes.

4.6 Applications of the Second Derivative

In this section we discuss some applications of the second derivative:

- problems of motion
- interpretation of points of inflection
- the second derivative test for local extrema

Consider an object that moves in a straight line with position function $s(t)$. We have seen (in section 3.2) that the slope of the position-time graph gives us information about the velocity of the object. Since the acceleration function is the second derivative of the position function

$$a = \frac{dv}{dt} = \frac{d^2s}{dt^2}$$

it follows that the concavity of the position-time graph gives us information about the acceleration of the object. This is illustrated in Example 1.

Example 1. An object moves in a straight line, with position function

$$s(t) = t^3 - 9t^2 + 24t, \quad 0 \le t \le 5$$

Graph the position, velocity, and acceleration as functions of time, and describe the motion of the object.

Solution. The velocity function is

$$\begin{aligned}
v(t) &= s'(t) \\
&= 3t^2 - 18t + 24 \\
&= 3(t - 4)(t - 2)
\end{aligned}$$

Analyzing the sign of $s'(t)$, we obtain:

	$0 \le t < 2$	$t = 2$	$2 < t < 4$	$t = 4$	$4 < t \le 5$
$s'(t)$	$+$	0	$-$	0	$+$
$s(t)$	increasing	local maximum	decreasing	local minimum	increasing

The acceleration function (second derivative) is

$$\begin{aligned}
a(t) &= s''(t) \\
&= 6t - 18 \\
&= 6(t - 3)
\end{aligned}$$

Analyzing the sign of $s''(t)$, we obtain:

	$0 \leq t < 3$	$t = 3$	$3 < t \leq 5$
$s''(t)$	$-$	0	$+$
$s(t)$	concave down	point of inflection	concave up

We now have enough information to graph the position function. Note that the graph of the velocity function is a parabola, with vertex at $t = 3$, and that the graph of the acceleration is a straight line.

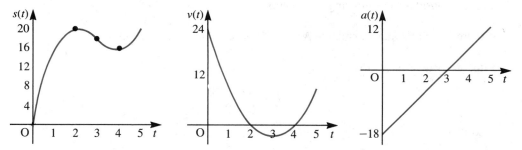

It is essential to note that the actual motion of the object occurs along a straight line, the s-axis. The three graphs enable us to state the direction of motion and whether the object is speeding up or slowing down. The term ''speed'' indicates the magnitude of the velocity, $|v|$. Note that to increase the speed when $v > 0$ we would need $a > 0$ (so that $|v| = v$ increases). In order to increase the speed when $v < 0$ we would need $a < 0$ (so that $|v| = -v$ again increases). With this understanding, we can use the three graphs to describe the motion as follows:

Time interval	Direction of motion	Speed $|v|$
$0 < t < 2$	positive direction $(v > 0)$	decreasing $(a < 0)$
$2 < t < 3$	negative direction $(v < 0)$	increasing $(a < 0)$
$3 < t < 4$	negative direction $(v < 0)$	decreasing $(a > 0)$
$4 < t < 5$	positive direction $(v > 0)$	increasing $(a > 0)$

Note also that the object is at rest $(v = 0)$ when $t = 2$, $s = 20$ and when $t = 4$, $s = 16$.

When $a = s''(t) > 0$, the graph of $s(t)$ is concave up, and when $a = s''(t) < 0$, it is concave down. At the point of inflection $(t = 3)$ of the graph of $s(t)$, the acceleration changes sign and the graph of $v(t)$ has a turning point (a local minimum). $\square$

In a problem of motion, the points of inflection of the position-time graph show when the acceleration changes sign and when the velocity has a local maximum or minimum, as in Example 1. Points of inflection are also important in other applications, as is illustrated in Example 2.

Example 2. Suppose that the number of houses in a new subdivision after t months of development is modelled by the function

$$N(t) = 1000\left[1 - \frac{2000}{2000 + t^3}\right], \quad 0 \le t \le 60$$

Sketch the graph of $N(t)$ and give an interpretation of the point of inflection.

Solution. Consider the following observations:

- there is a horizontal asymptote $N = 1000$, since $\lim\limits_{t \to +\infty} N(t) = 1000$.

- the derivative of $N(t)$ is

$$N'(t) = \frac{(6 \times 10^6)\,t^2}{(2000 + t^3)^2}$$

   so that

$$N'(0) = 0 \text{ and } N'(t) > 0 \text{ for } t > 0$$

- $N(0) = 0$ and $N(60) \approx 991$.

This leads to the graph shown here. It seems that there is one point of inflection for $t > 0$. To verify this, calculate the second derivative. After simplifying, we obtain

$$N''(t) = \frac{(24 \times 10^6)\,t(1000 - t^3)}{(2000 + t^3)^3}$$

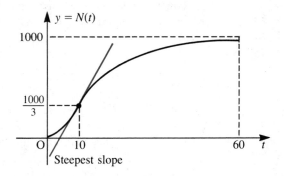

The equation $N''(t) = 0$ has the solution $t^3 = 1000$; that is, $t = 10$. Since

$$0 < t < 10 \text{ implies that } 1000 - t^3 > 0 \text{ and hence that } N''(t) > 0,$$

and since

$$t > 10 \text{ implies that } 1000 - t^3 < 0 \text{ and hence that } N''(t) < 0,$$

we obtain the following sign diagram for $N''(t)$.

	$0 < t < 10$	$t = 10$	$10 < t < 60$
$N''(t)$	+	0	−
graph of $N(t)$	concave up	point of inflection	concave down

Thus, the point $\left(10, \frac{1000}{3}\right)$ is the only point of inflection in the interval $0 < t < 60$.

The slope of the graph of $N(t)$ (the derivative $N'(t)$) represents the rate of construction, measured in houses built per month. From the graph, $N'(t)$ increases for $0 < t < 10$ (concave up) and decreases for $10 < t < 60$ (concave down). It follows that the maximum value of $N'(t)$ occurs at $t = 10$, that is, at the point of inflection. Thus the point of inflection shows when the rate of construction is a maximum.   □

The sign of the second derivative of a function provides a new method for classifying local extrema.

Suppose that

$$f'(c) = 0$$

and

$$f''(c) > 0$$

This implies that $x = c$ lies in an interval in which the graph is concave up. Hence $x = c$ **must correspond to a local minimum**.

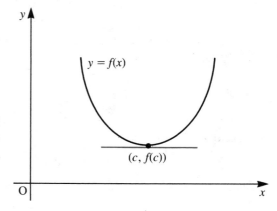

Similarly, if $f'(c) = 0$ and

$$f''(c) < 0$$

then $x = c$ lies in an interval in which the graph is concave down. Hence $x = c$ **must correspond to a local maximum**.

We summarize these results below.

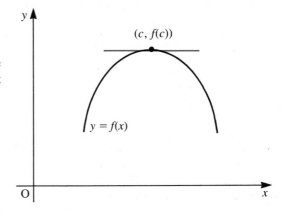

Second Derivative Test for Local Extrema

If $f'(c) = 0$ and $f''(c) > 0$, then $f(x)$ has a local minimum at $x = c$.
If $f'(c) = 0$ and $f''(c) < 0$, then $f(x)$ has a local maximum at $x = c$.

This test is applied in Example 3.

Example 3. Find and classify all local extrema of the function

$$f(x) = 3x^5 - 25x^3 + 60x$$

Solution. The derivative of $f(x)$ is

$$\begin{aligned} f'(x) &= 15x^4 - 75x^2 + 60 \\ &= 15(x^4 - 5x^2 + 4) \end{aligned}$$

which exists for all x. Solving $f'(x) = 0$, we obtain

$$x^4 - 5x^2 + 4 = 0$$

or

$$(x^2 - 1)(x^2 - 4) = 0$$

giving four values of x:

$$x = -1, \quad x = 1, \quad x = -2, \quad \text{and } x = 2$$

To apply the second-derivative test, differentiate $f'(x)$ to obtain

$$f''(x) = 15(4x^3 - 10x)$$

We evaluate the second derivative at the x-values for which $f'(x) = 0$, and the conclusions are stated in the table.

x	-2	-1	1	2
$f'(x)$	0	0	0	0
$f''(x)$	$-$	$+$	$-$	$+$
$f(x)$	local maximum	local minimum	local maximum	local minimum

On evaluating $f(x)$ at the local extrema, we obtain the following graph:

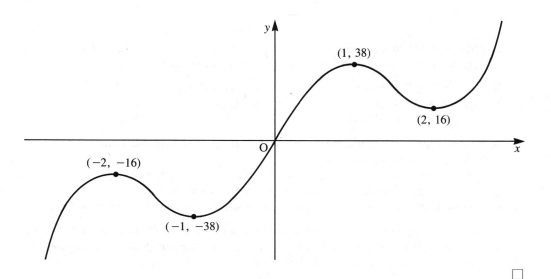

At first sight the second derivative test may appear to be an effective tool for classifying local extrema, but it has several drawbacks:

- The test gives no conclusion if $f''(c) = 0$.

- Evaluating the second derivative can result in lengthy calculations.

To illustrate the first point, we give three simple graphical examples:

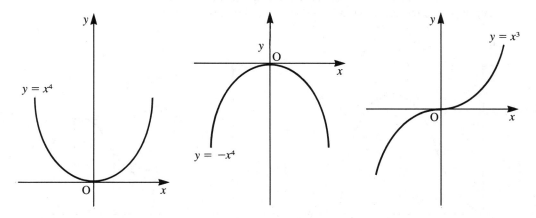

In each case $f'(0) = 0$, and $f''(0) = 0$. At $x = 0$, however, the three curves have a local minimum, a local maximum, and a point of inflection, respectively.

The first-derivative test in section 4.1 has none of these drawbacks. It applies more generally and requires that one calculate only the first derivative.

Exercises 4.6

1. A particle moves in a straight line with position function $s(t)$, $t \geq 0$. In each case sketch the graphs of the position, velocity, and acceleration functions.

    a. $s(t) = 2t^3 - 12t^2 + 18t - 3$ **b.** $s(t) = t^3 - 6t^2 + 9t + 6$
    c. $s(t) = t^3 - 3t^2 + 3t + 3$ **d.** $s(t) = t^4 - 108t + 4$
    e. $s(t) = 3t^4 - 16t^3 + 24t^2$

2. Referring to Exercise 1, use the graphs to answer the following questions:
    (i) When is the particle at rest?
    (ii) When is the particle moving in the positive (negative) direction?
    (iii) When is the speed of the particle increasing (decreasing)?
    (iv) What is the total distance travelled after 6 seconds of motion, starting at $t = 0$?

3. For the following situations, which occur when a car is being driven, state whether the velocity is positive or negative and whether the acceleration is positive or negative. In each case, state whether the speed, $|v|$, is increasing or decreasing.

    a. braking while moving forward
    b. accelerating while in reverse gear
    c. accelerating while in forward gear
    d. braking while moving backward

4. Consider these position-time graphs.
    (i) At what times is the velocity zero?
    (ii) At what times is the object moving in the positive (negative) direction?
    (iii) At what times is the acceleration zero?
    (iv) At what times is the acceleration positive (negative)?
    (v) When is the object slowing down (speeding up)?

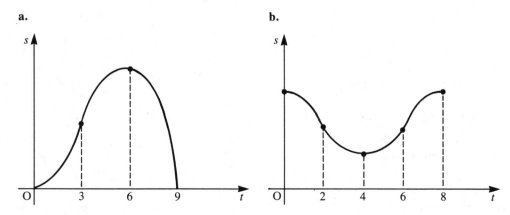

5. Referring to Exercise 4, make a rough sketch of the velocity and acceleration functions for each graph.

6. The position function of a particle moving in a straight line is

$$s(t) = \frac{10t^2}{32 + t^2}, \quad 0 \le t \le 10.$$

a. Sketch the graph of $s(t)$, indicating the points of inflection.
b. When is the velocity a maximum?
c. Sketch the graph of the velocity function.

7. A flu epidemic breaks out in Preston. The fraction of the population that is infected at time t (in weeks) is modelled by the function

$$f(t) = \frac{64t^2}{(4 + t)^4}, \quad 0 \le t \le 10$$

Sketch the graph of the function, showing all essential features. When is the largest fraction of people infected? When is the epidemic spreading most rapidly? Illustrate the results on your graph.

8. After a lake has been stocked with 1000 trout, the trout population is modelled by the function

$$N(t) = 1000 + \frac{10\ 000t^2}{t^2 + 100}$$

where t is the time in years.

a. What is the trout population after a long period of time?
b. When is the population increasing most rapidly?
c. Sketch the graph of $N(t)$ and illustrate the results in parts (a) and (b).

9. Find and classify all local extrema of each function, using the second derivative test.

a. $f(x) = x^2 - 10x + 3$

b. $f(x) = x^3 - 12x + 5$

c. $f(x) = 3x^4 - 16x^3 + 18x^2 + 2$

d. $f(x) = x + \dfrac{9}{x}$

e. $f(x) = x^2 + \dfrac{16}{x^2}$

f. $f(x) = (1 - x^2 + 2x^4)^3$

g. $f(x) = 3x^5 - 50x^3 + 135x$

h. $f(x) = x^2 + \dfrac{54}{x}$

10. Find and classify all local extrema of each function, using any suitable method.

a. $f(x) = x^4 - 2x^3$

b. $f(x) = \dfrac{x}{k^2 + x^2}$, k is a positive constant

c. $f(x) = x^5 + 5$

d. $f(x) = x^5 - 5x$

e. $f(x) = \dfrac{x^2 - 2x + 3}{x^2 + 2}$

f. $f(x) = \sqrt{1 - x^2 + 2x^4}$

g. $f(x) = x\sqrt{9 - x^2}$

Problems 4.6

1. For an object moving in air, the effect of air resistance can be represented by a force that is proportional to the velocity. If the position function of an object is

$$s(t) = \left(\frac{5t}{3+t}\right)^2$$

where s is measured in metres and t is measured in seconds, determine when the maximum air resistance occurs. Sketch the graph of $s(t)$ for $t > 0$ and interpret your result.

2. For the function $f(x) = x^2(a + \sqrt{a^2 - x^2})$, where a is a positive constant, calculate $f'(x)$ and $f''(x)$ for $x = 2\sqrt{2}\dfrac{a}{3}$. What can you deduce from your results?

3. The speed of an object moving in a straight line is $|v|$. Use the fact that $|v|^2 = v^2$ to show that the speed increases with respect to time when $va > 0$. (Hint: calculate the rate of change of the square of the speed).

4.7 Additional Curve-Sketching Techniques

In the preceding sections we have developed curve-sketching techniques for functions that have a derivative at all points at which the function is defined. However, there are simple functions for which the derivative does not exist at certain points. For example, in section 1.7 we considered the function

$$f(x) = |x|$$

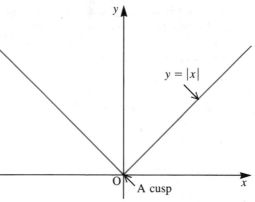

$y = |x|$

A cusp

and showed that $f'(0)$ does not exist. The reason for this is clear from the graph. At $x = 0$ the value of the derivative makes an abrupt change from -1 to 1, so that there is no tangent line at $(0, 0)$. We say that the graph has a cusp at $x = 0$.

In general, cusps often occur with functions involving absolute values and fractional powers. In this section we extend our curve-sketching techniques to this type of function.

Example 1. Sketch the graph of the function

$$f(x) = 1 - x^{\frac{2}{3}}$$

Solution. The derivative of $f(x)$ is

$$f'(x) = -\frac{2}{3x^{\frac{1}{3}}}$$

It follows that $f'(0)$ does not exist (since the denominator is zero when $x = 0$) and that $f'(x)$ increases without bound as $x \to 0$:

$$\lim_{x \to 0^+} f'(x) = -\infty, \quad \lim_{x \to 0^-} f'(x) = +\infty$$

Note that there is an abrupt change in $f'(x)$ at $x = 0$, from "large positive" to "large negative," and so the graph has a cusp when $x = 0$.

To sketch the graph, note that

$$f'(x) > 0 \text{ for } x < 0, \text{ so that } f(x) \text{ is increasing for } x < 0,$$

and

$$f'(x) < 0 \text{ for } x > 0, \text{ so that } f(x) \text{ is decreasing for } x > 0.$$

We also calculate the second derivative:

$$f''(x) = \frac{2}{9x^{\frac{4}{3}}}$$

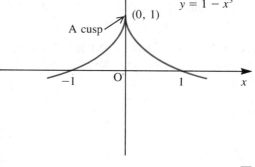

It follows that $f''(x) > 0$ for all $x \neq 0$, so that the graph is concave up for $x < 0$ and for $x > 0$. We obtain the graph shown to the right. Note that the function is even; that is,

$$f(-x) = f(x)$$

so that the graph is symmetric about the y-axis. □

We now consider a function that involves absolute values.

Example 2. Sketch the graph of

$$f(x) = x|x - 2|$$

Solution. Express $f(x)$ without the absolute value signs. Since

$$|x - 2| = \begin{cases} x - 2, & \text{if } x \geq 2 \\ -(x - 2), & \text{if } x < 2 \end{cases}$$

we obtain

$$f(x) = \begin{cases} x^2 - 2x, & \text{if } x \geq 2 \\ -x^2 + 2x, & \text{if } x < 2 \end{cases}$$

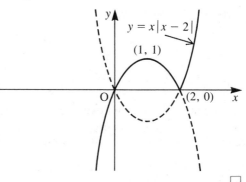

By sketching the parabolas $y = x^2 - 2x$ and $y = -x^2 + 2x$, we obtain the graph shown to the right. Observe that the graph has a cusp at $x = 2$, so that the derivative $f'(2)$ does not exist. □

We are now in a position to make an important observation. In Example 1, $f(x) = 1 - x^{\frac{2}{3}}$ has a local maximum at $x = 0$ and $f'(0)$ does not exist. In Example 2, $f(x) = x|x - 2|$ has a local minimum at $x = 2$ and $f'(2)$ does not exist. Therefore, a local minimum or local maximum may occur not only at points where $f'(x) = 0$ but also at points where $f'(x)$ does not exist. Such points are called "critical points."

Critical Points

A point $(c, f(c))$ is a critical point of $f(x)$ if either

$$f'(c) = 0$$

or

$$f'(c) \text{ does not exist.}$$

The number c is called a critical value of $f(x)$.

The first-derivative test (see section 4.1) may be used to identify local extrema, even in the case where $f'(x)$ does not exist. In Example 1 of this section,

$$f'(x) > 0 \text{ for } x < 0$$

and

$$f'(x) < 0 \text{ for } x > 0$$

so that $x = 0$ is a local maximum. A similar argument applies to the local minimum at $x = 2$ in Example 2.

We now give a detailed example of curve sketching involving cusps.

Example 3. Sketch the graph of the function

$$f(x) = x^{\frac{5}{3}} - 5x^{\frac{2}{3}}$$

and indicate all local extrema and points of inflection.

Solution. The derivative of $f(x)$ is

$$f'(x) = \frac{5}{3}x^{\frac{2}{3}} - \frac{10}{3}x^{-\frac{1}{3}}$$

$$= \frac{5}{3}\left[\frac{x - 2}{x^{\frac{1}{3}}}\right]$$

Notice that $f'(0)$ does not exist (since the denominator is zero and the numerator is non-zero when $x = 0$). Furthermore, $f'(x) = 0$ has only the solution $x = 2$ (when the numerator is zero). Thus $f(x)$ has two critical values, $x = 0$ and $x = 2$.

The sign of $f'(x)$ is determined by the sign of the factors $x - 2$ and $x^{\frac{1}{3}}$. The results are summarized in the table.

	$x<0$	$x=0$	$0<x<2$	$x=2$	$x>2$
$f'(x)$	+	does not exist	−	0	+
$f(x)$	increasing	local maximum (cusp)	decreasing	local minimum	increasing

The second derivative is

$$f''(x) = \frac{10}{9}x^{-\frac{1}{3}} + \frac{10}{9}x^{-\frac{4}{3}}$$

$$= \frac{10}{9}\left[\frac{x+1}{x^{\frac{4}{3}}}\right]$$

Note that $f''(0)$ does not exist and that $f''(x) = 0$ when $x = -1$. The sign of $f''(x)$ is determined by the sign of the factor $x + 1$, since $x^{\frac{4}{3}}$ is always positive. We summarize the results below.

	$x<-1$	$x=-1$	$-1<x<0$	$x=0$	$x>0$
$f''(x)$	−	0	+	does not exist	+
$f(x)$	concave down	point of inflection	concave up		concave up

The tables lead to the following graph.

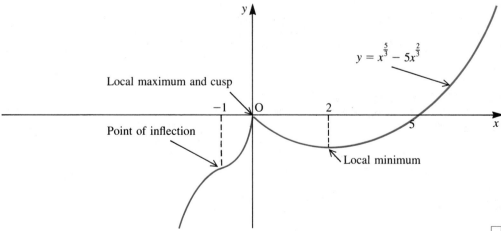

Local maximum and cusp

$y = x^{\frac{5}{3}} - 5x^{\frac{2}{3}}$

Point of inflection

Local minimum

As a final example, we show that if $f'(c)$ does not exist, the graph of $f(x)$ may have a vertical tangent line at $x = c$, instead of a cusp. This example also shows that a point of inflection may occur at a point where $f'(x)$ does not exist.

Example 4. Sketch the graph of the function

$$f(x) = x^{\frac{1}{3}}$$

Solution. The derivative of $f(x)$ is

$$f'(x) = \frac{1}{3}x^{-\frac{2}{3}}$$

$$= \frac{1}{3x^{\frac{2}{3}}}$$

Note that $f'(0)$ does not exist, so that $x = 0$ is a critical value of $f(x)$. It is important to determine the behaviour of $f'(x)$ as $x \to 0$. Since $f'(x) > 0$ for all $x \neq 0$ and the denominator of $f'(x)$ is zero when $x = 0$, we have

$$\lim_{x \to 0} f'(x) = +\infty$$

This means that there is a vertical tangent line at $x = 0$. In addition, $f(x)$ is increasing for $x < 0$ and $x > 0$.

The second derivative of $f(x)$ is

$$f''(x) = -\frac{2}{9}x^{-\frac{5}{3}}$$

Since $x^{\frac{5}{3}} > 0$ if $x > 0$ and $x^{\frac{5}{3}} < 0$ for $x < 0$, we obtain the following table:

	$x < 0$	$x = 0$	$x > 0$
$f''(x)$	$+$	does not exist	$-$
$f(x)$	concave up	point of inflection	concave down

The graph has a point of inflection when $x = 0$, even though $f'(0)$ and $f''(0)$ do not exist. Note that the curve crosses its tangent line at $x = 0$.

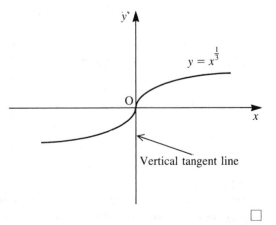

$y = x^{\frac{1}{3}}$

Vertical tangent line

To end the section we shall make a comment on horizontal asymptotes. For functions other than rational functions, there can be two distinct horizontal asymptotes, as $x \to +\infty$ and $x \to -\infty$. This can occur for functions involving fractional powers, such as

$$f(x) = \frac{x}{\sqrt{x^2 + 1}}$$

See Problems 1 and 2 in this section and Problem 2 in section 4.3.

Exercises 4.7

1. Sketch the graph of each function by elementary means (without using derivatives). Hence find all local extrema and describe the behaviour of the derivative at these points.

   a. $f(x) = |x^2 - 1|$ **b.** $f(x) = |x^2 - x|$
   c. $f(x) = |x^3 - 1|$ **d.** $f(x) = 2x - |x|$
   e. $f(x) = x - 2|x|$ **f.** $f(x) = x|x + 1|$

2. Sketch the graph of each function. State where the first and second derivatives do not exist. Indicate cusps, vertical tangent lines, and points of inflection.

   a. $f(x) = 3x^{\frac{2}{3}}$ **b.** $f(x) = 8 - x^{\frac{1}{3}}$

   c. $f(x) = 3(x - 1)^{\frac{1}{3}}$ **d.** $f(x) = x^{\frac{4}{3}} - 1$

   e. $f(x) = (x - 2)^{\frac{5}{3}}$ **f.** $f(x) = -3(x - 2)^{\frac{4}{3}}$

3. Sketch the graph of each function and label all essential features.

   a. $f(x) = x^{\frac{4}{3}} - 4x^{\frac{1}{3}}$ **b.** $f(x) = 3(x - 2)^{\frac{5}{3}} - 5x$

   c. $f(x) = [x(x - 1)]^{\frac{1}{3}}$ **d.** $f(x) = |x^3 - 3x|$

   e. $f(x) = \left| \dfrac{x}{x^2 - 1} \right|$ **f.** $f(x) = \left| \dfrac{x - 1}{x} \right|$

   g. $f(x) = x^2|x - 4|$ **h.** $f(x) = \dfrac{|x|}{x^2 + 1}$

Problems 4.7

1. Functions other than rational functions can have two different horizontal asymptotes, as $x \to +\infty$ and $x \to -\infty$. Consider the function

$$f(x) = \frac{x}{\sqrt{x^2 + 1}}$$

   a. By expressing $f(x)$ in the form $f(x) = \left(\dfrac{x}{|x|} \right) \dfrac{1}{\sqrt{1 + \dfrac{1}{x^2}}}$, evaluate

   $\lim\limits_{x \to +\infty} f(x)$ and $\lim\limits_{x \to -\infty} f(x)$.

   b. Use the result of part (a) and the derivative of $f(x)$ to sketch the graph of $f(x)$.

2. Find the horizontal and vertical asymptotes, and sketch the graphs.

a. $f(x) = \dfrac{3x + 5}{\sqrt{4x^2 + 1}}$

b. $f(x) = \dfrac{\sqrt{9x^2 + 5}}{x - 1}$

c. $f(x) = \dfrac{x - 1}{|x + 1|}$

d. $f(x) = \dfrac{x^3}{|x^3 - 1|}$

Review Exercises

1. a. Determine the local extrema of the function

$$f(x) = 3x^4 + 8x^3 - 6x^2 - 24x + 3$$

and sketch its graph.

b. Use your graph to predict the approximate location of the points of inflection.

2. For each function, make a rough sketch of the graph by finding the vertical and horizontal asymptotes. If there is no horizontal asymptote, find the dominant term in $f(x)$ as $x \to \pm\infty$ in order to sketch the graph.

a. $f(x) = \dfrac{2x + 1}{x - 1}$

b. $f(x) = \dfrac{(x - 1)(x - 2)}{x - 3}$

c. $f(x) = \dfrac{(x - 1)(x - 3)}{x - 2}$

d. $f(x) = \dfrac{(x - 1)(x - 3)}{(x - 2)^2}$

e. $f(x) = x^2 - \dfrac{4}{x + 1}$

f. $f(x) = \dfrac{x}{x^2 - 4x + 4}$

g. $f(x) = \dfrac{x^2 + 1}{4x^2 - 9}$

h. $f(x) = \dfrac{x^2 - 6x + 9}{x^2 + x - 2}$

3. Referring to Exercise 2, use the graph to predict the approximate location of the turning points, and then use the derivative to find their exact location.

4. Find the simplest rational function that satisfies the following conditions. Sketch the graph of the function.

a. $f(1) = 0 = f(2)$; the graph has vertical asymptotes at $x = 3$ and $x = 4$; $f(0) = 1$

b. $f(0) = 2$; $\displaystyle\lim_{x \to 1^+} f(x) = +\infty$; $\displaystyle\lim_{x \to 1^-} f(x) = +\infty$

5. For what value of k will $f(x) = x + \dfrac{k}{x}$ have a local maximum at $x = -2$?

6. The graph of the function

$$f(x) = \dfrac{ax + b}{(x - 1)(x - 4)}$$

has a horizontal tangent line at the point $(2, -1)$. Find a and b and show that $f(x)$ has a local maximum at $(2, -1)$. Sketch the graph.

7. By introducing suitable variables, express each statement in terms of derivatives.

    a. The grouse population of Bruce County is decreasing less rapidly than previously. (Let $N(t)$ denote the number of grouse at time t.)

    b. The price of gasoline continues to increase, but at a slower rate.

    c. The company's profit is increasing more rapidly than last year.

    d. Unemployment continues at a fixed level.

8. Find constants a, b, c, and d such that the graph of the function

$$f(x) = ax^3 + bx^2 + cx + d$$

has a local extremum at $(0, 3)$ and a point of inflection at $(1, -1)$. Sketch the graph of $f(x)$.

9. On the same set of axes, sketch the graphs of the functions

$$f(x) = x \quad \text{and} \quad g(x) = x + \frac{4}{x - 2}$$

Find local maxima and minima, points of inflection, and points of intersection of the two graphs if there are any.

10. On the basis of the information given, make a rough sketch of the graph of $f(x)$ near the point $(1, 1)$. In each case, $f(1) = 1$.

    a. $f'(1) = 0$, $f''(1) = 2$

    b. $f'(1) = 0$, $f''(1) = -3$

    c. $f'(1) = -2$, $f''(1) = -1$

    d. $f'(1) = 2$, $f''(1) = 0$, $f''(x) > 0$ if $x < 1$, $f''(x) < 0$ if $x > 1$

11. Consider the following graph of the function $f(x)$:

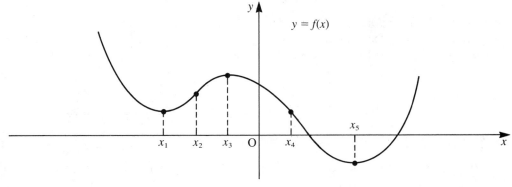

There are local extrema at x_1, x_3, and x_5; and points of inflection at x_2 and x_4. State the intervals in which the following conditions hold.

    a. $f'(x) > 0$, $f''(x) > 0$ **b.** $f'(x) > 0$, $f''(x) < 0$

    c. $f'(x) < 0$, $f''(x) > 0$ **d.** $f'(x) < 0$, $f''(x) < 0$

12. In this exercise you are given the graph of the derivative $f'(x)$ of a function $f(x)$. Answer the following questions about $f(x)$.

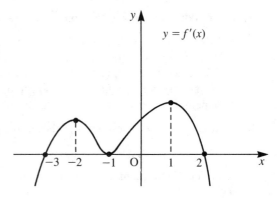

a. On what intervals is $f(x)$ increasing? decreasing? concave up? concave down?

b. Find all local extrema and points of inflection of $f(x)$.

c. Make a rough sketch of the graph of $f(x)$, assuming that $f(0) = 1$.

13. Consider the function $f(x) = \dfrac{1}{x^3 + 1}$.

a. Make a rough sketch of the graph of $f(x)$ by finding the vertical and horizontal asymptotes.

b. Your graph in part (a) will possibly be missing an essential feature. By finding where $f'(x)$ is zero, improve your sketch.

c. Based on your graph in part (b), how many points of inflection do you expect? Verify your conjecture by analyzing $f''(x)$.

14. Are the following statements true or false? If false, give an example of a function for which the statement is false.

a. If $f'(2) = 0$, then $f(x)$ has a local maximum or a local minimum when $x = 2$.

b. If $f(x)$ is a polynomial of degree 3, then its graph has one point of inflection.

c. If $f''(1) = 0$, then the graph of $f(x)$ has a point of inflection when $x = 1$.

d. If $f(x)$ is a rational function, then its graph has a horizontal asymptote.

15. Invent a cubic polynomial function whose graph is of the form shown. Find the turning points of your function.

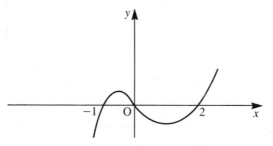

16. Invent a rational function that satisfies the following conditions and sketch the graph of your function.

a. $y = -2$ is a horizontal asymptote and $x = -1$ is a vertical asymptote

b. $x = 2$ is a vertical asymptote and $f(x)$ behaves like $y = \frac{1}{2}x$ when x is large

c. $y = 2$ is a horizontal asymptote and there are no vertical asymptotes

17. a. Sketch the graphs of the functions

$$f(x) = x^3 - 3x + 1 \quad \text{and} \quad g(x) = x + 1$$

on the same axes and find all points of intersection.

b. From the graphs in part (a), or by other means, find all values of x so that

$$x + 1 > x^3 - 3x + 1$$

18. Let $f(x) = |x|$. Sketch the graph of each function.

a. $y = f(x + 1)$ **b.** $y = f(x + 1) - 1$ **c.** $y = f(f(x + 1) - 1)$

Indicate at what points the derivative $\dfrac{dy}{dx}$ does not exist.

19. Let $f(x) = x^2 - 2x$. Sketch the graph of each function.

a. $y = |f(x)|$ **b.** $y = f(|x|)$

Indicate at what points the derivative $\dfrac{dy}{dx}$ does not exist.

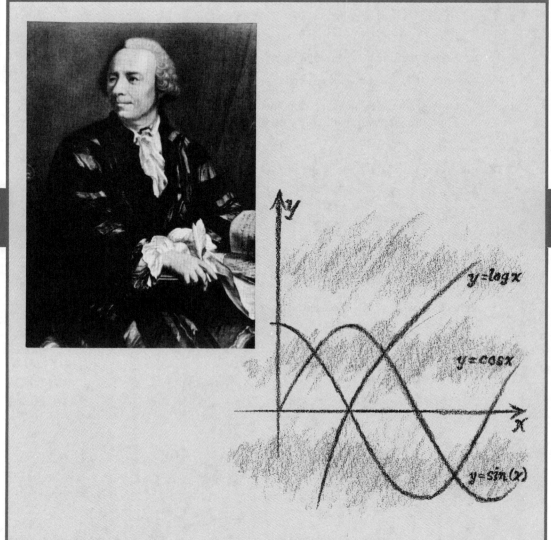

Leonard Euler *(1707–1783) was one of the foremost mathematicians of modern times. Born in Basel, Switzerland, and studying under Johann Bernoulli, Euler soon outstripped his teacher. Well versed in languages, physiology, medicine, geography and the physical sciences, he has had an enormous influence in the teaching of mathematics. It is said that all textbooks in Calculus are essentially copies of his three books on the subject. He is responsible for the modern treatment of logarithm and exponential functions and the notations, sin(x) and cos(x), used for the trigonometric functions, as well as the use of f(x) to denote an unspecified function. The most important "special number," after π and e, is the Euler constant:*

$$\gamma = \lim_{n \to \infty} (1 + \frac{1}{2} + \frac{1}{3} + \frac{1}{4} + \ldots + \frac{1}{n} - \ln n) = .5772156649015 \ldots$$

It is still unknown whether Euler's constant is rational or irrational.

Trigonometric Functions and Their Derivatives

CHAPTER 5

So far in our study of Calculus we have worked with functions that can be evaluated by using only the operations of addition, subtraction, multiplication, division, and extraction of roots. Examples of such functions are $f(x) = 2x^5 + x - 7$, $g(x) = \dfrac{2x^2 + 1}{x - 1}$, and $h(x) = \sqrt{x^2 - x}$.

These functions are referred to as algebraic functions, and they include polynomials and rational functions as special cases. Trigonometric functions, however, cannot be expressed in terms of algebraic functions and are thus a new type of function, with significantly different properties. For example, they are **periodic** functions.

Trigonometric functions play an important role in the description of oscillatory phenomena and periodic motion. Among the applications of trigonometric functions are the modelling of rotating machinery, planetary orbits, the rise and fall of tides, and the current in electrical circuits. Tables of the sine function were first compiled in the second century B.C. in connection with astronomy.

In this chapter we shall use the methods of Calculus to analyze the trigonometric functions.

5.1 Review of Basic Properties

Trigonometric functions are closely related to the circle and the number π. For a circle of radius r,

$$\text{Circumference} = 2\pi r \qquad\qquad (1)$$

and

$$\text{Area} = \pi r^2 \qquad (2)$$

Perhaps you have wondered about how these formulae can be justified and about the origins of the number π. In section 5.5, when we discuss the so-called fundamental trigonometric limit, we shall derive the area formula (2) from the circumference formula (1).

In order to define the sine and cosine functions,

$$f(\theta) = \sin \theta \quad \text{and} \quad g(\theta) = \cos \theta$$

for any real number θ, we regard θ as the measure of an angle. For this purpose we need to choose a unit for measuring angles. In Calculus, the most convenient unit is the radian, for reasons that will be discussed when we find the derivatives of the trigonometric functions in section 5.4.

A **radian** is the measure of the angle subtended at the centre of a circle of radius r
by an arc of length r. The length s of an
arc that subtends an angle of θ radians at
the centre of a circle of radius r is proportional to the angle; that is,

$$\frac{s}{r} = \frac{\theta}{1}$$

Therefore,

$$s = r\theta$$

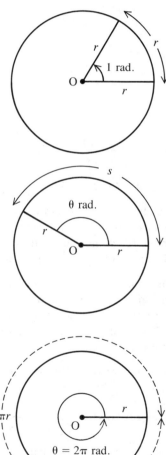

Since the circumference s of a circle of radius
r is $2\pi r$, it follows that **the measure of the
angle corresponding to one complete revolution is $\theta = 2\pi$ radians**.

The formula for the area of a sector of a
circle also assumes a simple form when
radian measure is used. The area of a sector
is proportional to its central angle θ.

$$\frac{\text{Area of sector}}{\text{Area of circle}} = \frac{\text{Angle subtended by sector}}{\text{Angle subtended by circle}}$$

Hence, by equation (2),

$$\frac{A}{\pi r^2} = \frac{\theta}{2\pi}$$

and

$$A = \frac{1}{2}r^2\theta$$

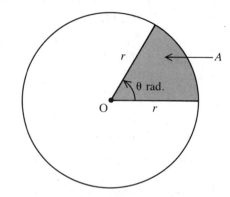

If we use ''degrees'' to measure angles, one complete revolution corresponds to 360 degrees. Hence 360 degrees corresponds to 2π radians, or

$$\pi \text{ radians} = 180 \text{ degrees}$$

This relation enables one to convert from degrees to radians. For example, an angle of 45° has a measure of $45 \times \frac{\pi}{180} = \frac{\pi}{4}$ radians. But, as mentioned earlier, we shall work exclusively with radian measure, so we suggest that you review the radian measure of the commonly used angles such as 30°, 60°, 90°, etc.

We are now in a position to define the trigonometric functions

$$f(\theta) = \sin\theta \quad \text{and} \quad g(\theta) = \cos\theta$$

for any real number θ. Given a number θ, we draw an angle of radian measure θ in a circle of radius r, thereby determining a unique point (x, y) on the circle. If $\theta > 0$, the angle is measured counterclockwise from the positive x-axis; if $\theta < 0$, the angle is measured in the clockwise direction. These functions are defined by

$$\cos\theta = \frac{x}{r}$$

and

$$\sin\theta = \frac{y}{r}$$

for any real number θ.

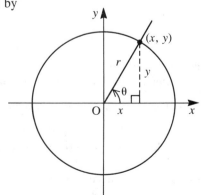

If the angle θ is between 0 and $\dfrac{\pi}{2}$ radians (0° and 90°), it is convenient to express $\sin \theta$ and $\cos \theta$ with reference to a right-angled triangle, i.e.,

$$\sin \theta = \frac{\text{opposite}}{\text{hypotenuse}}$$

and

$$\cos \theta = \frac{\text{adjacent}}{\text{hypotenuse}}$$

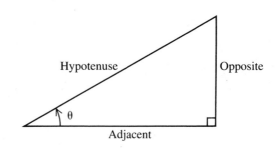

It is important to note that the ratios $\dfrac{x}{r}$ and $\dfrac{y}{r}$ are independent of the length of the radius of the circle and depend only on the value of θ. Since the two triangles in the diagram are similar, it follows that

$$\frac{x_1}{r_1} = \frac{x}{r} \quad \text{and} \quad \frac{y_1}{r_1} = \frac{y}{r}$$

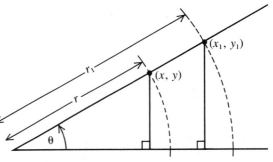

One is thus free to choose a circle of any convenient radius to define the sine and cosine functions. In particular, if we choose a unit circle ($r = 1$), it follows from the definitions of sine and cosine that the point P in the diagram has x and y coordinates equal to $\cos \theta$ and $\sin \theta$ respectively.

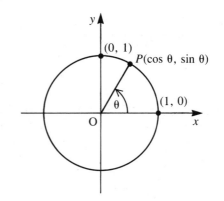

The functions $\cos \theta$ and $\sin \theta$ have been defined geometrically in the diagram above. With certain exceptions, the actual values of $\cos \theta$ and $\sin \theta$ cannot be found by elementary means; the exceptions are special values of θ such as $0, \dfrac{\pi}{6}, \dfrac{\pi}{4}, \dfrac{\pi}{3}, \dfrac{\pi}{2}$, and integral multiples of them.

The three following diagrams, which are based on an isosceles triangle and two equilateral triangles, should remind you how to calculate the cosine and sine of these numbers.

Calculators use algorithms that are based on university-level mathematics to approximate $\cos \theta$ and $\sin \theta$ for any number θ.

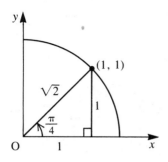

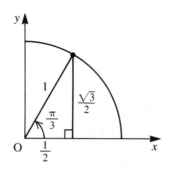

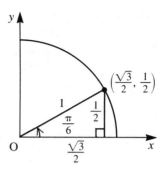

Example 1. Find $\cos\dfrac{17\pi}{6}$ by determining the coordinates of the appropriate point on the unit circle.

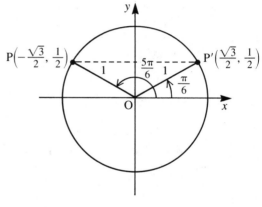

Solution. Since $\dfrac{17\pi}{6} = \dfrac{5\pi}{6} + 2\pi$, the angle $\theta = \dfrac{17\pi}{6}$ determines a point P in the second quadrant. The point P', which is the reflection of P in the y-axis, corresponds to the angle $\dfrac{\pi}{6}$ radians and hence has coordinates $\left(\dfrac{\sqrt{3}}{2}, \dfrac{1}{2}\right)$. Therefore, P has coordinates $\left(\dfrac{-\sqrt{3}}{2}, \dfrac{1}{2}\right)$. It follows that $\cos\dfrac{17\pi}{6}$ equals $\dfrac{-\sqrt{3}}{2}$, the x-coordinate of P.   □

We now derive some simple properties of $\cos\theta$ and $\sin\theta$, using the fact that $x = \cos\theta$ and $y = \sin\theta$ are the coordinates of the point on a unit circle determined by the angle θ. Since the equation of the circle is

$$x^2 + y^2 = 1$$

it follows that

$$\cos^2\theta + \sin^2\theta = 1$$

for all θ. It is also clear that $-1 \le x \le 1$ and $-1 \le y \le 1$, which implies that

$$-1 \le \cos\theta \le 1$$

and

$$-1 \le \sin\theta \le 1$$

for all θ.

Since one complete revolution corresponds to 2π radians, it follows that angles that differ by 2π radians correspond to the same point (x, y) on the circle. Therefore,

$$x = \cos(\theta + 2\pi) = \cos\theta$$

and

$$y = \sin(\theta + 2\pi) = \sin\theta$$

This means that $\cos\theta$ and $\sin\theta$ are **periodic functions** of period 2π.

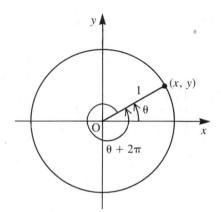

Finally, if the number θ determines the point (x, y) on the circle, then by symmetry, the number $-\theta$ determines the point $(x, -y)$. It follows from the definitions of the sine and cosine functions that

$$x = \cos(-\theta) = \cos\theta$$

and

$$-y = \sin(-\theta) = -\sin\theta$$

Recalling the definition of even and odd functions from section 4.4, we note that $\cos\theta$ is an even function of θ and $\sin\theta$ is an odd function of θ.

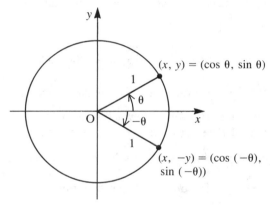

Properties of the Sine and Cosine Functions

Pythagorean Identity $\cos^2\theta + \sin^2\theta = 1$

Range $-1 \le \cos\theta \le 1$
$-1 \le \sin\theta \le 1$

Periodicity $\cos(\theta + 2\pi) = \cos\theta$
$\sin(\theta + 2\pi) = \sin\theta$

Symmetry $\sin(-\theta) = -\sin\theta$
$\cos(-\theta) = \cos\theta$

The range, periodicity, and symmetry properties are displayed in the graphs of the functions $f(\theta) = \sin\theta$ and $g(\theta) = \cos\theta$.

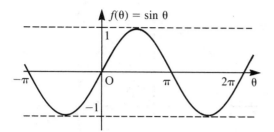

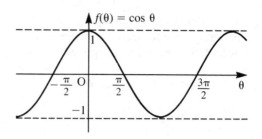

Example 2. Sketch the graph of $h(\theta) = 2\sin\left(3\theta + \dfrac{5\pi}{4}\right)$.

Solution. Recall that the graph of $f(\theta + b)$ is just the graph of $f(\theta)$ translated b units to left. Hence we rewrite our function as

$$h(\theta) = 2\sin\left[3\left(\theta + \frac{5\pi}{12}\right)\right]$$

and recognize that this is the graph of $2\sin 3\theta$ translated to the left by $\dfrac{5\pi}{12}$ units. Recall that the graph of $\sin 3\theta$ is similar to the graph of $\sin \theta$ but has three "loops" between 0 and π (the dotted curve in the diagram).

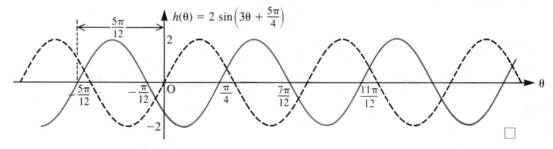

Example 3. Sketch the graph of $f(\theta) = |2\cos\theta + 1|$.

Solution. The graph of $2\cos\theta + 1$ is obtained by translating the graph of $2\cos\theta$ upward by one unit. Finally, the graph of $|2\cos\theta + 1|$ is obtained by reflecting in the θ-axis the points of the graph of $2\cos\theta + 1$ that are below the θ-axis.

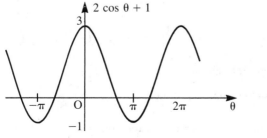

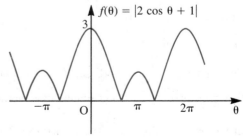

We now define the remaining trigonometric functions, tangent, secant, cotangent, and cosecant, for any real number θ, as follows:

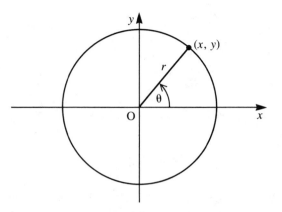

$$\tan \theta = \frac{y}{x}, \qquad \sec \theta = \frac{r}{x}$$

$$\cot \theta = \frac{x}{y}, \qquad \csc \theta = \frac{r}{y}$$

These functions can be expressed in terms of $\sin \theta$ and $\cos \theta$:

$$\tan \theta = \frac{\sin \theta}{\cos \theta}, \qquad \sec \theta = \frac{1}{\cos \theta}$$

$$\cot \theta = \frac{\cos \theta}{\sin \theta}, \qquad \csc \theta = \frac{1}{\sin \theta}$$

Using these relations, we can derive the properties of $\tan \theta$, $\sec \theta$, $\cot \theta$, and $\csc \theta$ from the properties of $\sin \theta$ and $\cos \theta$. For example, on dividing the Pythagorean identity

$$\cos^2 \theta + \sin^2 \theta = 1$$

by $\cos^2 \theta$, we obtain

$$1 + \tan^2 \theta = \sec^2 \theta$$

The graphs of the functions $\tan \theta$ and $\sec \theta$ are given below.

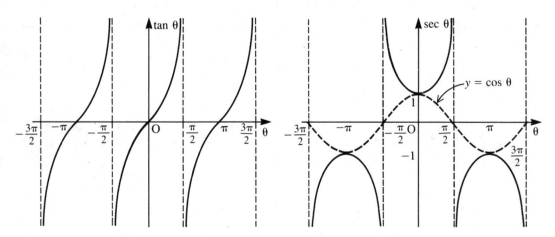

The functions $\tan \theta$ and $\sec \theta$ are defined for all θ such that $\cos \theta \neq 0$; that is, $\theta \neq \pm\frac{\pi}{2}, \pm\frac{3\pi}{2}, \ldots$. Their graphs have vertical asymptotes at these values.

In various situations, it is necessary to calculate the values of the remaining trigonometric functions, given the value of one of them.

Example 4. If $\sin \theta = \dfrac{3}{5}$ and $\dfrac{\pi}{2} < \theta < \pi$, find $\cos \theta$ and $\tan \theta$.

Solution. Since

$$\sin \theta = \frac{y}{r}$$

$$= \frac{3}{5}$$

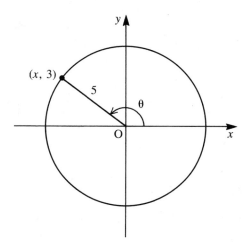

we draw a circle of radius 5. Then θ corresponds to the point $(x, 3)$ on this circle, lying in the second quadrant. Since

$$x^2 + 3^2 = 5^2$$

we obtain $x = -4$, the only solution for which $x < 0$. Hence,

$$\cos \theta = \frac{x}{r}$$

$$= -\frac{4}{5}$$

and

$$\tan \theta = \frac{y}{x}$$

$$= -\frac{3}{4}$$

□

Exercises 5.1

1. Find the trigonometric values by determining the coordinates of the appropriate point on the unit circle (see Example 1).

   a. $\sin \dfrac{\pi}{4}$ **b.** $\sin \dfrac{3\pi}{4}$ **c.** $\cos \dfrac{3\pi}{4}$

   d. $\cos \left(\dfrac{-\pi}{3} \right)$ **e.** $\sin \left(\dfrac{-7\pi}{6} \right)$ **f.** $\sin \dfrac{9\pi}{4}$

   g. $\cos \dfrac{3\pi}{2}$ **h.** $\cos \dfrac{7\pi}{6}$ **i.** $\sin 3\pi$

2. By using symmetry properties of a circle, express each quantity in terms of $\sin \theta$.

   a. $\sin (\pi + \theta)$ **b.** $\sin (\pi - \theta)$ **c.** $\sin (2\pi - \theta)$

3. By using symmetry properties of a circle, express each quantity in terms of $\cos \theta$.

   a. $\cos (\pi + \theta)$ **b.** $\cos (\theta - 2\pi)$ **c.** $\cos (\theta - \pi)$

4. Sketch the graph of each function and state the period.
   Recall that a function $f(x)$ is said to be periodic if there is a number T such that

   $$f(x + T) = f(x), \text{ for all } x.$$

   The smallest such positive number is called the period of $f(x)$.

   a. $\cos 2\theta$

   b. $2 \sin \dfrac{\theta}{2}$

   c. $2 \sin (\pi\theta) + 1$

   d. $1 - 3 \cos \dfrac{\pi\theta}{2}$

   e. $2 \sin \left(\theta - \dfrac{\pi}{6} \right)$

   f. $5 \cos \left(2\theta + \dfrac{\pi}{3} \right)$

   g. $|2 - 3 \sin \theta|$

   h. $|3 + 4 \cos \pi\theta|$

   i. $3 \sin \left(4\theta + \dfrac{3\pi}{2} \right)$

   j. $\tan \theta$

   k. $\tan 2\theta$

   l. $\sec 2\theta$

5. Using the graph of $\tan \theta$ as a guide, sketch the graph of $\cot \theta$.

6. Using the graph of $\sin \theta$ as a guide, sketch the graph of $\csc \theta$.

7. Use the Pythagorean identity to show that

   $$\cot^2 \theta + 1 = \csc^2 \theta$$

8. Write each expression in terms of $\sin \theta$ and $\cos \theta$. Simplify where possible.

   a. $\tan \theta + \cot \theta$

   b. $\sec \theta - \tan \theta$

   c. $\sec^2 \theta + \csc^2 \theta$

   d. $\dfrac{\tan \theta - \cot \theta}{\tan \theta + \cot \theta}$

9. The value of $\sin \theta$, $\cos \theta$, or $\tan \theta$ is given. Find the values of the two other functions if θ lies in the given interval.

   a. $\sin \theta = \dfrac{5}{13}, \quad \dfrac{\pi}{2} \le \theta \le \pi$

   b. $\cos \theta = \dfrac{1}{3}, \quad -\dfrac{\pi}{2} \le \theta \le 0$

   c. $\tan \theta = \dfrac{1}{2}, \quad \pi \le \theta \le \dfrac{3\pi}{2}$

   d. $\cos \theta = -\dfrac{1}{2}, \quad \pi \le \theta \le \dfrac{3\pi}{2}$

   e. $\tan \theta = -3, \quad \dfrac{\pi}{2} \le \theta \le \pi$

   f. $\sin \theta = -\dfrac{1}{\sqrt{3}}, \quad -\dfrac{\pi}{2} \le \theta \le 0$

10. By expressing $\tan (-\theta)$ in terms of sine and cosine, show that $\tan (-\theta) = -\tan \theta$.

Problems 5.1

1. A train passes through an intersection on a straight east-west track travelling due east at 120 km/h. At the same instant that the train passes through the intersection, a car crosses the overpass at 80 km/h and travels northeast on a straight road. For the following calculations neglect the height of the overpass.

   a. Find the distance between the two vehicles thirty minutes later.
   b. Express the distance r between the two vehicles after t hours as a function of t.

2. a. An object moves so that, at any time t, its position (x, y) is given by

$$x = 5 \cos t, \quad y = 5 \sin t$$

Sketch the path of the object.

b. Repeat part (a) if $x = 3 \cos t$ and $y = 4 \sin t$.

3. Sketch the graph of each function.

a. $f(\theta) = \sin|\theta|$ **b.** $f(\theta) = \tan|\theta|$

4. Design of a humidifier: A vertical circular disk of radius R is partially submerged in water and rotated slowly with its axis horizontal. Show that the area of the disk that is wet and exposed to the air is

$$A = R^2(\pi \sin^2 \theta - \theta + \sin \theta \cos \theta)$$

where θ is the indicated angle, measured in radians.

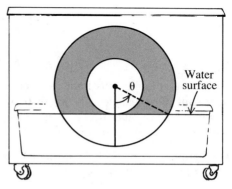

5. A pyramid has a square base with length a metres; the angle of inclination of the slant edges is $60°$.

a. Find the height h of the pyramid in terms of a.

b. Find the length of the slant height s in terms of a.

6. If $f(t) = -t$ for $-1 < t \leq 1$, and $f(t)$ is periodic with period 2, sketch the graph of $f(t)$ for $-3 \leq t \leq 3$. Is $f(t)$ a continuous function?

7. A stone is embedded in the tread of a tire. As the vehicle moves, the position of the stone is described by the equations

$$x = t - \sin t, \quad y = 1 - \cos t$$

at any time $t \geq 0$. Use a calculator to plot the position of the stone at various times t, with $0 \leq t \leq 2\pi$. Use the fact that $\sin t$ and $\cos t$ are periodic to sketch the path of the stone for $0 \leq t \leq 6\pi$. The curve that you have drawn is called a **cycloid**.

8. Plot the path of a point (x, y) that moves so that at any time t

$$x = \cos t, \quad y = \sin 3t$$

The curve traced by the moving point (x, y) is called a **Lissajous figure**. This curve can be displayed on an oscilloscope by providing voltages of the form $x = \cos t$ and $y = \sin 3t$ to the horizontal and vertical sweep terminals. If you have access to an oscilloscope, you could create many interesting curves of this type by using voltages of the form $x = \sin(at + b)$ and $y = \sin(ct + d)$.

5.2 The Addition Identities

Our main goal in this chapter is to find the derivatives of the trigonometric functions. We shall first consider the cosine function. If the cosine function could be expressed in terms of functions with known derivatives, we could find its derivative by applying the rules of differentiation. Unfortunately, this is not the case, and so we must use the definition of the derivative. At this stage it is convenient to use x as the independent variable. If $f(x) = \cos x$, then

$$f'(x) = \lim_{h \to 0} \frac{f(x + h) - f(x)}{h}$$
$$= \lim_{h \to 0} \frac{\cos(x + h) - \cos x}{h}$$

In order to simplify this limit we need an expansion for $\cos(x + h)$, that is, for the **cosine of a sum** of two angles. In this section, we shall derive an expansion for $\cos(A + B)$, and this will lead to other trigonometric identities that are useful in Calculus. We shall return to the calculation of the derivatives of the trigonometric functions in section 5.4.

Our intuition is of no help in finding an expansion for $\cos(A + B)$. A check with simple values for A and B shows that

$$\cos(A + B) \neq \cos A + \cos B$$

For example, if $A = \dfrac{\pi}{2}$ and $B = 0$, the left side is $\cos \dfrac{\pi}{2} = 0$, whereas the right side is

$\cos \dfrac{\pi}{2} + \cos 0 = 1$.

The correct expansion is

$$\cos(A + B) = \cos A \cos B - \sin A \sin B$$

This is an identity, valid for all angles A and B. Because of the importance of this identity we shall illustrate its use in a number of examples. At the end of this section we shall give a proof.

Example 1. Use the addition identity for the cosine function to calculate $\cos\left(\dfrac{7\pi}{12}\right)$.

Solution. Observe that $\dfrac{7\pi}{12}$ can be expressed in terms of angles for which we know the cosine:

$$\frac{7\pi}{12} = \frac{\pi}{4} + \frac{\pi}{3}$$

Therefore,

$$\cos\left(\frac{7\pi}{12}\right) = \cos\left(\frac{\pi}{4} + \frac{\pi}{3}\right)$$

$$= \cos\frac{\pi}{4}\cos\frac{\pi}{3} - \sin\frac{\pi}{4}\sin\frac{\pi}{3}$$

$$= \left(\frac{1}{\sqrt{2}}\right)\left(\frac{1}{2}\right) - \left(\frac{1}{\sqrt{2}}\right)\left(\frac{\sqrt{3}}{2}\right) \quad \text{(from the standard triangles in section 5.1)}$$

$$= \frac{1 - \sqrt{3}}{2\sqrt{2}}$$

The value is negative, which is expected, since $\frac{7\pi}{12}$ is in the second quadrant. □

Example 2. Prove the identity

$$\cos\left(\frac{\pi}{2} - C\right) = \sin C$$

Solution. Since the addition identity

$$\cos(A + B) = \cos A \cos B - \sin A \sin B$$

is valid for all A and B, we may choose $A = \frac{\pi}{2}$, $B = -C$. It follows that

$$\cos\left(\frac{\pi}{2} - C\right) = \cos\left(\frac{\pi}{2} + (-C)\right)$$

$$= \cos\frac{\pi}{2}\cos(-C) - \sin\frac{\pi}{2}\sin(-C)$$

Since $\cos\frac{\pi}{2} = 0$, $\sin\frac{\pi}{2} = 1$, and $\sin(-C) = -\sin C$,

$$\cos\left(\frac{\pi}{2} - C\right) = \sin C$$

as required. □

If we replace C by $\frac{\pi}{2} - C$ in the identity of Example 2, we obtain the related identity.

$$\sin\left(\frac{\pi}{2} - C\right) = \cos C$$

Example 3. Derive the addition identity

$$\sin(A + B) = \sin A \cos B + \cos A \sin B$$

Solution. We choose $C = A + B$ in the identity of Example 2, obtaining

$$\sin(A + B) = \cos\left[\frac{\pi}{2} - (A + B)\right]$$
$$= \cos\left[\left(\frac{\pi}{2} - A\right) + (-B)\right]$$
$$= \cos\left(\frac{\pi}{2} - A\right)\cos(-B) - \sin\left(\frac{\pi}{2} - A\right)\sin(-B)$$
$$= \sin A \cos B + \cos A \sin B \qquad\qquad \square$$

When we set $B = A$ in the addition identities for sine and cosine, we obtain two important identities:

$$\cos(A + A) = \cos A \cos A - \sin A \sin A$$

and

$$\sin(A + A) = \sin A \cos A + \cos A \sin A$$

which can be simplified to

$$\cos 2A = \cos^2 A - \sin^2 A$$

and

$$\sin 2A = 2 \sin A \cos A$$

The last two identities are referred to as the double-angle identities.

Example 4. If $\tan A = -\frac{1}{2}$, and A lies in the interval $\frac{\pi}{2} \le A \le \pi$, find $\sin 2A$ and $\cos 2A$ without using a calculator.

Solution. We use the double-angle identities. In order to evaluate $\sin A$ and $\cos A$, we first determine the coordinates of the point on a circle corresponding to the angle A, using the fact that

$$\tan A = \frac{y}{x} = -\frac{1}{2} \quad \text{and} \quad \frac{\pi}{2} < A < \pi$$

The radius of the circle is $r = \sqrt{(-2)^2 + (1)^2} = \sqrt{5}$. Hence,

$$\cos A = \frac{x}{r} = -\frac{2}{\sqrt{5}}$$

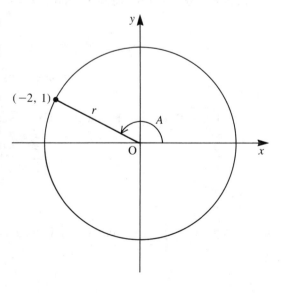

and

$$\sin A = \frac{y}{x} = \frac{1}{\sqrt{5}}$$

It follows from the double-angle identities that

$$\cos 2A = \cos^2 A - \sin^2 A$$
$$= \left(-\frac{2}{\sqrt{5}}\right)^2 - \left(\frac{1}{\sqrt{5}}\right)^2$$
$$= \frac{3}{5}$$

and that

$$\sin 2A = 2\sin A \cos A$$
$$= 2\left(\frac{1}{\sqrt{5}}\right)\left(\frac{-2}{\sqrt{5}}\right)$$
$$= -\frac{4}{5}$$

The signs indicate that the angle $2A$ lies in the fourth quadrant $\left(\frac{3\pi}{2} \leq 2A \leq 2\pi\right)$. $\square$

Having familiarized ourselves with some uses of the addition identity for cosine, we now turn to its proof. Recall that the distance $|AP|$ between two points $A(a, b)$ and $P(x, y)$ in the plane is

$$|AP| = \sqrt{(x - a)^2 + (y - b)^2}$$

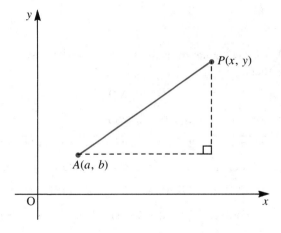

Theorem. $\cos(A + B) = \cos A \cos B - \sin A \sin B$

Proof. Consider a circle, with centre at $(0, 0)$ and radius 1, containing angles of measure A, $A + B$, and $-B$, as drawn. By definition of sine and cosine, the points M, N, P, and Q have coordinates as shown in the diagram.

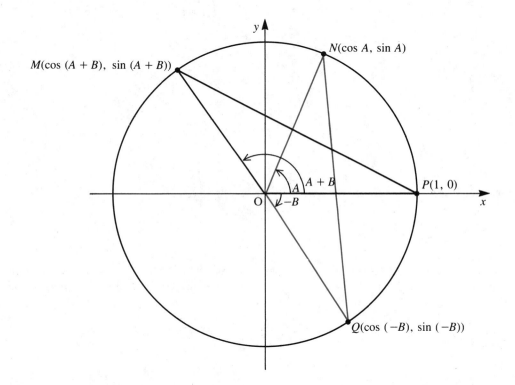

Since $\angle MOP$ and $\angle NOQ$ have equal measure $A + B$ by construction, $\triangle NOQ$ is congruent to $\triangle MOP$. This implies that

$$|MP| = |NQ|$$

If we use the distance formula, this equation becomes

$$\sqrt{[\cos(A + B) - 1]^2 + \sin^2(A + B)} = \sqrt{[\cos A - \cos(-B)]^2 + [\sin A - \sin(-B)]^2}$$

On squaring both sides and expanding the brackets, we obtain

$$\cos^2(A + B) - 2\cos(A + B) + 1 + \sin^2(A + B)$$

$$= \cos^2 A - 2\cos A \cos(-B) + \cos^2(-B) + \sin^2 A - 2\sin A \sin(-B) + \sin^2(-B)$$

Since

$$\sin^2 x + \cos^2 x = 1, \quad \cos(-x) = \cos x, \quad \text{and} \quad \sin(-x) = -\sin x$$

the above equation can be simplified to

$$1 - 2\cos(A + B) + 1 = 1 - 2\cos A \cos B + 1 + 2\sin A \sin B$$

Hence,

$$\cos(A + B) = \cos A \cos B - \sin A \sin B \qquad \square$$

Here is a summary of the identities that were derived in this section.

Addition Identities

$$\cos(A + B) = \cos A \cos B - \sin A \sin B$$
$$\sin(A + B) = \sin A \cos B + \cos A \sin B$$

Complementary Identities

$$\cos\left(\frac{\pi}{2} - A\right) = \sin A$$

$$\sin\left(\frac{\pi}{2} - A\right) = \cos A$$

Double-Angle Identities

$$\cos 2A = \cos^2 A - \sin^2 A$$
$$\sin 2A = 2\sin A \cos A$$

Note the interdependence of these identities. The addition identities are reduced to the complementary identities if we set $A = \frac{\pi}{2}$ and $B = -A$, and they are reduced to the double-angle identities if we set $B = A$. We encourage you to memorize these identities, but keep in mind that the second and third pair can be quickly derived from the first pair. Other related identities are established in Exercises 3 and 8.

We conclude this section with an example that illustrates the use of addition identities in the sketching of trigonometric graphs.

Example 5. Sketch the graph of the function

$$y = \sqrt{3}\,\sin x + \cos x$$

Solution. Consider the coefficients $\sqrt{3}$ and 1 of $\sin x$ and $\cos x$ as the adjacent and opposite sides of a right-angled triangle. The hypotenuse is then of length 2, and the angle indicated in the diagram is $\dfrac{\pi}{6}$ radians.

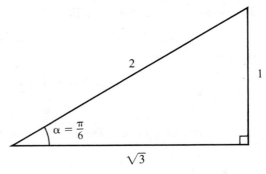

Now rewrite y in the form

$$y = 2\left(\frac{\sqrt{3}}{2}\sin x + \frac{1}{2}\cos x\right)$$

From the triangle, $\cos\dfrac{\pi}{6} = \dfrac{\sqrt{3}}{2}$ and $\sin\dfrac{\pi}{6} = \dfrac{1}{2}$, and hence

$$y = 2\left(\sin x \cos\frac{\pi}{6} + \cos x \sin\frac{\pi}{6}\right)$$

This is the expanded form of the addition identity for the sine function. Hence,

$$y = 2\sin\left(x + \frac{\pi}{6}\right)$$

We can thus obtain the graph by translating the graph of $y = 2\sin x$ to the left by $\dfrac{\pi}{6}$ units.

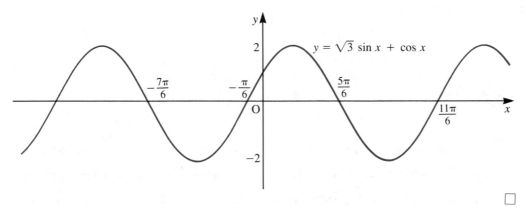

Exercises 5.2

1. Use the identity for $\cos(A + B)$ to calculate each quantity without using a calculator.

a. $\cos\dfrac{\pi}{12}$ **b.** $\cos\dfrac{5\pi}{12}$ **c.** $\cos\dfrac{11\pi}{12}$

2. Use the identity for $\sin(A + B)$ to calculate each quantity without using a calculator.

   a. $\sin\dfrac{7\pi}{12}$ 　　　　　**b.** $\sin\dfrac{13\pi}{12}$ 　　　　　**c.** $\sin\dfrac{19\pi}{12}$

3. Prove the identities by replacing B by $-B$ in the addition identities.

   a. $\cos(A - B) = \cos A \cos B + \sin A \sin B$
   b. $\sin(A - B) = \sin A \cos B - \cos A \sin B$

4. Express each quantity in terms of $\sin x$ and $\cos x$.

   a. $\sin\left(\dfrac{\pi}{3} + x\right)$ 　　　　　**b.** $\cos\left(x + \dfrac{3\pi}{4}\right)$

   c. $\cos\left(\dfrac{\pi}{4} - x\right)$ 　　　　　**d.** $\sin(2\pi - x)$

5. Find an equivalent expression in terms of a single trigonometric function.

   a. $\sin 2x \cos x + \cos 2x \sin x$
   b. $\cos 5x \cos 4x + \sin 5x \sin 4x$
   c. $\cos 3x \sin 5x - \sin 3x \cos 5x$
   d. $\cos x \cos 4x - \sin x \sin 4x$

6. If $\cos A = \dfrac{1}{3}$, with $0 < A < \dfrac{\pi}{2}$, and $\sin B = \dfrac{1}{4}$, with $\dfrac{\pi}{2} < B < \pi$, calculate each quantity.

   a. $\cos(A + B)$ 　　　　　**b.** $\sin(A + B)$
   c. $\cos 2A$ 　　　　　　　**d.** $\sin 2B$
   e. $\cos 4A$ 　　　　　　　**f.** $\sin 4B$

7. If $\sin A = -\dfrac{1}{\sqrt{5}}$, with $-\dfrac{\pi}{2} < A < 0$, and $\cos B = -\dfrac{1}{\sqrt{3}}$, with $\dfrac{\pi}{2} < B < \pi$, calculate each quantity.

   a. $\cos(A - B)$ 　　　　　**b.** $\sin(A - B)$
   c. $\cos(2A - B)$ 　　　　　**d.** $\sin(A - 2B)$

8. Use the double-angle identity for $\cos 2A$ and the identity $\cos^2 A + \sin^2 A = 1$ to prove each identity.

   a. $\cos 2A = 2\cos^2 A - 1$ 　　　　　**b.** $\cos 2A = 1 - 2\sin^2 A$
   　　　　$180 - 270$

9. If $\tan A = \dfrac{1}{3}$ and $\pi < A < \dfrac{3\pi}{2}$, calculate each quantity. In what quadrant does the angle $2A$ lie?

   a. $\sin 2A$ 　　　　　　　**b.** $\cos 2A$

10. If $\sec A = -2$ and $\dfrac{\pi}{2} < A < \pi$, calculate each quantity.

   a. $\sin\left(A + \dfrac{\pi}{4}\right)$ 　　　　　**b.** $\cos\left(A - \dfrac{\pi}{4}\right)$

11. If x is an acute angle such that $\tan 2x = -\frac{24}{7}$, find $\sin x$ and $\cos x$.

12. Sketch the graph of each function, using the method of Example 5.

    a. $y = \sin x + \cos x$ **b.** $y = \sqrt{3} \sin x - 3 \cos x$

Problems 5.2

1. a. Graph the function $y = \sin^2 x$ by writing $\sin^2 x = (\sin x)(\sin x)$ and considering the graph of $\sin x$.

    b. Confirm your graph in part (a) by using the identity

$$\cos 2x = 1 - 2\sin^2 x$$

    to rewrite the function $y = \sin^2 x$.

2. Graph the function $y = \sin^n x$, $0 \le x \le \pi$, for different positive integers n, on the same axes. What happens to the shape of the graph as n becomes increasingly large?

3. a. Given that

$$a \sin x + b \cos x = A \sin (x + \alpha)$$

    for all real x, relate the constants A and α to the constants a and b. This shows that it is always possible to express $a \sin x + b \cos x$ in the form $A \sin (x + \alpha)$.

    b. Show that it is always possible to express $a \sin x + b \cos x$ in the form $B \cos (x + \beta)$, where B and β are constants.

5.3 Trigonometric Identities and Equations

It is important to distinguish between two types of equations. The first is an equation that is valid for all values of the variable, such as

$$x^2 - 4 = (x - 2)(x + 2)$$

This type of equation is called an **identity**. In the previous section we encountered the basic trigonometric identity

$$\cos (A + B) = \cos A \cos B - \sin A \sin B$$

and other identities that follow from it. Identities are used for simplifying expressions or for rewriting an expression in a form that is more convenient or that makes some desired result obvious.

The second type of equation is one that is only satisfied by certain specific values of the variable, called **the solutions of the equation**. For example, the equation

$$x^2 = 2$$

is only satisfied if $x = \sqrt{2}$ or $x = -\sqrt{2}$. As a second example, the points of intersection of the graphs of $y = \cos 2x$ and $y = \cos x$ are found by solving the equation

$$\cos 2x = \cos x$$

This problem will be solved shortly. In addition, the equation $f'(x) = 0$, which one solves to find the points at which the tangent line to the graph of $y = f(x)$ is horizontal, is also of this second type.

In this section, we shall discuss further applications of the trigonometric identities of section 5.2. We shall then solve some equations that include trigonometric functions in preparation for further work in the Calculus of trigonometric functions later in the chapter. It is important to realize that only very special trigonometric equations can be solved exactly. There are, however, techniques such as Newton's method that can be used to find approximate solutions for equations that cannot be solved exactly.

For example, the equation

$$\cos x = x$$

which gives the point of intersection of $y = \cos x$ and $y = x$, cannot be solved exactly. This problem will be addressed in section 5.7.

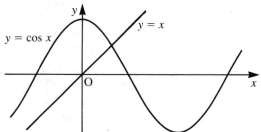

Example 1. Prove the identity

$$\tan (A + B) = \frac{\tan A + \tan B}{1 - \tan A \tan B}$$

Solution. A useful method for proving trigonometric identities is to express all functions in terms of sines and cosines. For the left side, we obtain

$$\tan (A + B) = \frac{\sin (A + B)}{\cos (A + B)}$$

$$= \frac{\sin A \cos B + \cos A \sin B}{\cos A \cos B - \sin A \sin B}$$

For the right side, we obtain

$$\frac{\tan A + \tan B}{1 - \tan A \tan B} = \frac{\dfrac{\sin A}{\cos A} + \dfrac{\sin B}{\cos B}}{1 - \dfrac{\sin A \sin B}{\cos A \cos B}}$$

$$= \frac{\left(\dfrac{\sin A}{\cos A} + \dfrac{\sin B}{\cos B}\right) \cos A \cos B}{\left(1 - \dfrac{\sin A \sin B}{\cos A \cos B}\right) \cos A \cos B}$$

$$= \frac{\sin A \cos B + \cos A \sin B}{\cos A \cos B - \sin A \sin B}$$

Since the left side and right side of the original equation have the same form, the identity is proved. $\square$

To prove an identity, one usually attempts to make the given left and right sides assume identical forms, as in the previous example. One can of course make use of known identities, and it often helps to rearrange the terms algebraically; for example, factor a difference of squares, expand brackets, take out a common factor, introduce a common denominator, etc. In Example 1, we found it helpful to express "tan" in terms of "sin" and "cos," and this is often a useful strategy. It is important to keep in mind, however, that there is often more than one way to prove an identity.

Example 2. Prove the identity

$$\sin 3x = 3 \sin x - 4 \sin^3 x$$

Solution. We start with the left side and write

$$
\begin{aligned}
\sin 3x &= \sin(x + 2x) \\
&= \sin x \cos 2x + \cos x \sin 2x \\
&= \sin x (\cos^2 x - \sin^2 x) + \cos x (2 \sin x \cos x) \\
&= 3 \sin x \cos^2 x - \sin^3 x \\
&= 3 \sin x (1 - \sin^2 x) - \sin^3 x \\
&= 3 \sin x - 4 \sin^3 x
\end{aligned}
$$

This agrees with the right side, and the proof is complete.   □

The following example illustrates an indirect approach to deriving an identity.

Example 3. Prove that

$$\cos X + \cos Y = 2 \cos \left(\frac{X + Y}{2} \right) \cos \left(\frac{X - Y}{2} \right)$$

Solution. Start with the addition identity

$$\cos(A + B) = \cos A \cos B - \sin A \sin B$$

Replace B by $-B$ in this identity to obtain

$$\cos(A - B) = \cos A \cos B + \sin A \sin B$$

since $\cos(-B) = \cos B$ and $\sin(-B) = -\sin B$. Now add the previous two equations to obtain

$$\cos(A + B) + \cos(A - B) = 2 \cos A \cos B$$

In order to obtain the desired identity, we relabel the variables, letting

$$A + B = X \quad \text{and} \quad A - B = Y$$

This implies that

$$A = \frac{X + Y}{2} \quad \text{and} \quad B = \frac{X - Y}{2}$$

so the last identity assumes the desired form

$$\cos X + \cos Y = 2 \cos \left(\frac{X + Y}{2} \right) \cos \left(\frac{X - Y}{2} \right)$$

    □

There are similar identities for expressing $\cos X - \cos Y$ and $\sin X \pm \sin Y$ as products. (See Exercise 2 in this section.) We do not recommend that you memorize these formulae. What is important is to understand the method of deriving these identities from the addition identities for sine and cosine.

We now consider two examples in which we solve trigonometric equations.

Example 4. Solve the following equation for x.

$$8 \sin^2 x - 10 \sin x - 7 = 0$$

Solution. Observe that the equation is a quadratic equation in $\sin x$. Letting

$$u = \sin x$$

we obtain

$$8u^2 - 10u - 7 = 0$$

which can be factored, yielding

$$(4u - 7)(2u + 1) = 0$$

Hence,

$$u = \frac{7}{4} \quad \text{or} \quad u = -\frac{1}{2}$$

and therefore

$$\sin x = \frac{7}{4} \quad \text{or} \quad \sin x = -\frac{1}{2}$$

Since $-1 \le \sin x \le 1$, the equation $\sin x = \frac{7}{4}$ has no solutions.

The diagram indicates two solutions of the equation $\sin x = -\frac{1}{2}$, for $0 \le x \le 2\pi$. Noting that $\sin \frac{\pi}{6} = \frac{1}{2}$, we obtain these two solutions as

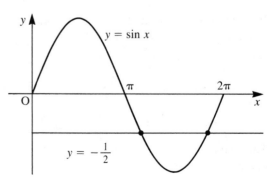

$$x = \pi + \frac{\pi}{6}$$

$$= \frac{7\pi}{6}$$

and

$$x = 2\pi - \frac{\pi}{6}$$

$$= \frac{11\pi}{6}$$

Since $\sin x$ is periodic of period 2π, the general solution is

$$x = \frac{7\pi}{6} + 2n\pi, \quad n \in Z$$

and

$$x = \frac{11\pi}{6} + 2n\pi, \quad n \in Z$$

where Z is the set of integers. □

Example 5. Find the points of intersection of the curves $y = \cos x$ and $y = \cos 2x$, in the interval $0 \leq x \leq 2\pi$.

Solution. We must solve the equation

$$\cos 2x = \cos x$$

for x. Using the double-angle identity for $\cos 2x$, we can write

$$\begin{aligned}
\cos 2x &= \cos^2 x - \sin^2 x \\
&= \cos^2 x - (1 - \cos^2 x) \\
&= 2\cos^2 x - 1
\end{aligned}$$

Thus, the equation $\cos 2x = \cos x$ assumes the form

$$2\cos^2 x - \cos x - 1 = 0$$

which is a quadratic equation in $\cos x$. Factoring, we obtain

$$(\cos x + 1)(\cos x - 1) = 0$$

and hence

$$\cos x = -\frac{1}{2} \quad \text{or} \quad \cos x = 1$$

Each of these equations has two solutions in the interval $0 \leq x \leq 2\pi$, namely

$$x = \frac{2\pi}{3} \quad \text{and} \quad x = \frac{4\pi}{3}$$

and

$$x = 0 \quad \text{and} \quad x = 2\pi$$

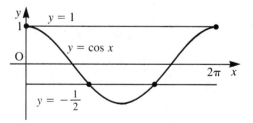

Thus the points of intersection of the given curves are

$$\left(\frac{2\pi}{3}, -\frac{1}{2}\right), \quad \left(\frac{4\pi}{3}, -\frac{1}{2}\right),$$
$$(0, 1) \quad \text{and} \quad (2\pi, 1)$$

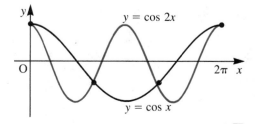

□

Exercises 5.3

1. Prove each identity.

   a. $\cos^4 x - \sin^4 x = \cos 2x$

   b. $\sin^4 A + 2\cos^2 A - \cos^4 A = 1$

   c. $\cos 3A = -3\cos A + 4\cos^3 A$

   d. $\cos^4 \phi = \frac{1}{8}(3 + 4\cos 2\phi + \cos 4\phi)$

   e. $\dfrac{\sin 2x}{1 + \cos 2x} = \tan x$

   f. $\dfrac{1 - \cos x}{\sin x} = \tan\left(\dfrac{x}{2}\right)$

   g. $\sin 2A = \dfrac{2\tan A}{1 + \tan^2 A}$

   h. $\cos x = \dfrac{1 - \tan^2\left(\frac{x}{2}\right)}{1 + \tan^2\left(\frac{x}{2}\right)}$

   i. $\tan 2A = \dfrac{2\tan A}{1 - \tan^2 A}$

   j. $\sec 2A = \dfrac{\sec^2 A}{2 - \sec^2 A}$

   k. $\sin 4x = 8\cos^3 x \sin x - 4\cos x \sin x$

   l. $\dfrac{1 + \tan x}{1 - \tan x} = \tan\left(x + \dfrac{\pi}{4}\right)$

   m. $\tan 3x = \dfrac{3\tan x - \tan^3 x}{1 - 3\tan^2 x}$

   n. $\dfrac{1 - \cos 6x}{\sin 6x} = \tan 3x$

2. By following the method used in Example 3, derive the following identities.

   a. $\cos X - \cos Y = -2\sin\left(\dfrac{X + Y}{2}\right)\sin\left(\dfrac{X - Y}{2}\right)$

   b. $\sin X + \sin Y = 2\sin\left(\dfrac{X + Y}{2}\right)\cos\left(\dfrac{X - Y}{2}\right)$

   c. $\sin X - \sin Y = 2\cos\left(\dfrac{X + Y}{2}\right)\sin\left(\dfrac{X - Y}{2}\right)$

3. Solve each equation.

   a. $\cos x = \dfrac{1}{\sqrt{2}}, \quad -2\pi \le x \le 2\pi$

   b. $\sin 2x = -\dfrac{\sqrt{3}}{2}, \quad -\pi \le x \le \pi$

   c. $\sin^2 x - \sin x = 0$

   d. $\cos^2 x - 2 = 0$

   e. $2\sin^2 x + \sin x - 1 = 0, \quad 0 \le x \le 4\pi$

   f. $2\sec^2 x - 5\sec x + 2 = 0, \quad 0 \le x \le 2\pi$

   g. $3\sin x = \cos x$

   h. $\sin 2x = \sin x$

4. Find the points of intersection of each pair of curves in the given interval. Illustrate your results by sketching the curves.

   a. $y = \sin 2x, \quad y = \sin x, \quad 0 \le x \le 2\pi$

   b. $y = \sin 2x, \quad y = \tan x, \quad 0 \le x \le 2\pi$

   c. $y = \cos 2x, \quad y = \sin x, \quad -\pi \le x \le \pi$

   d. $y = \tan 2x, \quad y = 2\sin x, \quad -\dfrac{\pi}{4} \le x \le \dfrac{3\pi}{4}$

   e. $y = \sin 3x, \quad y = \sin x, \quad 0 \le x \le 2\pi$

5. If $\tan\dfrac{\theta}{2} = u$, show that

$$\sin\theta = \frac{2u}{1 + u^2} \quad\text{and}\quad \cos\theta = \frac{1 - u^2}{1 + u^2}$$

Problems 5.3

1. Prove the identity

$$\frac{1}{1 + \sin x} = \sec^2 x - \tan x \sec x$$

2. Solve the equation

$$\sqrt{3}\,\sin x + \cos x = 1$$

(Hint: See Example 5 and Problem 3 of section 5.2.)

3. a. Noting that $\tan(-B) = -\tan B$, establish an identity for $\tan(A - B)$ in terms of $\tan A$ and $\tan B$.

b. Noting that the slope of a straight line is $\tan\theta$, where θ is the angle that the line makes with the positive x-axis, find the acute angle of intersection of the lines $2x + y - 6 = 0$ and $3x - y - 4 = 0$.

4. Prove the identity

$$\frac{\sin x + \sin 2x + \sin 3x}{\cos x + \cos 2x + \cos 3x} = \tan 2x$$

(Suggestion: The identities in Exercise 2 can be used to give a quick proof.)

5. a. Prove the identity

$$\cos kx = \frac{\sin\left[\left(k + \tfrac{1}{2}\right)x\right] - \sin\left[\left(k - \tfrac{1}{2}\right)x\right]}{2\sin\left(\tfrac{x}{2}\right)}$$

b. Hence, prove the identity

$$\cos x + \cos 2x + \cos 3x = \frac{\sin\left(\tfrac{7}{2}x\right)}{2\sin\left(\tfrac{x}{2}\right)} - \frac{1}{2}$$

c. Similarly, show that

$$\sum_{k=1}^{n}\cos kx = \frac{\sin\left[\left(n + \tfrac{1}{2}\right)x\right]}{2\sin\left(\tfrac{x}{2}\right)} - \frac{1}{2}$$

5.4 The Derivatives of cos x and sin x

Having developed the identity

$$\cos(A + B) = \cos A \cos B - \sin A \sin B$$

we now return to the problem of differentiating the function $f(x) = \cos x$. For $f(x) = \cos x$, the definition of the derivative gives

$$f'(x) = \lim_{h \to 0} \frac{\cos(x + h) - \cos x}{h}$$

If we use the addition identity with $A = x$ and $B = h$, the difference quotient can be written as

$$\frac{\cos(x + h) - \cos x}{h} = \frac{\cos x \cos h - \sin x \sin h - \cos x}{h}$$

Group the terms that have $\cos x$ as a factor and then separate the quotient into a sum of two terms, to get

$$\frac{\cos(x + h) - \cos x}{h} = \frac{-\sin x \sin h + \cos x (\cos h - 1)}{h}$$

$$= -(\sin x)\left(\frac{\sin h}{h}\right) + (\cos x)\left(\frac{\cos h - 1}{h}\right)$$

It follows that

$$f'(x) = \lim_{h \to 0} \left[-(\sin x)\left(\frac{\sin h}{h}\right) + (\cos x)\left(\frac{\cos h - 1}{h}\right) \right]$$

$$= -\sin x \left[\lim_{h \to 0} \frac{\sin h}{h} \right] + \cos x \left[\lim_{h \to 0} \frac{\cos h - 1}{h} \right]$$

by the sum property of limits. Note that $\sin x$ and $\cos x$ are constants in this limit process, since x does not vary as $h \to 0$.

We now face the problem of evaluating the limits

$$\lim_{h \to 0} \frac{\sin h}{h} \quad \text{and} \quad \lim_{h \to 0} \frac{\cos h - 1}{h}$$

In each case, the numerator and denominator both tend to zero, and we are unable to evaluate the limits by means of some cancellation procedure. For now we investigate these limits, using a calculator. Consider the following table, where the angle h is measured in radians.

h (radians)	$\dfrac{\sin h}{h}$	$\dfrac{\cos h - 1}{h}$
0.1	0.998 334	−0.049 958
0.01	0.999 983	−0.004 999
0.001	0.999 999	−0.000 499

The calculations summarized in the table suggest that

$$\lim_{h \to 0} \frac{\sin h}{h} = 1 \quad \text{and} \quad \lim_{h \to 0} \frac{\cos h - 1}{h} = 0$$

These results will be proved in the next section, where it will be shown that the second limit is a direct consequence of the first. The first of these limits is referred to as the **fundamental trigonometric limit**.

By substituting these limits in the expression for the derivative of the function $f(x) = \cos x$, we obtain

$$f'(x) = (-\sin x)(1) + (\cos x)(0)$$
$$= -\sin x$$

Summarizing, we have established the derivative of the cosine function.

$$\frac{d}{dx}(\cos x) = -\sin x$$

In words, **the derivative of the cosine function is the negative of the sine function.**

Note that this derivative depends on the fundamental trigonometric limit, which in turn depends on the fact that we have selected radians as the unit of angular measurement. The table of values for $\dfrac{\sin h}{h}$ would be quite different if h were measured in degrees (see Problem 5). We shall have more to say on this topic when we prove the fundamental trigonometric limit in section 5.5.

We shall now illustrate the use of this result in some examples.

Example 1. Find the derivative $\dfrac{dy}{dx}$ for each function.

a. $y = \cos(x^2)$ **b.** $y = \cos^2 x$

Solution.

a. To differentiate this composite function, we use the Chain Rule, writing

$$y = \cos u \quad \text{and} \quad u = x^2$$

Then

$$\frac{dy}{dx} = \frac{dy}{du}\frac{du}{dx}$$
$$= (-\sin u)(2x)$$
$$= -2x \sin (x^2)$$

when we substitute for u.

b. In this composite function, the outer function is the power function, since $y = \cos^2 x = (\cos x)^2$. We again use the Chain Rule, writing

$$y = u^2 \quad \text{and} \quad u = \cos x$$

Then

$$\frac{dy}{dx} = \frac{dy}{du}\frac{du}{dx}$$
$$= (2u)(-\sin x)$$
$$= -2 \sin x \cos x \qquad \square$$

In applying the Chain Rule in Example 1, we introduced the variable u, in order to make the method as clear as possible. With practice, however, it is possible to dispense with this intermediate step, and we urge you to make this your goal. For example, if

$$y = \cos (x^2)$$

we can immediately write

$$\frac{dy}{dx} = (-\sin (x^2))(2x)$$

First differentiate the outermost function "cos( )" to get "$-\sin( )$," **evaluated at the inner function**, and then multiply by the derivative of the inner function x^2.

We now use the identities

$$\cos \left(\frac{\pi}{2} - x\right) = \sin x \quad \text{and} \quad \sin \left(\frac{\pi}{2} - x\right) = \cos x$$

to find the derivative of $\sin x$. Let

$$y = \sin x$$

By the first identity

$$y = \cos \left(\frac{\pi}{2} - x\right)$$

Knowing the derivative of the cosine function, we can use the Chain Rule to find $\dfrac{dy}{dx}$.

$$\frac{dy}{dx} = \left[-\sin\left(\frac{\pi}{2} - x\right) \right](-1)$$

$$= \sin\left(\frac{\pi}{2} - x\right)$$

Hence, by the second identity

$$\frac{dy}{dx} = \cos x$$

Summarizing, we have:

$$\frac{d}{dx}(\sin x) = \cos x$$

Using the Chain Rule, we can now differentiate composite functions of $\sin x$. For example

$$\frac{d}{dx}[3\sin(2x)] = 6\cos 2x, \qquad \frac{d}{dx}[\sin(3x^2)] = 6x\cos(3x^2)$$

Example 2. Show that the tangent line to the graph of $\sin x$ at the origin makes an angle of $\dfrac{\pi}{4}$ radians with the x-axis.

Solution. Let $y = \sin x$. Then

$$\frac{dy}{dx} = \cos x$$

Hence, when $x = 0$, the slope of the tangent line is

$$m = \cos 0$$
$$= 1$$

Recall that the angle of inclination θ formed with the x-axis by a line of slope m satisfies

$$\tan \theta = m$$

(see the diagram). Thus, the tangent line to the graph of $\sin x$ at $(0, 0)$ makes an angle of $\dfrac{\pi}{4}$ with the x-axis.

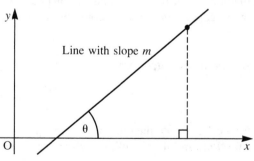

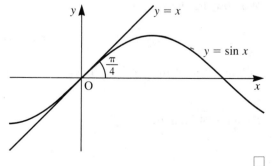

Example 3. Find the maximum value and minimum value of the function

$$f(x) = \cos 2x + 2\sin x$$

on the interval $0 \le x \le \dfrac{3\pi}{4}$.

Solution. By the Algorithm for Extreme Values (section 3.4), the maximum and minimum values occur at a point on the graph where $f'(x) = 0$, or at an end point of the interval. The derivative of $f(x)$ is

$$f'(x) = -2\sin 2x + 2\cos x$$

The equation $f'(x) = 0$ is

$$-\sin 2x + \cos x = 0$$

Use a double angle identity to obtain

$$-2\sin x \cos x + \cos x = 0$$

and hence,

$$\cos x(-2\sin x + 1) = 0$$

This implies that

$$\cos x = 0 \quad \text{or} \quad \sin x = \frac{1}{2}$$

Therefore,

$$x = \frac{\pi}{2} \quad \text{and} \quad x = \frac{\pi}{6}$$

are the solutions in the given interval.

Evaluate $f(x)$ at $\dfrac{\pi}{6}$ and $\dfrac{\pi}{2}$ and at the end points, to obtain the results summarized in the table.

x	0	$\dfrac{\pi}{6}$	$\dfrac{\pi}{2}$	$\dfrac{3\pi}{4}$
$f(x)$	1	$\dfrac{3}{2}$	1	$\sqrt{2}$

The maximum value is $\dfrac{3}{2}$, and the minimum value is 1.

Exercises 5.4

1. Find $\dfrac{dy}{dx}$.

a. $y = 3\cos 4x$

b. $y = \cos\left(3x + \dfrac{\pi}{2}\right)$

c. $y = \cos(2x^3)$

d. $y = \cos^3 2x$

e. $y = \cos(x^2 + x)$

f. $y = (x + \cos x)^2$

g. $y = \cos\left(\pi x + \dfrac{1}{\pi}\right)$

h. $y = \cos \pi x + \dfrac{1}{\pi}$

i. $y = 2\sin \pi x + x^2$

j. $y = 3\sin(x^2 - 1)$

k. $y = 3\sin^2 x$

l. $y = (\sin 2x + \cos x)^3$

m. $x = \sin y$

2. Calculate $\dfrac{d^2y}{dx^2}$ in each part of Exercise 1.

3. Differentiate each function.

a. $f(x) = x\cos x$

b. $g(u) = u^3 \sin 2u$

c. $f(y) = y^2 \cos(3y^3)$

d. $h(u) = \sin(\cos \pi u)$

e. $f(x) = \sin x \cos x$

f. $h(t) = \dfrac{\sin 2t}{\cos 2t}$

g. $v(t) = \sin^2(\sqrt{t})$

h. $v(t) = \sqrt{1 + \cos t + \sin^2 t}$

i. $g(y) = \sin^2 \pi y \cos \pi y$

j. $h(x) = \sin x \sin 2x \sin 3x$

k. $f(t) = \sqrt{2 + \sin^2 5t}$

l. $g(u) = (u + \sin 3u)^2$

m. $h(x) = \dfrac{x^2}{2 - \cos \pi x}$

n. $h(t) = \sin \dfrac{1}{t}$

o. $h(y) = \dfrac{\sin 2y}{1 + \sin 2y}$

p. $m(x) = (x^2 + \cos^2 x)^3$

4. Find $\dfrac{dy}{dx}$ in each case, where A, B, m, and n are constants.

a. $y = \cos(Ax + B)$

b. $y = A\cos^n Bx$

c. $y = \sin^m(x^n)$

d. $y = Ax^n \sin^m Bx$

5. Find the maximum and minimum value of each function on the given interval.

a. $f(x) = 2\cos x + x, \quad -\pi \le x \le \pi$

b. $f(x) = 2\sin x - x, \quad 0 \le x \le 2\pi$

c. $f(x) = \sin x + 2x, \quad 0 \le x \le 2\pi$

d. $f(x) = 2\cos x - \cos 2x, \quad \dfrac{\pi}{2} \le x \le \dfrac{3\pi}{2}$

e. $f(x) = \sin^2 x - \sin x, \quad -\pi \le x \le \pi$

f. $f(x) = x\sin x + \cos x, \quad -\dfrac{\pi}{4} \le x \le \pi$

6. Find the equation of the tangent line to the curve at each of the given points.

    a. $\cos(x + 2y) = 2x + 2y - \pi$, $\left(\dfrac{\pi}{2}, 0\right)$

    b. $x\sin(xy - y^3) = \dfrac{x^2 - y}{y}$, $(1, 1)$

7. What angle does the tangent line to the curve $y = \dfrac{1}{\sqrt{3}}\sin 3x$ at the origin make with the x-axis?

8. If $y = A\cos kt + B\sin kt$, where A, B, and k are constants, show that

$$y'' + k^2 y = 0$$

9. Find the equation of the tangent line to the graph of the function at the indicated point. Use the second derivative to determine whether the graph lies above or below the tangent. Sketch the graph near the indicated point.

    a. $f(x) = x\sin 2x$, $x = \dfrac{\pi}{4}$

    b. $f(x) = \sin^2 x$, $x = \dfrac{\pi}{3}$

    c. $f(x) = \cos(\pi x^2 + \pi)$, $x = \dfrac{1}{2}$

Problems 5.4

1. Use the tangent approximation (see section 3.6) to show that

$$\sin x \approx x, \text{ when } x \text{ is close to } 0$$

If $x > 0$, is the approximation too large or too small?

2. Let $f(x) = \sqrt{1 + \sin(x^2 - 2)}$. Use the tangent approximation at $x = \sqrt{2}$ to find an approximate value of $f(1.5)$. Check the accuracy of your answer with a calculator.

3. Let $f(x) = \cos x$ and let $p(x) = a + bx + cx^2$.

    a. Find the constants a, b, and c by requiring that

$$p(0) = f(0), \quad p'(0) = f'(0), \quad \text{and} \quad p''(0) = f''(0)$$

    b. Sketch the graph of $\cos x$ and $p(x)$ in the same diagram. By making a table of values, show that

$$\cos x \approx p(x)$$

for x close to 0 (say, $|x| < 0.5$). For what values of x will the approximation give five-place accuracy?

4. Suppose that b satisfies the relation

$$\tan b - b = 0$$

  a. Show that the tangent line to the curve $y = \sin x$ at the point $(b, \sin b)$ passes through the origin.

  b. Sketch the graph of $y = \sin x$ and draw two such tangent lines for positive values of b.

  c. Sketch the graphs of $y = \tan x$ and $y = x$ in order to locate approximately the values of b in part (b). How many solutions does the equation

$$\tan x - x = 0$$

have?

5. a. Evaluate $\lim\limits_{h \to 0} \dfrac{\sin h}{h}$, where h is the measure of an angle in degrees. (Use a calculator to determine $\dfrac{\sin 10°}{10}$, $\dfrac{\sin 5°}{5}$, $\dfrac{\sin 1°}{1}$, etc., to get an estimate for this limit.)

  b. Evaluate $\lim\limits_{h \to 0} \dfrac{\cos h - 1}{h}$, where h is the measure of an angle in degrees.

  c. What modifications would have to be made to the derivatives

$$\frac{d}{dx} \sin x = \cos x \quad \text{and} \quad \frac{d}{dx} \cos x = -\sin x$$

if x were the measure of an angle in degrees instead of in radians?

5.5 The Fundamental Trigonometric Limit

In the previous section we obtained the derivative of the cosine function by assuming the validity of the fundamental trigonometric limit.

$$\lim_{h \to 0} \frac{\sin h}{h} = 1$$

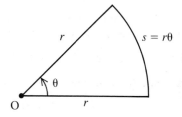

In this section we shall prove this limit by using the formula for the length of the arc of a circle,

$$s = r\theta$$

where θ is the radian measure of the angle subtended by the arc. We shall avoid using the area formula for the circle, since its derivation makes use of the limit that we wish to prove. A derivation of the formula for the area of a circle, using the fundamental trigonometric limit, is outlined in Problem 1 of this section.

Theorem. $\displaystyle\lim_{h \to 0} \frac{\sin h}{h} = 1$, where h is the radian measure of an angle.

Proof. Draw an angle of radian measure $h > 0$ in a circle of radius 1, forming an arc PQ of length h. The tangent line is drawn at P, and the lines QR and QS are drawn perpendicular to OP and PS respectively.

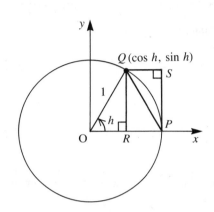

From the diagram, it follows that

$$|QR| < |PQ| < \text{arc}(PQ) < |PS| + |QS|$$

where $|QR|$ denotes the length of the line segment QR, etc. In addition, referring to the diagram, we obtain

$$|QR| = |PS| = \sin h$$
$$|QS| = |OP| - |OR| = 1 - \cos h$$

and

$$\text{arc}(PQ) = h$$

It follows from the above inequality that

$$\sin h < h < \sin h + (1 - \cos h)$$

When we divide by $\sin h$, the inequality becomes

$$1 < \frac{h}{\sin h} < 1 + \frac{1 - \cos h}{\sin h}$$

Now use the Pythagorean identity (in factored form)

$$(1 - \cos h)(1 + \cos h) = \sin^2 h$$

to obtain

$$\frac{1 - \cos h}{\sin h} = \frac{\sin h}{1 + \cos h}$$

Therefore

$$1 < \frac{h}{\sin h} < 1 + \frac{\sin h}{1 + \cos h}$$

From the results,

$$\lim_{h \to 0} \sin h = 0 \quad \text{and} \quad \lim_{h \to 0} \cos h = 1$$

and from the properties of limits, it follows that

$$\lim_{h \to 0} \left[1 + \frac{\sin h}{1 + \cos h} \right] = 1$$

Since the function $\dfrac{h}{\sin h}$ lies between 1 and the function $1 + \dfrac{\sin h}{1 + \cos h}$, whose limit is 1, we may conclude that

$$\lim_{h \to 0} \frac{h}{\sin h} = 1$$

Hence,

$$\lim_{h \to 0} \frac{\sin h}{h} = 1 \qquad\qquad \square$$

We now use the fundamental trigonometric limit to prove the second limit that was used in section 5.4.

Example 1. Prove that

$$\lim_{h \to 0} \frac{1 - \cos h}{h} = 0$$

Solution. The Pythagorean identity, in factored form, is

$$(1 - \cos h)(1 + \cos h) = \sin^2 h$$

Hence,

$$\frac{1 - \cos h}{h} = \left(\frac{\sin h}{h} \right)\left(\frac{\sin h}{1 + \cos h} \right)$$

On using the properties of limits we obtain

$$\lim_{h \to 0} \frac{1 - \cos h}{h} = \left(\lim_{h \to 0} \frac{\sin h}{h} \right)\left(\lim_{h \to 0} \frac{\sin h}{1 + \cos h} \right)$$
$$= (1)(0)$$
$$= 0$$

The fundamental trigonometric limit can sometimes be used to evaluate other limits in which both the denominator and numerator tend to zero. $\qquad \square$

Example 2. Evaluate $\lim\limits_{x \to 0} \dfrac{1 - \cos 4x}{x^2}$.

Solution. **By the double angle and Pythagorean identities,**

$$\cos 4x = \cos^2 2x - \sin^2 2x$$
$$= 1 - 2\sin^2 2x$$

Hence,

$$\lim_{x \to 0} \frac{1 - \cos 4x}{x^2} = \lim_{x \to 0} \frac{2\sin^2 2x}{x^2}$$

$$= \lim_{u \to 0} \frac{2\sin^2 u}{\left(\dfrac{u}{2}\right)^2} \quad \text{(Let } 2x = u\text{)}$$

$$= 8 \lim_{u \to 0} \left(\frac{\sin u}{u}\right)^2$$

$$= 8(1)^2$$

$$= 8 \qquad \qquad \square$$

Exercises 5.5

1. Use the fundamental trigonometric limit to evaluate

$$\lim_{h \to 0} \frac{\sin 2h}{h}$$

in two ways.

   a. First use the double-angle identity for $\sin 2h$.
   b. Then make the change of variable $u = 2h$.

2. Use the fundamental trigonometric limit to evaluate each limit.

   a. $\lim\limits_{h \to 0} \dfrac{\sin 3h}{h}$

   b. $\lim\limits_{x \to 0} \dfrac{\sin \pi x}{x}$

   c. $\lim\limits_{u \to 0} \dfrac{\tan u}{u}$

   d. $\lim\limits_{x \to 0} \dfrac{\tan 10x}{x}$

   e. $\lim\limits_{t \to 0} \dfrac{1 - \cos t}{t^2}$

   f. $\lim\limits_{x \to 0} \dfrac{1 - \cos 2x}{x \sin x}$

   g. $\lim\limits_{x \to 0} \dfrac{\sin 3x}{4x}$

   h. $\lim\limits_{x \to 0} \dfrac{\sin 3x}{\sin 4x}$

   i. $\lim\limits_{h \to 0} \dfrac{\sin^2 h}{h}$

   j. $\lim\limits_{x \to 0} \dfrac{\sin(\sin x)}{\sin x}$

Problems 5.5

1. Choose n equally spaced points on a circle of radius r. Join each point to its neighbour and to the centre O, forming n equal triangles. Let $A(n)$ be the sum of the areas of the n triangles. Calculate the area A of the circle by taking the limit of $A(n)$ as n increases without bound.

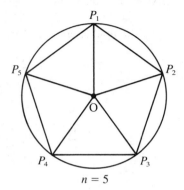

$n = 5$

$$A = \lim_{n \to \infty} A(n)$$

a. Show that the area of one triangle is

$$r^2 \sin\left(\frac{\pi}{n}\right) \cos\left(\frac{\pi}{n}\right)$$

b. Use the fundamental trigonometric limit to show that

$$\lim_{n \to \infty} n \sin\left(\frac{\pi}{n}\right) = \pi$$

c. Hence, show that

$$A = \pi r^2$$

2. This problem describes a proof of the fundamental trigonometric limit that assumes the area formula for a circle. From the figure, it follows that

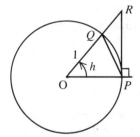

Area $\triangle OPQ$ < Area sector (OPQ) < Area $\triangle OPR$

a. Show that

$$\cos h < \frac{h}{\sin h} < \frac{1}{\cos h},$$

$$\text{for } 0 < h < \frac{\pi}{2}$$

b. Show that

$$\lim_{h \to 0} \frac{\sin h}{h} = 1$$

3. Sketch the graph of the function

$$f(x) = \frac{\sin x}{x}, \quad x \neq 0$$

5.6 Further Trigonometric Derivatives

In this section we shall study the derivatives of the remaining trigonometric functions—tangent, secant, cotangent, and cosecant. Since these functions can be expressed in terms of sine and cosine, as follows, we can find their derivatives by applying the rules of differentiation.

$$\tan x = \frac{\sin x}{\cos x} \qquad \sec x = \frac{1}{\cos x}$$

$$\cot x = \frac{\cos x}{\sin x} \qquad \csc x = \frac{1}{\sin x}$$

Example 1. Find the derivative of each function.

a. $\tan x$

b. $\sec x$

Solution

a. By the quotient rule,

$$\frac{d}{dx}(\tan x) = \frac{d}{dx}\left(\frac{\sin x}{\cos x}\right)$$

$$= \frac{\cos x \dfrac{d}{dx}(\sin x) - \sin x \dfrac{d}{dx}(\cos x)}{\cos^2 x}$$

$$= \frac{\cos x (\cos x) - \sin x (-\sin x)}{\cos^2 x}$$

$$= \frac{\cos^2 x + \sin^2 x}{\cos^2 x}$$

$$= \frac{1}{\cos^2 x}$$

This can be expressed in terms of $\sec x$:

$$\frac{d}{dx}(\tan x) = \sec^2 x$$

b. Express $\sec x$ in terms of $\cos x$, as

$$\sec x = (\cos x)^{-1}$$

Then, by the Chain Rule,

$$\frac{d}{dx}(\sec x) = -(\cos x)^{-2}\frac{d}{dx}(\cos x)$$

$$= \frac{\sin x}{\cos^2 x}$$

This can be expressed in terms of $\tan x$ and $\sec x$, yielding

$$\frac{d}{dx}(\sec x) = \sec x \tan x$$

□

The derivatives of $\cot x$ and $\csc x$ can be found in a similar way (see Exercise 3 in this section). We now summarize the six trigonometric derivatives.

Trigonometric Derivatives

$$\frac{d}{dx}(\sin x) = \cos x \qquad \frac{d}{dx}(\cos x) = -\sin x$$

$$\frac{d}{dx}(\tan x) = \sec^2 x \qquad \frac{d}{dx}(\cot x) = -\csc^2 x$$

$$\frac{d}{dx}(\sec x) = \sec x \tan x \qquad \frac{d}{dx}(\csc x) = -\csc x \cot x$$

We encourage you to memorize these derivative formulae. Note that all the "co-functions" (cosine, cotangent, cosecant) have a minus sign in their derivative. But keep in mind that the final four derivatives can be quickly derived from the first two, as we have shown.

We now illustrate the use of these results in some examples.

Example 2. Find $\frac{dy}{dx}$ for each function.

a. $y = \tan (x^2 + 3x)$ **b.** $y = \sec^3 \pi x$

Solution

a. By the Chain Rule,

$$\frac{dy}{dx} = \sec^2 (x^2 + 2x) \frac{d}{dx}(x^2 + 3x)$$

$$= (2x + 3) \sec^2 (x^2 + 2x)$$

b. Write $y = \sec^3 \pi x$ as

$$y = (\sec \pi x)^3$$

in order to emphasize the form of the composite function. By the Chain Rule,

$$\frac{dy}{dx} = 3 \sec^2 \pi x \frac{d}{dx}(\sec \pi x)$$

$$= 3 \sec^2 \pi x [\sec \pi x \tan \pi x \frac{d}{dx}(\pi x)]$$

$$= 3 \pi \sec^3 \pi x \tan \pi x \qquad \square$$

Example 3. Show that $(0, 0)$ is a point of inflection of the graph of $f(x) = \tan x$.

Solution. A point of inflection occurs when the second derivative changes sign. The derivative of $f(x)$ is

$$f'(x) = \sec^2 x$$

Differentiate again, applying the Chain Rule, to obtain

$$f''(x) = \frac{d}{dx}(\sec^2 x)$$
$$= 2 \sec x \frac{d}{dx}(\sec x)$$
$$= 2 \sec x (\sec x \tan x)$$

Hence,

$$f''(x) = 2 \tan x \sec^2 x$$

Observe that $f''(0) = 0$. To determine the sign of $f''(x)$ on the interval $-\frac{\pi}{2} < x < \frac{\pi}{2}$, note that $\sec^2 x > 0$ for all x, so we only need to consider the sign of $\tan x$. Since

$$\tan x > 0, \quad \text{if } 0 < x < \frac{\pi}{2}$$

and

$$\tan x < 0, \quad \text{if } -\frac{\pi}{2} < x < 0$$

we obtain the following table.

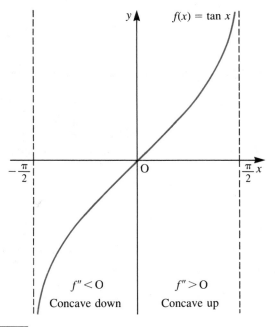

	$-\frac{\pi}{2} < x < 0$	$x = 0$	$0 < x < \frac{\pi}{2}$
$f''(x)$	$-$	0	$+$
graph of $f(x)$	concave down	point of inflection	concave up

Since the sign of $f''(x)$ changes at $x = 0$, it follows that $(0, 0)$ is a point of inflection. □

Example 4. Find the turning points (local extrema) of the function

$$f(x) = 2x - \tan x, \text{ where } -\frac{\pi}{2} < x < \frac{\pi}{2},$$

and sketch the graph of $f(x)$.

Solution. The derivative of $f(x)$ is

$$f'(x) = 2 - \sec^2 x$$

To find the turning points, we solve $f'(x) = 0$; that is,

$$2 - \sec^2 x = 0$$

Expressing this in terms of $\cos x$, we obtain

$$\cos^2 x = \frac{1}{2}$$

and hence

$$\cos x = \pm \frac{1}{\sqrt{2}}$$

Since $\cos x$ is positive in the given interval, we discard the minus sign, obtaining the solutions

$$x = -\frac{\pi}{4} \quad \text{and} \quad x = \frac{\pi}{4}$$

In order to determine whether these values give turning points, we observe that the sign of $f'(x)$ does not change on each of the subintervals

$$-\frac{\pi}{2} < x < -\frac{\pi}{4}, \quad -\frac{\pi}{4} < x < \frac{\pi}{4}, \quad \text{and} \quad \frac{\pi}{4} < x < \frac{\pi}{2}$$

since $x = \pm\frac{\pi}{4}$ are the only values at which $f'(x)$ is zero. We can thus determine the sign of $f'(x)$ by evaluating it at one point of each sub-interval:

$$f'\left(-\frac{\pi}{3}\right) = -2, \quad f'(0) = 1, \quad f'\left(\frac{\pi}{3}\right) = -2$$

This leads to the following table and graph.

	$-\frac{\pi}{2} < x < -\frac{\pi}{4}$	$x = -\frac{\pi}{4}$	$-\frac{\pi}{4} < x < \frac{\pi}{4}$	$x = \frac{\pi}{4}$	$\frac{\pi}{4} < x < \frac{\pi}{2}$
$f'(x)$	$-$	0	$+$	0	$-$
$f(x)$	decreasing	local minimum	increasing	local maximum	decreasing

Note that the vertical asymptotes of $y = -\tan x$ give rise to vertical asymptotes in the graph of $f(x)$. Also note that $f(x)$ is an odd function,

$$f(-x) = -f(x)$$

so that its graph is symmetric under reflection through the origin. It is also helpful to obtain a rough sketch of the graph by regarding $f(x)$ as the sum of $2x$ and $-\tan x$, whose graphs are shown as dotted lines. $\square$

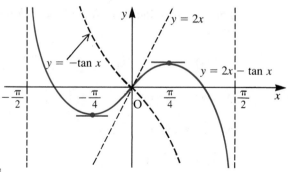

Exercises 5.6

1. Find $\dfrac{dy}{dx}$ in each case.

   a. $y = 2\tan x - \tan 2x$

   b. $y = 3\sec(2x^2 + 1)$

   c. $y = 3\sec 5x \tan^2 5x$

   d. $y = \sqrt{x^2 + \sec^2 x}$

   e. $y = \dfrac{x^2}{\tan \pi x}$

   f. $y = \tan(x^2) - \tan^2 x$

   g. $y = \sqrt{x}\,\sec\sqrt{x}$

   h. $y = x^2 \tan\left(\dfrac{1}{x}\right)$

   i. $y = \tan(xy)$

   j. $x\tan y = y\tan x$

   k. $y = \tan(\sin x)$

   l. $y = \sin(\tan x)$

2. Use the identity

$$\sec^2 x = 1 + \tan^2 x$$

and the derivative of $\tan x$ to find the derivative of $\sec x$.

3. Use the derivatives of $\sin x$ and $\cos x$ to find the derivatives of $\cot x$ and $\csc x$, in the form given in the text.

4. Find $\dfrac{dy}{dx}$ in each case.

   a. $y = \cot 2x + \csc 2x$

   b. $y = 2x^3 \cot x$

   c. $y = (x + \csc x)^2$

   d. $y = \sqrt{\pi^2 + \csc^2 x}$

   e. $y = 3\cot\sqrt{x^2 + 1}$

   f. $y = \dfrac{\cot x}{1 + \csc^2 x}$

   g. $y = \sqrt{x}\,\csc\left(\dfrac{1}{\sqrt{x}}\right)$

   h. $y = \cot^2 2x \csc 2x$

   i. $\cot(x + y) = 2y$

   j. $\cot(xy^2) - 4y + 3 = 0$

   k. $y = \dfrac{\tan x - 1}{\tan x + 1}$

   l. $y = (\cot x + \sin x)^2$

5. Find the equation of the tangent line and the equation of the normal line to the curve $y + 2x\tan(\pi xy) = x - 1$ at the point $(1, 0)$.

6. For each function $f(x)$, find all local extrema. Using this information, sketch the graph of $f(x)$.

a. $f(x) = \tan 3x - 4x$, $\quad -\dfrac{\pi}{6} < x < \dfrac{\pi}{6}$

b. $f(x) = x - \tan x$, $\quad -\dfrac{\pi}{2} < x < \dfrac{\pi}{2}$

c. $f(x) = \tan^2 x$, $\quad -\dfrac{\pi}{2} < x < \dfrac{\pi}{2}$

d. $f(x) = 8\tan\left(\dfrac{x}{4}\right) - x$, $\quad -2\pi < x < 2\pi$

7. Let $f(x) = 6\tan x - \tan 2x$, where $-\dfrac{\pi}{4} < x < \dfrac{\pi}{4}$.

a. Find the equation of the tangent line when $x = 0$.
b. Find the points of the graph at which the tangent line is horizontal.
c. Sketch the graph.

8. Use the identity $\cot x = \dfrac{1}{\tan x}$ and the derivative of $\tan x$ to find the derivative of $\cot x$.

9. Let $f(x) = \sec x$. Investigate the sign of $f''(x)$ and show that it agrees with the shape of the graph of $\sec x$ drawn in section 5.1. Are there any points of inflection?

Problems 5.6

1. Consider the function
$$f(x) = (\sec x + \tan x)^n, \text{ where } n \text{ is a constant}$$
and show that
a. $f'(x) = nf(x)\sec x$
b. $f''(x) = f'(x)(n\sec x + \tan x)$

2. Evaluate $\displaystyle\lim_{h \to 0} \dfrac{\tan\left(\dfrac{\pi}{4} + h\right) - 1}{h}$.

(Hint: Think of the definition of the derivative.)

3. a. Find the tangent approximation (see section 3.6) for $f(x) = \tan x$ at the following points.

    (i) $x = 0$ (ii) $x = \dfrac{\pi}{4}$

b. Use the tangent approximations in part (a) to calculate the following.

    (i) $\tan(0.13)$ (ii) $\tan\left(\dfrac{\pi}{4} - 0.1\right)$

Check the accuracy of your answers with a calculator.

4. Use the tangent approximation of $f(x) = \sec x$ at $x = \dfrac{\pi}{3}$ to calculate $\sec\left(\dfrac{4\pi}{9}\right)$.

5. Consider the function

$$f(x) = \tan x + \sec x, \text{ where } -\frac{\pi}{2} < x < \frac{\pi}{2}$$

   a. Evaluate $\lim\limits_{x \to -\frac{\pi}{2}^+} f(x)$.

   b. Prove that $f(x) > 0$ for $-\dfrac{\pi}{2} < x < \dfrac{\pi}{2}$.

   c. Sketch the graph of $f(x)$.

6. Consider the function

$$f(x) = \tan bx - ax, \text{ where } -\frac{\pi}{2b} < x < \frac{\pi}{2b}$$

For what values of the positive constants a and b is $f(x)$ increasing on the given interval?

5.7 Applications of Trigonometric Functions

Trigonometric functions are included in many interesting mathematical models. We begin with a related-rates problem.

Example 1. A TV camera, located 1000 m from the site of a rocket launch, records the event. The rocket is launched vertically, and its elevation s (in metres) t seconds after lift-off is $s = 200t^2$. How rapidly must the camera angle be increased in order to maintain a view of the rocket, 5 s after lift-off?

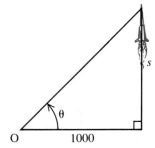

Solution. Let s be the height of the rocket (in metres), and let θ be the angle of elevation (in radians) at an arbitrary time t. It is given that

$$s = 200t^2$$

and hence

$$\frac{ds}{dt} = 400t$$

Since we want to find $\dfrac{d\theta}{dt}$, we look for a relation between θ and s. From the diagram, which represents the situation at an arbitrary time $t > 0$, we see that

$$\tan \theta = \frac{s}{1000}$$

for all $t > 0$. Differentiate both sides of this equation with respect to t to obtain

$$\frac{d}{dt}(\tan \theta) = \frac{1}{1000}\frac{ds}{dt}$$

Use the Chain Rule for the left side, and substitute $400t$ for $\dfrac{ds}{dt}$, to obtain

$$\sec^2 \theta \frac{d\theta}{dt} = \frac{2t}{5}$$

We now substitute $t = 5$ into this equation. In order to evaluate $\sec^2 \theta$ when $t = 5$, we use the equations $s = 200 t^2$ and $\tan \theta = \dfrac{s}{1000}$ to obtain

$$\tan \theta = \frac{200(5^2)}{1000}$$
$$= 5$$

The Pythagorean identity divided by $\cos^2 \theta$ implies that

$$\sec^2 \theta = 1 + \tan^2 \theta$$
$$= 1 + (5)^2$$
$$= 26$$

Thus, when $t = 5$, the equation for $\dfrac{d\theta}{dt}$ yields

$$26\frac{d\theta}{dt} = \frac{2}{5}(5)$$
$$= 2$$

so that

$$\frac{d\theta}{dt} = \frac{1}{13}$$

Thus 5 s after launch the camera angle must be increased at a rate of $\frac{1}{13}$ radians per second. $\square$

We now do an optimization problem.

Example 2. An irrigation channel is constructed by bending a sheet of metal that is 3 m wide, as shown in the diagram. What angle θ will maximize the carrying capacity?

Solution. The carrying capacity will be maximized if the cross-sectional area is maximized. Let $A(\theta)$ be the cross-sectional area when the ''bending angle''is θ radians.

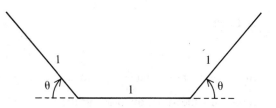

We restrict θ to the interval $0 \leq \theta \leq \dfrac{\pi}{2}$, because bending past the vertical will reduce the carrying capacity.

Since the channel is symmetrical,

$$A(\theta) = \text{Area (rectangle } ABCD) + 2 \times \text{Area } (\triangle ADE)$$
$$= |AB||AD| + |DE||AD|$$

From $\triangle ADE$

$$\sin \theta = |AD| \quad \text{and} \quad \cos \theta = |DE|$$

since $|AE| = 1$. Hence,

$$A(\theta) = \sin \theta + \sin \theta \cos \theta, \quad \text{for } 0 \leq \theta \leq \dfrac{\pi}{2}$$

To find the maximum of $A(\theta)$ on the interval $0 \leq \theta \leq \dfrac{\pi}{2}$, apply the Algorithm for Extreme Values of section 3.4. Differentiate $A(\theta)$, using the Product Rule for the second term, to obtain

$$A'(\theta) = \cos \theta + \cos^2 \theta - \sin^2 \theta$$

The equation $A'(\theta) = 0$ is

$$\cos^2 \theta - \sin^2 \theta + \cos \theta = 0$$

Therefore,

$$2 \cos^2 \theta + \cos \theta - 1 = 0$$

or

$$(2 \cos \theta - 1)(\cos \theta + 1) = 0$$

Hence,

$$\cos \theta = \tfrac{1}{2} \quad \text{or} \quad \cos \theta = -1$$

Since $0 \leq \theta \leq \dfrac{\pi}{2}$, we discard the second case. The first case yields

$$\theta = \frac{\pi}{3}$$

On evaluating $A(\theta)$ at $\dfrac{\pi}{3}$ and at the end points of the interval $0 \leq \theta \leq \dfrac{\pi}{2}$, we obtain the following results.

θ	0	$\dfrac{\pi}{3}$	$\dfrac{\pi}{2}$
$A(\theta)$	0	$\dfrac{3\sqrt{3}}{4}$	1

Since $\dfrac{3\sqrt{3}}{4} > 1$, $A(\theta)$ attains its maximum value when $\theta = \dfrac{\pi}{3}$. Thus a bending angle of $\dfrac{\pi}{3}$ radians will maximize the carrying capacity of the channel. $\qquad \square$

In Example 3, the curve sketching techniques of Chapter 4 are applied to a trigonometric function.

Example 3. Sketch the graph of the function

$$f(x) = 2\cos x + x, \text{ for } 0 \le x \le 2\pi$$

by studying the properties of the first and second derivatives.

Solution. First analyze the sign of the first derivative.

$$f'(x) = -2\sin x + 1$$

It follows that $f'(x) = 0$ when

$$\sin x = \frac{1}{2}$$

that is, when

$$x = \frac{\pi}{6} \quad \text{and} \quad x = \frac{5\pi}{6}$$

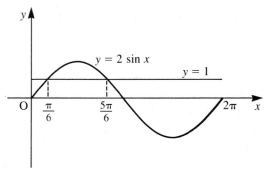

The sign of $f'(x)$ can be found by considering the graphs of $y = 2\sin x$ and $y = 1$. We see that $f'(x) < 0$ when $2\sin x > 1$, that is, when $\frac{\pi}{6} < x < \frac{5\pi}{6}$. In the intervals $0 < x < \frac{\pi}{6}$ and $\frac{5\pi}{6} < x \le 2\pi$, $2\sin x < 1$ and hence $f'(x)$ is positive.

x	$0 \le x < \frac{\pi}{6}$	$\frac{\pi}{6}$	$\frac{\pi}{6} < x < \frac{5\pi}{6}$	$\frac{5\pi}{6}$	$\frac{5\pi}{6} < x \le 2\pi$
$f'(x)$	$+$	0	$-$	0	$+$
$f(x)$	increasing	local maximum	decreasing	local minimum	increasing

We now analyze the sign of the second derivative.

$$f''(x) = -2\cos x$$

It follows that $f''(x) = 0$ when $x = \frac{\pi}{2}$ and $x = \frac{3\pi}{2}$. The sign of $f''(x)$ is the sign of $-\cos x$ and is summarized in the table.

x	$0 \le x < \frac{\pi}{2}$	$\frac{\pi}{2}$	$\frac{\pi}{2} < x < \frac{3\pi}{2}$	$\frac{3\pi}{2}$	$\frac{3\pi}{2} < x \le 2\pi$
$f''(x)$	$-$	0	$+$	0	$-$
$f(x)$	concave down	point of inflection	concave up	point of inflection	concave down

The final graph incorporates all the information that we have obtained. It may be helpful to calculate function values at the local extrema and the points of inflection.

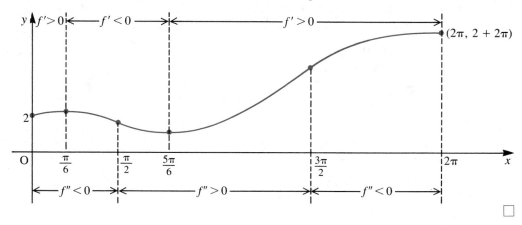

Exercises 5.7

1. An object is suspended from the end of a spring. Its displacement from the equilibrium position is

$$s = 8 \sin(10\pi t)$$

Calculate the velocity and acceleration of the object at any time t and show that

$$\frac{d^2s}{dt^2} + 100\pi^2 s = 0$$

2. The displacement s (in centimetres) of the midpoint of a vibrating violin string (the A string) at time t is

$$s = 0.05 \sin(880\pi t)$$

where t is measured in seconds. Find the velocity v and acceleration a of the midpoint of the string, and show that

$$a = -(880\pi)^2 s$$

3. One end of a ladder of length 5 m slides down a vertical wall. When the upper end of the ladder is 3 m above the ground, it has a downward velocity of 0.5 m/s. Find the rate at which the angle of elevation θ is changing at that time.

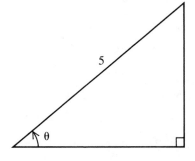

4. A balloon rises into the air, starting at a point P. An observer 100 m from P looks at the balloon, and the angle θ between her line of sight and the ground increases at a rate of $\frac{1}{20}$ radians per second. Find the velocity of the balloon when $\theta = \frac{\pi}{4}$.

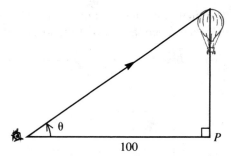

5. A V-shaped trough 5 m long is made from a rectangular sheet of aluminum 100 cm wide by bending it down the middle. What angle between the sides of the trough will maximize its capacity?

6. The hypotenuse of a right-angled triangle is 12 cm in length. Find the measure of the angles in the triangle that maximize its perimeter.

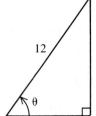

7. Sketch the graph of each function, indicating the intervals on which the function is increasing, decreasing, concave up, and concave down.

    a. $f(x) = x - 2\cos x$ **b.** $f(x) = x + 2\sin x$
    c. $f(x) = \sqrt{3}\,x - 2\sin x$ **d.** $f(x) = x - 2\sin^2 x$

8. For each function, find all points where $f'(x) = 0$ and determine their nature using the second derivative test. Use this information to sketch the graph of each function.

    a. $f(x) = \left(\sin x + \frac{1}{2}\right)^2, \quad 0 \le x \le 2\pi$

    b. $f(x) = \dfrac{3}{2 + \cos x}, \quad -\dfrac{\pi}{2} \le x \le \dfrac{3\pi}{2}$

    c. $f(x) = 2\sin^3 x - 3\sin x, \quad 0 \le x \le \pi$

9. Sketch the graph of each function using any appropriate techniques. Label the essential features. Except where noted, the interval is $-2\pi \le x \le 2\pi$.

    a. $f(x) = \cos^2 x$ **b.** $f(x) = \cos x - \sin x$

    c. $f(x) = 8\sin x - \tan x, \quad -\dfrac{\pi}{2} < x < \dfrac{\pi}{2}$ **d.** $f(x) = \cos x - \cos 2x$

    e. $f(x) = |\sin x|$ **f.** $f(x) = \sin|x|$

10. The voltage V being supplied to an electrical circuit at time t is

$$V = 100\sin 50t + 50\sin 100t$$

Find the maximum and minimum values of V over one period.

11. A particle moving along a straight line has the position function
$$s(t) = t \sin (\pi t)$$

a. Find the velocity and acceleration of the particle when $t = \frac{3}{2}$.

b. Is the particle moving towards or away from the origin when $t = \frac{3}{2}$? Is the particle slowing down or speeding up when $t = \frac{3}{2}$?

12. A line L through the point $(0, 1)$ is rotating about the point $(0, 1)$ at the rate of one revolution per minute in a clockwise direction. At what rate is the point of intersection of L and the x-axis moving along the x-axis when $x = 5$?

13. A lighthouse searchlight 1 km from shore makes one revolution every 45 s. How fast is the spot of light moving along a wall on the shore when the spot is 500 m from the point P?

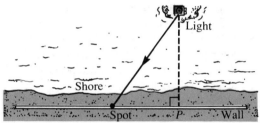

14. An isosceles triangle is inscribed in a circle of radius R. Find the value of θ that maximizes the area of the triangle.

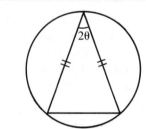

15. A light is suspended above the centre of a circular table of radius 1 m. The light intensity I at a point P on the edge of the table is proportional to $\cos \theta$ and inversely proportional to l^2. Express I in terms of θ, and determine how high the light should be in order to maximize I.

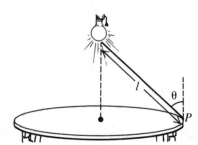

16. Find the maximum and minimum values of each function on the given interval.

a. $f(x) = \dfrac{13}{5 \sin x + 12 \cos x}, \quad 0 \le x \le \dfrac{\pi}{2}$

b. $f(x) = \sec x - x, \quad 0 \le x \le \dfrac{5\pi}{12}$

c. $f(x) = \sin x \cos^2 x, \quad 0 \le x \le \dfrac{\pi}{2}$

17. a. By graphing $y = \cos x$ and $y = x$, show that the equation

$$\cos x = x$$

has one solution.

b. Apply Newton's method (see section 3.7) to approximate this solution. Show that the recurrence formula has the form

$$x_{n+1} = \frac{x_n \sin x_n + \cos x_n}{1 + \sin x_n}$$

Problems 5.7

1. A boy is whirling a conker on a string 0.5 m long in a vertical circle at 6 rev/s. If the sun is directly overhead, find the velocity of the conker's shadow when the conker is in the two o'clock position.

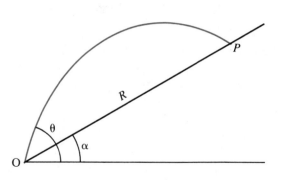

2. A stack of lumber of mass 3000 kg is dragged across a level floor by means of a chain attached to skids under the stack. The force F in the chain is related to the angle θ between the chain and the floor by

$$F = \frac{(30\ 000)k}{k \sin \theta + \cos \theta}$$

where k is the "coefficient of friction."

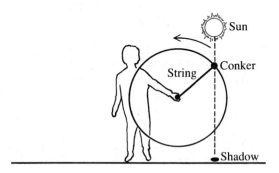

If θ can take on values in the interval $0 \le \theta \le \frac{\pi}{4}$ and $k = \frac{5}{12}$, find the angle θ that will minimize F.

3. The range R (in metres) of a projectile fired with a velocity v (in metres per second) at an angle θ to the horizontal along a surface inclined at an angle α to the horizontal is

$$R = \frac{2v^2}{g}\left[\frac{\sin(\theta - \alpha)\cos\theta}{\cos^2\alpha}\right]$$

Find the value of θ for which the range is a maximum.

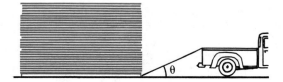

4. a. By graphing $y = \tan x$ and $y = mx$, where m is a constant, determine the values of m for which the equation

$$\tan x = mx$$

has a solution in the interval $0 < x < \dfrac{\pi}{2}$.

b. Use Newton's method to find the solution of $\tan x = 2x$ in the interval $0 < x < \dfrac{\pi}{2}$.

5. Two corridors, 3 m and 4 m wide respectively, meet at right angles. Find the length of the longest thin straight rod that can pass horizontally around the corner.

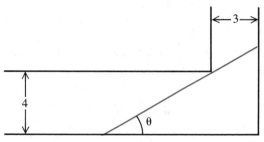

6. Repeat Problem 5 for corridors of width a metres and b metres respectively.

7. A runner in a circular arena moves from A to B at a speed of 2 m/s. A light at L casts a shadow of the runner on the curved wall of the arena at S. How fast is the shadow moving when the runner at R has moved one quarter of the distance from A to B?

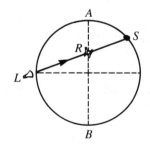

8. An isosceles triangle ABC is circumscribed about a circle of radius 3 cm. Find the minimum possible area of the triangle.

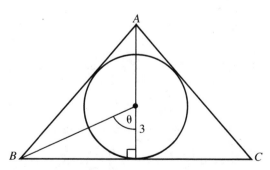

9. In Problem 8, find the minimum possible perimeter of the triangle.

10. Refer to Problem 4 in section 5.1. Show that in order to maximize the wetted area exposed to air, the centre of the disk should be at a distance $h = \dfrac{R}{\sqrt{1 + \pi^2}}$ above the surface of the water.

11. The diagram shows a rotating wheel
    and a connecting rod AB; the point B
    slides back and forth along the line OB.
    The length of the rod is 4 times the
    radius of the wheel. The wheel rotates
    counterclockwise at a rate of 400 rpm.

    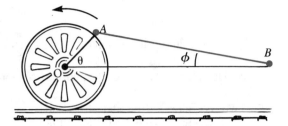

    a. Find the maximum value of the angle
    ϕ as the wheel rotates.
    (Hint: Use the Law of Sines.)

    b. Find $\dfrac{d\phi}{dt}$, the angular velocity of the connecting rod in radians per minute, when

    $\theta = \dfrac{\pi}{6}$.

    c. Show that the distance OB is

    $$OB = R(\cos\theta + \sqrt{16 - \sin^2\theta})$$

    where R is the radius of the wheel.

    d. Find the velocity of the point B when $\theta = \dfrac{\pi}{4}$ and when $\theta = \dfrac{3\pi}{4}$, assuming that
    $R = 0.5$ m.

12. Sketch the graph of $y = \dfrac{1}{1 - 2\sin x}$, showing all vertical asymptotes and turning points.

13. A bicycle is moving at a rate of 4 m/s. It has wheels of radius 40 cm, and a reflector is
    attached to the front spokes 30 cm from the centre of the wheel. If the reflector is at its
    lowest point at $t = 0$, what is the vertical component of the reflector's velocity at $t = 5$ s?

14. A circle of radius R rolls along the x-axis. A point (x, y) on the circumference travels
    along a path called a cycloid, given by the pair of equations

    $$x = R(t - \sin t) \quad \text{and} \quad y = R(1 - \cos t)$$

    where t is time (see Problem 7 in section 5.1). Show that the speed of this moving point,

    given by $\sqrt{\left(\dfrac{dx}{dt}\right)^2 + \left(\dfrac{dy}{dt}\right)^2}$, is $2R\left|\sin\left(\dfrac{t}{2}\right)\right|$.

15. At time $t = 0$, two particles are at the point $A(1, 0)$ on the circle with radius 1, centred
    at the origin. The first particle leaves the circle on a tangential path and moves upwards
    at the rate of 2 m/s. The second particle moves counterclockwise around the circle at a
    rate of 1 radian/s. Find the rate of change of the distance between the particles at $t = \pi$ s.

16. Consider the function $f(x) = x \sin \left(\frac{1}{x}\right)$, where $x > 0$.

    a. Show that

$$-x < x \sin \left(\frac{1}{x}\right) < x, \text{ for } x > 0$$

    b. Find all x-intercepts of $f(x)$.
    c. Sketch the graph of $f(x)$.
    d. Does $\lim\limits_{x \to 0^+} f(x)$ exist?

17. Sketch the graph of the function $f(x) = \sin \left(\frac{1}{x}\right)$, where $x > 0$. Does $\lim\limits_{x \to 0^+} f(x)$ exist?

18. Sketch the graph of $f(x) = \dfrac{\sin x}{x}$, $x \neq 0$. Does $\lim\limits_{x \to +\infty} f(x)$ exist?

Review Exercises

1. Find all solutions of the equation

$$2 \sin^2 x - 3 \sin x - 2 = 0$$

    between $-\pi$ and π.

2. Prove the identity

$$\frac{\sin 4x}{1 - \cos 4x} = \cot x - \frac{1}{2} \csc x \sec x$$

3. Find y' and y'' in each case.

    a. $y = 3 \sin 2x - 4 \cos 2x$ **b.** $y = \tan 3x$
    c. $y = \pi x \cos (\pi x) - \sin (\pi x)$ **d.** $y = \sin^2 2x + \cos^2 2x$
    e. $y = \cot^3 x$ **f.** $y = x \tan 2x$
    g. $y = \tan (3x^2) - \sec (3x^2)$ **h.** $y = \cos^2 (3x)$

    i. $y = \sin (x^3)$ **j.** $y = \dfrac{1}{2 - \cos x}$

4. a. Find the equation of the tangent line to the curve $y = x \sin x$ at the point where $x = \dfrac{\pi}{2}$.

    b. Use the second derivative to determine whether the curve lies above or below the tangent line near $x = \dfrac{\pi}{2}$.

5. The position function of a particle that moves in a straight line is
$x(t) = 2\pi t + \cos(2\pi t)$.

    a. Find the velocity of the particle at time t.
    b. Find the acceleration of the particle at time t.
    c. For what values of t in the interval $0 \le t \le 3$ is the particle at rest?
    d. What is the maximum velocity of the particle?

6. A particle moves along the x-axis so that at time t its position function is
$x(t) = \sin(\pi t^2)$ for $-1 \le t \le 1$.

    a. Find the velocity of the particle at time t.
    b. Find the acceleration of the particle at time t.
    c. For what values of t does the particle change direction?
    d. Find all values of t for which the particle is moving to the left.

7. Consider the function $y = \sin^2(\pi x)$. Show that

    a. $y' = \pi \sin(2\pi x)$ **b.** $y'' + 4\pi^2 y = 2\pi^2$

8. Suppose that a person's blood pressure at time t (in seconds) is

$$p = 100 + 18 \sin 7t$$

    a. Find the maximum value of p (the systolic pressure) and the minimum value of p (the diastolic pressure).
    b. How many heartbeats per minute are predicted by the formula for p?

9. A drawbridge with arms of length 10 m is constructed as shown in the diagram.

If the arms rotate at $\dfrac{\pi}{60}$ radians/s as the bridge is raised, how fast is the distance AB changing when the angle of inclination is $\theta = \dfrac{\pi}{6}$ radians?

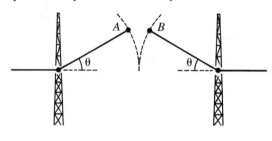

10. Find all local extrema of the function

$$f(x) = \sin x (1 - \cos x), \text{ where } 0 \le x \le 2\pi$$

Use the fact that $f(x)$ is periodic to sketch the graph for $-4\pi \le x \le 4\pi$.

11. A helicopter leaves the ground at a point 80 m from an observer and rises vertically at a rate of 2.5 m/s. How fast is the angle of elevation of the observer's line of sight to the helicopter increasing when the helicopter is at an altitude of 60 m?

12. The height of an object thrown downward from an initial altitude of 200 m is

$$h(t) = 200 - 12t - 5t^2$$

The object is being tracked by a searchlight 100 m from where the object will hit the ground. How fast is the angle of elevation of the searchlight changing after 3 s?

13. a. Sketch the graph of the function $f(x) = \cos x + \cos 2x$, for $0 \leq x \leq \pi$, by finding when the derivative of $f(x)$ is zero.

b. Extend your graph in part (a) to the interval $-\pi \leq x \leq \pi$ by using the fact that $f(x)$ is an even function.

c. Extend your graph in part (b) to the interval $-3\pi \leq x \leq 3\pi$ by using the fact that $f(x)$ is a periodic function of period 2π.

14. a. Show that the curve $y = x \sin x$ is tangent to the line $y = x$ whenever $\sin x = 1$, and is tangent to the line $y = -x$ whenever $\sin x = -1$.

b. Show that
$$-x \leq x \sin x \leq x, \text{ for } x \geq 0$$

c. Sketch the graph of $y = x \sin x$.

15. Find the maximum value attained by each function.

a. $f(x) = \sin x - \dfrac{1}{2}$

b. $f(x) = \left| \sin x - \dfrac{1}{2} \right|$

16. If $\tan(xy) = x$, find $\dfrac{dy}{dx}$ at the point $\left(1, \dfrac{\pi}{4} \right)$.

17. Suppose that $\sqrt{6} \sin x + \sqrt{2} \cos x = 2$, where $0 \leq x \leq 2\pi$. Find $\cos 2x$. (Use the method of Example 5 in section 5.2.)

18. The current I in an electrical circuit is
$$I = 10 \sin 100t + 20 \cos 100t$$

Find the peak current (maximum value of I) without using the derivative. (Use the method of Example 5 in section 5.2.)

19. If $\sin^2 x + \sin^2 y = \dfrac{5}{4}$, and $\dfrac{dx}{dt} = -1$, find $\dfrac{dy}{dt}$ at the point $(x, y) = \left(\dfrac{2\pi}{3}, \dfrac{3\pi}{4} \right)$.

20. Find the length of the shortest ladder that will reach from ground level to a high vertical wall if it must clear a 2 m vertical fence that is 3 m from the wall.
(Hint: The use of an angle as a variable can simplify this problem.)

21. a. If $-\dfrac{\pi}{2} < A < \dfrac{\pi}{2}$ and $A \neq -\dfrac{\pi}{4}$, prove that
$$\frac{\sin 2A - \cos 2A + 1}{\sin 2A + \cos 2A + 1} = \tan A$$

b. Use the result in part (a) to evaluate
$$\lim_{\theta \to -\frac{\pi}{2}} \frac{\sin \theta - \cos \theta + 1}{\sin \theta + \cos \theta + 1}$$

22. Show that the function $f(x) = x + \sin x$ has no local extrema. Sketch its graph for $-\pi \leq x \leq 3\pi$ and show all points of inflection.

23. Consider a circle of radius 1 centred at the origin. Straight lines drawn from the point $P(x, 0)$, are tangent to the circle at A and B. What is the maximum area of $\triangle OAB$, and what is the corresponding value of x?

24. A rectangle $PQRS$ is inscribed, as sketched, in the region between the x-axis and the part of the graph of $y = \cos 4x$ specified by $-\dfrac{\pi}{8} \le x \le \dfrac{\pi}{8}$. Determine the coordinates of P for which the perimeter of $PQRS$ is a maximum.

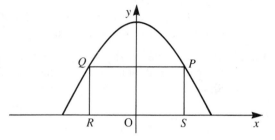

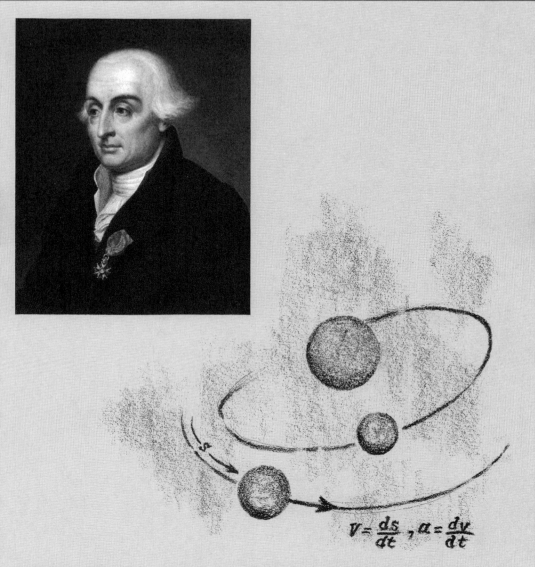

$$v = \frac{ds}{dt} \ , \ a = \frac{dv}{dt}$$

Joseph Louis Lagrange *(1736–1813) was a French-Italian mathematician and astronomer, born (as Giuseppe Lagrangia) in Turin, Italy. He became attracted to these areas after reading an article by the astronomer Halley. At the age of nineteen he was appointed a professor at the Royal Artillary School in Turin. He communicated some of his mathematical discoveries to Euler. By age twenty-five, he was regarded by some to be the greatest living mathematician. In later years, after moving to France, he was greatly admired by Napoleon. One of his greatest achievements was the application of mathematics to problems in celestial mechanics (the motion of heavenly bodies as a result of gravitational forces) and the development of a branch of mathematics called "Calculus of Variations" (which is precisely the technique now used to solve problems such as Johann Bernoulli's brachistochrone problem). In spite of his fame he remained a shy and modest man. He also married a sixteen-year-old when he was in his fifties!*

Derivatives of Logarithm and Exponential Functions

CHAPTER 6

We turn now to a study of two classes of functions that occur frequently in problems to which the methods of Calculus are applied. The exponential and logarithm functions are like the trigonometric functions in that they cannot be evaluated by means of simple arithmetic (addition, subtraction, multiplication, division, and extraction of roots). Exponential functions occur in many applications, for example the description of population growth, radioactive decay, and the cooling of a hot object. Logarithms provide the basis for the *pH* measure of chemical acidity, the decibel measure of sound intensity, and the Richter scale for measuring the magnitude of earthquakes.

We shall begin by reviewing some properties of exponential and logarithm functions.

6.1 Review

For any positive number a, the function

$$f(x) = a^x$$

is called **an exponential function with base** a. It is helpful to consider the graphs of two typical exponential functions,

$$y = 2^x \quad \text{and} \quad y = 3^x$$

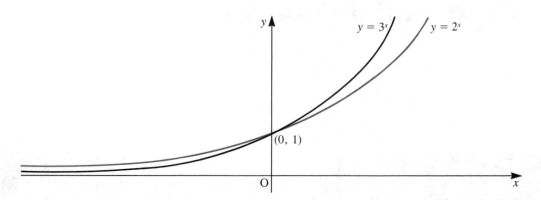

If the base a is greater than 1, then a^x increases very rapidly as $x \to +\infty$, and the larger the base the more rapid the rate of increase. On the other hand, for $a > 1$, a^x tends to zero very rapidly as $x \to -\infty$; for example, if $x = -100$, then 2^x may be written as $\dfrac{1}{2^{100}}$ which is small and positive.

To illustrate the behaviour of a^x for values of a less than 1, consider the function

$$f(x) = \left(\frac{1}{2}\right)^x$$

Since

$$\left(\frac{1}{2}\right)^x = (2^{-1})^x$$
$$= 2^{-x}$$

it follows that any exponential function with base $a < 1$ can be expressed in terms of an exponential function with base $a > 1$. The graph of the function

$$f(x) = \left(\frac{1}{2}\right)^x = 2^{-x}$$

is obtained by reflecting the graph of $y = 2^x$ in the y-axis, as shown in the diagram.

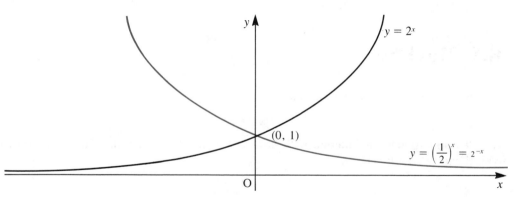

There is thus no essential loss of generality in restricting the base a to be greater than 1, and we shall do this.

Recall the following properties of exponents:

Properties of Exponents

$$a^p a^q = a^{p+q} \qquad \frac{a^p}{a^q} = a^{p-q}$$

$$a^0 = 1 \qquad (a^p)^q = a^{pq}$$

These properties are called the "laws of exponents," and hold for all real numbers p and q. They will be used routinely when we work with exponential functions. Note that $a^0 = 1$ results from setting $p = q$ in the quotient law. Note too that if we set $p = 0$ in the quotient law, we obtain

$$a^{-q} = \frac{1}{a^q}, \text{ for all } q$$

The logarithm of a number is defined by using the exponential function. If the numbers x and y, with $x > 0$, are related by

$$x = a^y$$

where a is a constant greater than 1, then y is called the logarithm of x with base a, and we write the **logarithm function**

$$y = \log_a x$$

Definition of Logarithm

For $x > 0$, $y = \log_a x$ means $x = a^y$

We can think of $\log_a x$ as the exponent to which the base a must be raised in order to give x.

It is important to recognize that a statement such as $y = \log_3 9$ can be written in the equivalent form $9 = 3^y$; this makes it clear that $y = \log_3 9 = 2$. Here are some other examples to illustrate this equivalence:

$$3 = \log_{10} 1000 \text{ is equivalent to } 1000 = 10^3$$

$$\frac{2}{3} = \log_8 4 \text{ is equivalent to } 4 = 8^{\frac{2}{3}}$$

$$1 = \log_5 5 \text{ is equivalent to } 5 = 5^1$$

$$0 = \log_c 1 \text{ is equivalent to } 1 = c^0$$

$$-1 = \log_a\left(\frac{1}{a}\right) \text{ is equivalent to } \frac{1}{a} = a^{-1}$$

The graph of the logarithm function

$$f(x) = \log_a x$$

can be found by expressing $y = \log_a x$ in the equivalent form $x = a^y$. The graph is simply the reflection of the curve $y = a^x$ in the line $y = x$, since the roles of x and y have been interchanged. The graphs of a^x and $\log_a x$, where $a > 1$, are shown in the diagram.

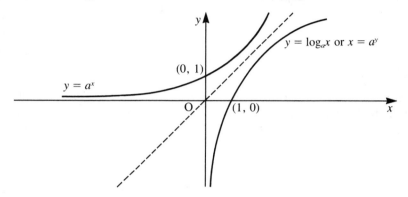

Note the following observations that can be made from the graphs:

- The domain of $y = a^x$ is $\{x \in R\}$.

- The range of $y = a^x$ is $\{y \in R \mid y > 0\}$.

- The domain of $y = \log_a x$ is $\{x \in R \mid x > 0\}$.

- The range of $y = \log_a x$ is $\{y \in R\}$.

Since $a^0 = 1$, the graph of $y = a^x$ (for any base a) passes through the point $(0, 1)$. Likewise, since $\log_a 1 = 0$, the graph of $y = \log_a x$ passes through the point $(1, 0)$. The graphs also display the fact that a^x and $\log_a x$ are **continuous functions** on their domains.

The following four properties of logarithms are direct consequences of the properties of exponents that were stated earlier.

Properties of Logarithms

$$\log_a (xy) = \log_a x + \log_a y, \text{ for } x, y > 0$$

$$\log_a \left(\frac{x}{y}\right) = \log_a x - \log_a y, \text{ for } x, y > 0$$

$$\log_a 1 = 0$$

$$\log_a (x^y) = y \log_a x, \text{ for } x > 0 \text{ and for all } y$$

These **"laws of logarithms"** will be used extensively in the following chapters. It is a common error to write $\log_a (x + y) = \log_a x + \log_a y$, whereas in fact $\log_a x + \log_a y = \log_a (xy)$.

Since the graphs of a^x and $\log_a x$ are related by reflection in the line $y = x$, these functions are **inverse functions** of one another (just as x^3 and $x^{\frac{1}{3}}$ are inverse functions of one another). If we substitute $y = \log_a x$ for y in $x = a^y$, we obtain

$$a^{\log_a x} = x$$

On the other hand, if we substitute $x = a^y$ for x in $y = \log_a x$, we obtain

$$\log_a (a^y) = y$$

In order to clarify the significance of these equations, write

$$f(x) = a^x \quad \text{and} \quad g(x) = \log_a x$$

Then the equations $a^{\log_a x} = x$ and $\log_a (a^y) = y$ become

$$f(g(x)) = x \quad \text{and} \quad g(f(y)) = y$$

In other words, if the exponential function and logarithm function are applied successively to a number, the number is left unchanged. This reiterates the fact that $\log_a x$ and a^x are inverse functions of one another.

If we choose $y = 1$ in the equation $\log_a (a^y) = y$, we obtain the important result that

$$\log_a a = 1$$

These last three results are known as the inverse identities.

The Inverse Identities

$$a^{\log_a x} = x, \text{ for all } x > 0$$

$$\log_a (a^y) = y, \text{ for all } y$$

$$\log_a a = 1$$

Finally, we derive the **change of base identity** for logarithms. This identity will allow us to express a logarithm with a certain base in terms of a more convenient base. For example, suppose we wish to express

$$y = \log_a x$$

in terms of a logarithm with base b. First switch to exponent form to obtain

$$x = a^y$$

Now take the logarithm with base b of each side of this equation, obtaining

$$\log_b x = \log_b a^y$$
$$= y \log_b a$$

On substituting for y, and rearranging, we obtain

$$\log_a x = \frac{\log_b x}{\log_b a}$$

This tells us that we can calculate logarithms to base a if we know logarithms to base b. For example, we can calculate $\log_2 100$ even though our calculators don't have a $\boxed{\log_2}$ key, as follows:

$$\log_2 100 = \frac{\log_{10} 100}{\log_{10} 2}$$

$$= \frac{2}{0.301}$$

$$= 6.64$$

Exercises 6.1

1. Express each equation in equivalent logarithmic form.

    a. $3^3 = 27$ **b.** $4^{-2} = \frac{1}{16}$

    c. $6^0 = 1$ **d.** $2^x = 7$

    e. $a^1 = a$ **f.** $x^3 = 3$

2. Express each equation in equivalent exponential form.

    a. $\log_3 \left(\frac{1}{3}\right) = -1$ **b.** $\log_{11}(121) = 2$

    c. $x = \log_5 7$ **d.** $y = \log_x 2$

    e. $\log_{125} x = \frac{1}{3}$ **f.** $\frac{1}{2} = \log_9 3$

3. Simplify each expression.

    a. $\log_5 125$ **b.** $\log_3 81$

    c. $\log_{10}(10\ 000)$ **d.** $\log_{10}(0.0001)$

    e. $10^{\log_{10} 3}$ **f.** $5^{\log_5 7}$

    g. $3^{-2\log_3 5}$ **h.** $10^{-3\log_{10} 2}$

    i. $\log_3 \left(5^3 9^{-3} 25^{-\frac{3}{2}}\right)$ **j.** $\log_2 20 - \log_2 5$

    k. $\log_{10} 3 + \log_{10}\left(\frac{1}{30}\right)$ **l.** $\dfrac{\log_{10} 27}{\log_{10} 3}$

    m. $\log_5(5^4)$ **n.** $\dfrac{\log_2 100}{\log_2 10}$

    o. $\log_b \sqrt{b}$ **p.** $b^{\log_b 10}$

4. Solve each equation for x.

    a. $\log_{10} x = 2$ **b.** $\log_5 x = 3$

    c. $\log_3 x = -2$ **d.** $\log_{10} x = 2 \log_{10} 5$

    e. $\log_3 x = 3 \log_3 10$ **f.** $\log_3 x = \log_3 24 - \log_3 6$

    g. $\log_2 (2x) = 0$ **h.** $\log_3 (5x) = 1$

    i. $\log_2 (2^x) = 10$ **j.** $\log_5 (10^x) = 7$

    k. $\log_x 27 = 2$ **l.** $\log_{x^2} 81 = 1$

    m. $\log_2 (8x) = 3 \log_2 x$ **n.** $\log_x (2x^3 - 8) = 3$

5. The point $\left(2, \frac{1}{2}\right)$ lies on the graph of $y = \log_b x$. Find b.

6. Sketch the graph of $f(x) = \log_{10} (10x)$, and find its x-intercept. Show that this graph is the graph of $\log_{10} x$ translated vertically by 1 unit.

7. Sketch the graph of each function and find its x-intercept.

    a. $y = \log_3 (x - 1)$ **b.** $y = \log_{10} (x + 2)$

    c. $y = \log_2 (4x - 8)$ **d.** $y = \log_3 (9x)$

8. Sketch the graph of each function and find its x-intercept.

    a. $y = 5^x - 1$ **b.** $y = 2^{-x} - 4$

    c. $y = 3^{x+2}$ **d.** $y = 5^{2-x}$

9. Use the change of base identity

$$\log_a x = \frac{\log_b x}{\log_b a}$$

to evaluate each quantity.

    a. $\dfrac{\log_5 81}{\log_5 3}$ **b.** $\dfrac{\log_2 25}{\log_2 5}$

    c. $\dfrac{\log_7 2}{\log_7 8}$ **d.** $M^{\left[\frac{\log_b 5}{\log_b M}\right]}$

10. If I_0 is the intensity of barely audible sound, then the decibel (dB) measure of the loudness, L, of a sound of intensity I is given by

$$L = \log_{10} \left[\frac{I}{I_0}\right]$$

    a. What is the loudness (in dB) of a sound of intensity I_0? $10 I_0$? $10^{10} I_0$?

    b. A loudness of 140 dB is considered to be the pain threshold. What is the intensity I of such a sound?

11. An earthquake of minimal intensity I_0 is given a value 0 on the Richter scale. An earthquake of intensity I has a magnitude

$$R = \log_{10}\left[\frac{I}{I_0}\right]$$

on the Richter scale.

a. Express I in terms of R and I_0.

b. Show that increasing the intensity of the earthquake by a factor of 10 will increase the Richter magnitude by 1.

12. The *pH* value of a chemical solution measures the acidity or alkalinity of the solution. The formula is

$$pH = -\log_{10}[H^+]$$

where $[H^+]$ is the concentration of hydrogen ions in the solution (in moles per litre).

a. Distilled water has a hydrogen ion concentration of 10^{-7} moles per litre. What is its *pH* value?

b. Tomatoes have $[H^+] = 6.3 \times 10^{-5}$. Find the *pH* value.

c. Acidic solutions have $pH < 7$ and basic solutions have $pH > 7$. Which type of solution has the higher concentration of hydrogen ions?

Problems 6.1

1. Find where the graphs of $y = 2\log_{10}x$ and $y = \log_{10}2x$ intersect. Sketch the graphs.

2. Sketch the graph of each function.

    a. $f(x) = 2^{-|x|}$ **b.** $f(x) = |1 - 2^{-x}|$

3. If $\log_{10}2 = x$, express $\log_2 5$ in terms of x.

4. Sketch the graph of each function.

    a. $y = \log_{10}|x|$ **b.** $y = |\log_{10}x|$

6.2 A Fundamental Limit and the Number *e*

The next step in studying the logarithm and exponential functions is to find their derivatives. We shall start with the logarithm function

$$f(x) = \log_a x, \quad x > 0$$

In order to find $f'(x)$ we use the definition of the derivative, since $\log_a x$ cannot be expressed in terms of functions with known derivatives. Furthermore, the problem of simplifying the difference quotient cannot be resolved for logarithm functions by algebraic manipulation such as "rationalizing." We encountered this type of situation when finding the derivative of the cosine function. That problem led to the fundamental trigonometric limit

$$\lim_{h \to 0} \frac{\sin h}{h} = 1$$

With the logarithm function, we shall encounter a second fundamental limit, namely

$$\lim_{t \to 0} (1 + t)^{\frac{1}{t}}$$

One might guess that this limit equals 1, since $1 + t \to 1$ as $t \to 0$, and 1 raised to any power equals 1. This conclusion is false, however. The argument is invalid, since $1 + t$ never actually equals 1 in the limit process, and the exponent $\frac{1}{t}$ increases without bound as $t \to 0$. We thus investigate this limit numerically, with the results summarized in the following table.

t	-0.01	-0.001	-0.0001	0.0001	0.001	0.01
$(1 + t)^{\frac{1}{t}}$	2.731 999	2.719 642	2.718 418	2.718 146	2.716 924	2.704 814

It appears that $\lim_{t \to 0} (1 + t)^{\frac{1}{t}}$ does exist and has a value between 2.718 146 and 2.718 418.

There is no simple proof, however, that this limit exists. By an indirect method of proof it can be shown that the limit is an irrational number whose value, accurate to 12 decimal places, is

$$2.718\ 281\ 828\ 459$$

This number is called e, in honour of the 18th century mathematician Leonhard Euler (pronounced "oiler"). Thus we can consider the following equation to be the definition of the number e.

Definition of e

$$e = \lim_{t \to 0} (1 + t)^{\frac{1}{t}}$$

We shall see that the number e plays as fundamental a role in connection with the logarithm and exponential functions as π does in connection with the circle and the trigonometric functions.

The definition of e implies that

$$(1 + t)^{\frac{1}{t}} \approx e$$

for any number t that is **sufficiently close to zero**. The essential point is that the exponent is the reciprocal of the number that is added to 1. We can thus write the definition of e symbolically as

$$\lim_{[\ ] \to 0} (1 + [\ ])^{\frac{1}{[\ ]}} = e$$

where any variable can be inserted in [ ]. For example,

$$\lim_{u^2 \to 0} (1 + u^2)^{\frac{1}{u^2}} = e$$

and since $u \to 0$ as $u^2 \to 0$, this limit can be expressed as

$$\lim_{u \to 0} (1 + u^2)^{\frac{1}{u^2}} = e$$

If the exponent is not equal to the reciprocal of the additive term, however, the limit may not equal e, as Example 1 shows.

Example 1. Evaluate $\lim_{h \to 0} (1 + 2h)^{\frac{1}{h}}$.

Solution. Let $2h = t$. Then $\dfrac{1}{h} = \dfrac{2}{t}$ and

$$(1 + 2h)^{\frac{1}{h}} = \left[(1 + t)^{\frac{2}{t}} \right]$$

$$= \left[(1 + t)^{\frac{1}{t}} \right]^2$$

Since $t \to 0$ as $h \to 0$, it follows that

$$\lim_{h \to 0} (1 + 2h)^{\frac{1}{h}} = \lim_{t \to 0} \left[(1 + t)^{\frac{1}{t}} \right]^2$$

$$= \left[\lim_{t \to 0} (1 + t)^{\frac{1}{t}} \right]^2$$

$$= e^2$$

An equivalent definition of the number e can be given in terms of an integer variable. Let $t = \dfrac{1}{n}$, where n takes on positive integer values. Then $n \to +\infty$ as $t \to 0^+$ and the definition of e can be expressed as follows:

$$e = \lim_{n \to +\infty} \left(1 + \frac{1}{n} \right)^n$$

Exercises 6.2

1. Use the fundamental limit

$$\lim_{t \to 0} (1 + t)^{\frac{1}{t}} = e$$

to evaluate each limit.

a. $\lim_{h \to 0} \left((1 + h)^{\frac{3}{h}}\right)$

b. $\lim_{x \to 0} \left(1 + \frac{x}{5}\right)^{\frac{1}{x}}$

c. $\lim_{u \to 0} (1 + 3u)^{\frac{1}{u}}$

d. $\lim_{y \to 0} (1 + 4y)^{\frac{2}{y}}$

e. $\lim_{t \to 0} (1 + \sin t)^{\frac{1}{\sin t}}$

f. $\lim_{\theta \to \frac{\pi}{2}} (1 + \cos \theta)^{\frac{1}{\cos \theta}}$

2. Use the fundamental limit

$$\lim_{n \to +\infty} \left(1 + \frac{1}{n}\right)^{n} = e$$

to evaluate each limit.

a. $\lim_{n \to +\infty} \left(1 + \frac{2}{n}\right)^{n}$

b. $\lim_{m \to +\infty} \left(1 + \frac{1}{m^2}\right)^{m^2}$

c. $\lim_{n \to +\infty} \left(1 + \frac{3}{n}\right)^{n}$

d. $\lim_{p \to +\infty} \left(1 + \frac{1}{p + 100}\right)^{p}$

Problems 6.2

1. Use the fundamental limit

$$\lim_{t \to 0} (1 + t)^{\frac{1}{t}} = e$$

to evaluate each limit.

a. $\lim_{u \to 0} (1 + u^2)^{\frac{1}{u}}$

b. $\lim_{u \to 0} (1 + u)^{\frac{1}{u^2}}$

Explain intuitively why neither answer involves e.

2. An amount of P dollars earns interest at $r\%$ per year. If the interest is compounded n times per year, show that after 1 year the amount has increased to

$$P\left(1 + \frac{r}{100n}\right)^{n} \text{ dollars}$$

What will the amount be after 1 year with "continuous compounding" of interest (i.e., $n \to +\infty$)? Does continuous compounding have a significant benefit compared to daily compounding?

6.3 The Derivative of the Logarithm Function

The fundamental limit

$$\lim_{t \to 0} (1 + t)^{\frac{1}{t}} = e$$

enables us to find the derivative of the logarithm function

$$f(x) = \log_a x, \quad x > 0$$

By the definition of the derivative,

$$f'(x) = \lim_{h \to 0} \frac{f(x + h) - f(x)}{h}$$

$$= \lim_{h \to 0} \frac{\log_a (x + h) - \log_a x}{h}$$

$$= \lim_{h \to 0} \frac{\log_a \left(\dfrac{x + h}{x} \right)}{h} \qquad \text{(quotient property for logarithms)}$$

$$= \lim_{h \to 0} \left[\frac{1}{h} \log_a \left(1 + \frac{h}{x} \right) \right]$$

In order to apply the fundamental limit, let

$$t = \frac{h}{x}$$

Since x is a fixed positive number, it follows that $t \to 0$ as $h \to 0$. Thus, on eliminating h in the expression for $f'(x)$, we obtain

$$f'(x) = \lim_{t \to 0} \left[\left(\frac{1}{x} \right) \left(\frac{1}{t} \log_a (1 + t) \right) \right]$$

The second expression in parentheses can be rewritten as

$$\log_a (1 + t)^{\frac{1}{t}}$$

by using the power property of logarithms, and the factor $\dfrac{1}{x}$ can be taken outside the limit as a constant. Therefore,

$$f'(x) = \frac{1}{x} \lim_{t \to 0} \left[\log_a (1 + t)^{\frac{1}{t}} \right]$$

$$= \frac{1}{x} \log_a \left[\lim_{t \to 0} (1 + t)^{\frac{1}{t}} \right]$$

$$= \frac{1}{x} \log_a e$$

by the definition of e. Interchanging the limit and logarithm operations is justified by the fact that the logarithm function is continuous (as shown by its graph). This point is discussed in Problem 8. In summary, for $x > 0$ and for any $a > 0$, $a \neq 1$, we have shown that

$$\frac{d}{dx}(\log_a x) = \frac{1}{x}\log_a e$$

The value of the constant $\log_a e$ depends on the **base a of the logarithm function**. This derivative formula would be particularly simple if $\log_a e$ were equal to one. Since $\log_a a = 1$, we have

$$\log_e e = 1$$

and thus if we choose $a = e$ in the derivative formula, we obtain

$$\frac{d}{dx}(\log_e x) = \frac{1}{x}$$

When one is working with logarithm functions in Calculus, it is customary to choose base e, since then the derivative formula is simple. For this reason the logarithm function with base e has been given a special name, the **natural logarithm** of x, and a special notation, $\ln x$, pronounced ''lon x''.

The Natural Logarithm

For $x > 0$, the natural logarithm of x is defined by

$$\ln x = \log_e x$$

We now give the derivative formula for the natural logarithm function in this notation.

Derivative of ln x

$$\frac{d}{dx}(\ln x) = \frac{1}{x}, \text{ for } x > 0$$

The exponential function that corresponds to the natural logarithm function is denoted e^x. The inverse identities that relate $\ln x$ and e^x are obtained by setting $a = e$ in the inverse identities in section 6.1.

The Inverse Identities

$$e^{\ln x} = x, \text{ for all } x > 0$$

$$\ln(e^y) = y, \text{ for all real } y$$

$$\ln e = 1$$

Example 1. Sketch the graph of the natural logarithm function

$$f(x) = \ln x, \quad x > 0$$

showing its tangent line when $x = e$.

Solution. The graph has the general shape of the logarithm graph $y = \log_a x$, with $a > 1$. The conditions $\ln 1 = 0$ and $\ln e = 1$ determine two points on the graph. The derivative

$$f'(x) = \frac{1}{x}$$

which is positive for $x > 0$, confirms that $\ln x$ is increasing for all $x > 0$. The slope of the tangent line at $(e, 1)$ is

$$f'(e) = \frac{1}{e}$$

Thus the equation of the tangent line at $(e, 1)$ is

$$y - 1 = \frac{1}{e}(x - e)$$

which can be simplified to

$$y = \frac{1}{e}x$$

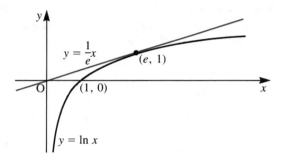

This tangent line passes through the origin, and we obtain the given diagram.

Note that $\ln x$ increases without bound as $x \to +\infty$. In addition, the graph of $\ln x$ has the y-axis as a vertical asymptote.

Using limit notation, we write

$$\lim_{x \to +\infty} \ln x = +\infty \quad \text{and} \quad \lim_{x \to 0+} \ln x = -\infty$$

Observe also that the derivative of $\ln x$ tends to 0 as $x \to +\infty$. This is related to the fact that although $\ln x \to +\infty$ as $x \to +\infty$, it does so at a very slow rate (for example, $\ln 10^6 = 6 \ln 10 \approx 13.8$). The graph appears to level off, but in fact it continues to rise indefinitely, and there is no horizontal asymptote. Problems 2 and 3 shed more light on the behaviour of $\ln x$ as $x \to +\infty$.

Example 2. If $f(x) = x(\ln x)^3$, for $x > 0$, find $f'\left(\frac{1}{e}\right)$.

Solution. By the product rule,

$$f'(x) = (1)(\ln x)^3 + x\frac{d}{dx}(\ln x)^3$$

By the Chain Rule,

$$\frac{d}{dx}(\ln x)^3 = 3(\ln x)^2 \frac{d}{dx}(\ln x)$$
$$= \frac{3(\ln x)^2}{x}$$

Hence,

$$f'(x) = (\ln x)^3 + 3(\ln x)^2$$

and

$$f'\left(\frac{1}{e}\right) = \left(\ln\frac{1}{e}\right)^3 + 3\left(\ln\frac{1}{e}\right)^2$$

Since $\ln\dfrac{1}{e} = \ln e^{-1} = -\ln e = -1$,

$$f'\left(\frac{1}{e}\right) = 2$$ □

Example 3. Referring to Example 2, find all points at which the graph of $f(x)$ has a horizontal tangent line.

Solution. From Example 2,

$$f(x) = x(\ln x)^3$$

and

$$f'(x) = (\ln x)^3 + 3(\ln x)^2, \text{ for } x > 0$$

For a horizontal tangent line, $f'(x) = 0$, so

$$(\ln x)^2(\ln x + 3) = 0$$

Hence,

$$\ln x = 0 \quad \text{or} \quad \ln x = -3$$

On solving for x, we get

$$x = e^0 = 1 \quad \text{or} \quad x = e^{-3}$$

and the corresponding function values are

$$f(1) = 0, \quad f(e^{-3}) = -\frac{27}{e^3}$$

Thus the tangent line is horizontal at $(1, 0)$ and $\left(\dfrac{1}{e^3}, -\dfrac{27}{e^3}\right)$.   □

Example 4. If $f(x) = [\ln{(\cos{x})}]^2$, find $f'\left(\dfrac{\pi}{4}\right)$.

Solution. **For this function, the Chain Rule has to be applied twice.**

$$f'(x) = 2\ln{(\cos{x})}\frac{d}{dx}[\ln{(\cos{x})}]$$

$$= 2[\ln{(\cos{x})}]\left(\frac{1}{\cos{x}}\right)\frac{d}{dx}(\cos{x})$$

$$= 2[\ln{(\cos{x})}]\left(\frac{1}{\cos{x}}\right)(-\sin{x})$$

$$= -2\tan{x}\,\ln{(\cos{x})}$$

Hence,

$$f'\left(\frac{\pi}{4}\right) = -2\tan{\frac{\pi}{4}}\ln\left(\cos{\frac{\pi}{4}}\right)$$

$$= -2\ln\left(\frac{1}{\sqrt{2}}\right)$$

$$= -2\ln\left(2^{-\frac{1}{2}}\right)$$

$$= \ln{2} \qquad\qquad \square$$

When working with $\ln{x}$ and e^x, it is usually best not to evaluate all answers numerically with a calculator but to leave them in terms of symbols such as e, $\sqrt{e}$, and $\ln{2}$ where appropriate. However, expressions such as $\ln\left(\dfrac{1}{\sqrt{2}}\right)$, as in the last example, or $e^{-2\ln{2}}$, should be simplified.

It is customary in Calculus and its applications **to work exclusively with the natural logarithm function** $\ln{x}$. Note, however, that $\log_a{x}$ can be related to $\ln{x}$ by choosing $b = e$ in the change of base identity in section 6.1.

$$\log_a{x} = \frac{\ln{x}}{\ln{a}}$$

This shows that any logarithm function with base a, $\log_a{x}$, is just the constant $\dfrac{1}{\ln{a}}$ times the natural logarithm function, $\ln{x}$. All the properties of $\log_a{x}$ may therefore be obtained from the corresponding properties for $\ln{x}$. For example,

$$\frac{d}{dx}(\log_a{x}) = \frac{1}{x}\left(\frac{1}{\ln{a}}\right)$$

Finally, note that the differentiation formula

$$\frac{d}{dx}(\ln{x}) = \frac{1}{x}$$

fills a gap in the following table.

$f(x)$	$-\dfrac{1}{3x^3}$	$-\dfrac{1}{2x^2}$	$-\dfrac{1}{x}$	?	x	$\dfrac{x^2}{2}$	$\dfrac{x^3}{3}$	$\dfrac{x^4}{4}$	$\dfrac{x^5}{5}$
$f'(x)$	$\dfrac{1}{x^4}$	$\dfrac{1}{x^3}$	$\dfrac{1}{x^2}$	$\dfrac{1}{x}$	1	x	x^2	x^3	x^4

The missing function (?) is of course $\ln x$. This will be useful when we are faced with the problem of finding a function whose derivative is given. (See Chapters 7 and 8.)

Exercises 6.3

1. Find the derivative of each function.

   a. $f(x) = \ln(x - 2)$ **b.** $f(x) = 3\ln(4 - 3x)$
   c. $f(x) = \ln(x^2 + 5)$ **d.** $f(x) = \ln x^2 + \ln 5$

   e. $g(t) = \ln\left(\sqrt{t} + \dfrac{1}{\sqrt{t}}\right)$ **f.** $h(t) = t^2 \ln t$

   g. $f(x) = (\ln x)^4$ **h.** $f(x) = \ln(x^4)$
   i. $f(t) = (t \ln t)^4$ **j.** $f(v) = (\ln v + v)^3$
   k. $g(u) = (\sin u)(\ln u)$ **l.** $f(y) = \ln(\sin y)$

   m. $f(x) = \dfrac{\ln x}{3 + \ln x}$ **n.** $g(t) = \ln(\sin t + \cos t)$

   o. $y = \cos^2(\ln x)$ **p.** $y = \sin(\ln u)$

   q. $y = \ln\sqrt{9 - x^2}$ **r.** $y = \ln\left[\dfrac{1 + x}{1 - x}\right]$

2. Find the domain of each function and sketch its graph. In each case find the equation of the tangent line at the x-intercept of the graph.

   a. $f(x) = \ln(x + 1)$ **b.** $f(x) = \ln(2x + 5)$
   c. $f(x) = \ln(2 - x)$ **d.** $f(x) = \ln(1 - 3x)$

3. **a.** By differentiating and simplifying, show that each pair of functions has the same derivative.

   (i) $f(x) = \ln(10x^2), \quad g(x) = \ln(x^2)$
   (ii) $f(x) = \ln(\sin 2x), \quad g(x) = \ln(\sin x) + \ln(\cos x)$
   (iii) $f(x) = \ln(\tan x), \quad g(x) = \ln(\sin x) - \ln(\cos x)$

   b. For each pair of functions in part a, show that

   $$f(x) - g(x) = k, \text{ where } k \text{ is a constant}$$

4. Show that the curve

   $$y = \ln x - (x - 1) + \frac{1}{2}(x - 1)^2$$

   has a horizontal tangent and a point of inflection at the point $(1, 0)$.

5. Let $y = \ln(\sec x)$. Show that

$$\left(\frac{dy}{dx}\right)^2 = e^{2y} - 1$$

6. Find $\dfrac{dy}{dx}$ at the given point.

    a. $\ln y - x = 0$, $(1, e)$
    b. $x \ln y + xy = 2$, $(2, 1)$
    c. $\ln(x^2 + y^2) + \sin x = 1$, $(0, \sqrt{e})$

7. Verify that the graph of $y = \ln x$ is concave down for all $x > 0$.

8. Let $f(x) = \ln(\ln x)$.

    a. Find the domain of $f(x)$.
    b. Find the slope of the tangent line to the graph of $f(x)$ at its x-intercept.

9. Consider the curve $y = (x \ln x)^2$. Find all points at which the curve has a horizontal tangent line.

10. Let $f(x) = [\ln(4 - x^2)]^2$.

    a. Find the domain of $f(x)$.
    b. Find all points at which the graph of $f(x)$ has a horizontal tangent line.

11. Use the properties of exponentials and logarithms and the relations

$$e^{\ln x} = x, \text{ for } x > 0$$

and

$$\ln(e^y) = y, \text{ for all } y$$

to reduce the following expressions to simplest form (i.e., eliminate all exponents and roots).

    a. $\ln(e^{-2})$ **b.** $\ln\left[\dfrac{\sqrt{2}}{\sqrt{3}}\right]$

    c. $e^{-2 \ln 3 + 3 \ln 2}$ **d.** $e^{-\ln\left(\frac{1}{e}\right)}$

    e. $\ln(3^{-e}e^3)$ **f.** $\ln\left(\dfrac{\sqrt{\pi}}{e}\right)$

12. Solve each equation for x.

    a. $\ln x + 3 = 0$ **b.** $2 \ln x - 5 = 0$
    c. $(\ln x)^2 - 4 = 0$ **d.** $(\ln x)^2 + (\ln x) - 2 = 0$
    e. $2 \ln x = \ln(4x + 5)$

13. Evaluate $\displaystyle\lim_{h \to 0} \frac{\ln(3 + h) - \ln 3}{h}$

(Hint: Think of the definition of the derivative.)

14. In this section, when we used the definition of the derivative to differentiate $\log_a x$, we obtained the formula

$$\frac{d}{dx}(\log_a x) = \frac{1}{x}\log_a e$$

At the end of this section, we used the change of base formula to show that

$$\frac{d}{dx}(\log_a x) = \frac{1}{x}\left(\frac{1}{\ln a}\right)$$

Show that the two formulae are equivalent.

Problems 6.3

1. The number of bacteria in a culture t hours after incubation began is given by

$$N = 1000e^{\frac{t}{5}}, \quad t \geq 0$$

How long will the population take to double, starting at $t = 0$? Starting at $t = 5$?

2. By constructing a table of values for $\dfrac{\ln x}{x}$, with $x = 10, 10^2, \ldots, 10^6$, make a conjecture concerning

$$\lim_{x \to +\infty} \frac{\ln x}{x}$$

3. Evaluate $\lim\limits_{x \to +\infty} \dfrac{\ln x}{x}$ as follows.

   a. By sketching the graphing of $y = \ln t$ and the tangent line to this graph at $(e, 1)$ (see Example 1), show that

   $$0 < \ln t \leq \frac{t}{e}, \text{ for } t > 1$$

   b. Let $t = \sqrt{x}$ in the result of part (a) and show that

   $$0 < \frac{\ln x}{x} \leq \frac{2}{e\sqrt{x}}, \text{ for } x > 1$$

   c. Hence, evaluate

   $$\lim_{x \to +\infty} \frac{\ln x}{x}$$

4. Sketch the graph of $f(x) = \dfrac{\ln x}{x}$.

5. Use the result of part (a) of Problem 3 to evaluate

$$\lim_{x \to +\infty} \frac{(\ln x)^n}{x}$$

for any positive number n.

(Hint: Let $t = x^{\frac{1}{2n}}$.)

6. Use the tangent approximation (see section 3.6) for $f(x) = \ln x$ at $x = 1$ to show that

$$\ln x \approx x - 1$$

for x close to 1. Compare the values of $\ln x$ and $x - 1$ for x-values of 0.90, 0.95, 1.00, 1.05, and 1.10.

7. a. Use the tangent approximation to show that

$$\sqrt{1 + \ln x} \approx 1 + \frac{1}{2}(x - 1)$$

for x close to 1.

b. Use the result of part (a) to approximate $\sqrt{1 + \ln(0.94)}$. Check the accuracy of your answer with a calculator.

8. Prove that if

$$\lim_{x \to a} g(x) = L$$

and if $f(y)$ is continuous at $y = L$, then

$$\lim_{x \to a} f(g(x)) = f(\lim_{x \to a} g(x))$$

In words, "a limit can be taken inside a continuous function."

Hint: By the definition of a continuous function,

$$\lim_{y \to L} f(y) = f(L)$$

Make the substitution $y = g(x)$.

9. Verify that the function defined implicitly by

$$\ln(x + y) = xy$$

has a local minimum at $(0, 1)$.

(Hint: Find y' and y'' implicitly and then use these along with the given information.)

6.4 The Exponential Function

In this section we shall study the exponential function $f(x) = e^x$ and find its derivative.

The graph of e^x has the general shape of an exponential function such as 2^x or 3^x (recall that $e \approx 2.718$ and see the first graph in section 6.1). Since e^x and $\ln x$ are inverse functions, their graphs are images of each other under reflection in the line $y = x$.

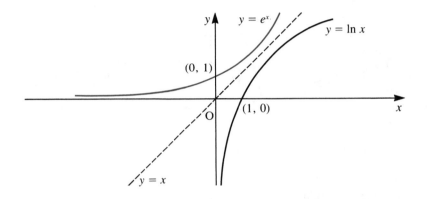

Note the limits

$$\lim_{x \to +\infty} e^x = +\infty \quad \text{and} \quad \lim_{x \to -\infty} e^x = 0$$

The latter corresponding to the fact that $y = e^x$ has the x-axis as a horizontal asymptote.

Knowing the graph of e^x, one can sketch the graphs of related functions such as $2 - e^x$, e^{-x}, and $8 - e^{-3x}$. For example, the graph of $y = e^{-x}$ is obtained by reflecting the graph of e^x in the y-axis.

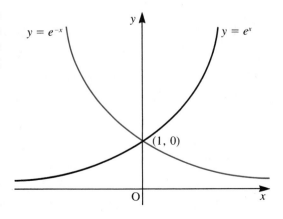

Example 1. Sketch the graph of $y = 8 - e^{-3x}$, and find its x-intercept.

Solution. We obtain the graph in two stages. The graph of $y = e^{-3x}$ is reflected in the x-axis to give $y = -e^{-3x}$, which is then translated upwards by 8 units.

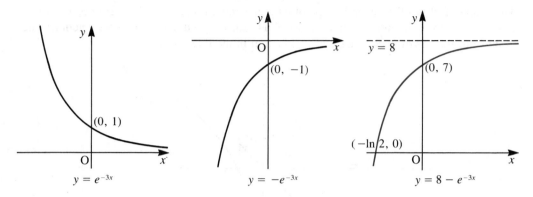

The x-intercept is obtained by letting $y = 0$, giving

$$e^{-3x} = 8$$

We take the natural logarithm of both sides, obtaining

$$\ln(e^{-3x}) = \ln 8$$

This can be simplified using the properties of logarithms.

$$-3x \ln e = \ln(2^3)$$
$$-3x(1) = 3 \ln 2$$
$$x = -\ln 2$$

We now proceed to find the **derivative of e^x**.

We start with

$$y = e^x$$

or, equivalently,

$$\ln y = x$$

This equation defines y implicitly as a function of x. Differentiate both sides with respect to x, obtaining

$$\frac{d}{dx}(\ln y) = 1$$

By the Chain Rule,

$$\frac{d}{dy}(\ln y)\frac{dy}{dx} = 1$$

and hence

$$\frac{1}{y}\frac{dy}{dx} = 1$$

Multiply both sides by y and, since $y = e^x$, we obtain

$$\frac{dy}{dx} = e^x$$

Derivative of e^x

$$\frac{d}{dx}(e^x) = e^x$$

The exponential function with base e has the striking property that **its derivative is the same function** (see also Problem 1). Geometrically this means that for the graph of $y = e^x$, the slope at any point equals the y-coordinate of the point. One consequence of this is discussed in Problem 2.

Example 2. Find the derivative of each function.

a. $f(x) = e^{5x}$ **b.** $g(x) = (\cos 3x)\,e^{-2x}$

Solution.

a. Apply the Chain Rule, writing

$$y = e^u \quad \text{and} \quad u = 5x$$

It follows that

$$\frac{dy}{dx} = \frac{dy}{du}\frac{du}{dx}$$
$$= e^u(5)$$

Hence,

$$f'(x) = 5e^{5x}$$

b. Apply the Product Rule, to obtain

$$g'(x) = \left[\frac{d}{dx}(\cos 3x)\right]e^{-2x} + \cos 3x\left[\frac{d}{dx}(e^{-2x})\right]$$

On using the Chain Rule, we obtain

$$g'(x) = -3\sin 3x\, e^{-2x} + \cos 3x(-2e^{-2x})$$
$$= -e^{-2x}(3\sin 3x + 2\cos 3x)$$

Example 3. Sketch the graph of the function $f(x) = e^{-x^2}$.

Solution. First, observe that $f(x)$ is an even function,

$$f(-x) = f(x)$$

so that the graph is symmetric about the y-axis. Since $e^{-x^2} = \dfrac{1}{e^{x^2}}$, $f(x)$ will tend to zero as x increases without bound.

$$\lim_{x \to +\infty} f(x) = 0$$

Using the Chain Rule, we differentiate to obtain

$$f'(x) = -2xe^{-x^2}$$

Hence, $f'(0) = 0$, and the tangent line is horizontal at $x = 0$. In addition, $f'(x) < 0$ for $x > 0$, and so $f(x)$ is a decreasing function for $x > 0$.

We thus obtain the following graph:

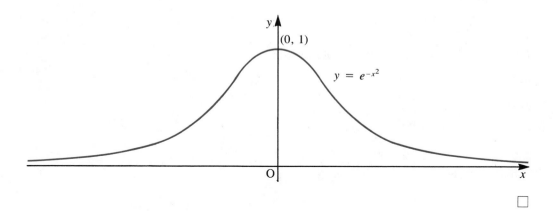

The shape of the graph implies that there are two points of inflection. These points can be found using the second derivative (see Exercise 5).

Example 4. Find the maximum and minimum values of $f(x) = xe^{-2x}$ on the interval $0 \le x \le \ln 3$.

Solution. Use the Algorithm for Extreme Values (see section 3.4). By the Product and Chain Rules, the derivative of $f(x)$ is

$$f'(x) = (1)e^{-2x} + x\frac{d}{dx}(e^{-2x})$$
$$= e^{-2x} + x(-2e^{-2x})$$
$$= e^{-2x}(1 - 2x)$$

Note that $f'(x) = 0$ implies that

$$x = \frac{1}{2}$$

since $e^{-2x} > 0$ for all x. Now evaluate $f(x)$ at $x = \frac{1}{2}$ and at the end points of the interval. Note that

$$f(\ln 3) = (\ln 3)e^{-2\ln 3}$$

which simplifies to

$$f(\ln 3) = \frac{1}{9}\ln 3$$

since

$$e^{-2\ln 3} = e^{\ln (3^{-2})}$$
$$= 3^{-2}$$

x	0	$\frac{1}{2}$	$\ln 3$
$f(x)$	0	$\frac{1}{2e} \approx 0.18$	$\frac{1}{9}\ln 3 \approx 0.12$

Thus, on the interval $0 \le x \le \ln 3$, the maximum value is $\frac{1}{2e}$, and the minimum value is 0.

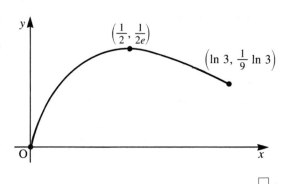

Exercises 6.4

1. Starting from the graph of e^x, sketch the graph of each function and find all intercepts.

a. $y = e^{-2x}$ **b.** $y = e^{2x} - 9$

c. $y = e^{-2x} - 4$ **d.** $y = 1 - 4e^x$

e. $y = |1 - 4e^x|$ **f.** $y = |e^{-2x} - 4|$

2. Differentiate each function.

a. $f(x) = 5e^{3x}$

b. $f(x) = 2e^{x^2 - x}$

c. $f(t) = 3e^{2\sin t}$

d. $f(t) = 3e^{\sin 2t}$

e. $g(x) = x^3 e^{-5x}$

f. $h(x) = [\sin(\pi x)]e^{3x}$

g. $p(u) = (e^{2u} - e^{-2u})^2$

h. $f(v) = \sqrt{v}e^{\sqrt{v}}$

i. $g(v) = \ln(\pi + e^{2v})$

j. $h(u) = \dfrac{e^{3u}}{1 + e^{3u}}$

k. $f(x) = e^{\sqrt{x}}\ln\sqrt{x}$

l. $f(x) = \ln\left[\dfrac{e^x + 1}{x + 1}\right]$

m. $f(x) = \ln(e^x + e^{-x})$

n. $f(x) = x\sqrt{1 + e^{\pi x}}$

o. $y = \dfrac{e^x}{\ln x}$

p. $y = e^{\sqrt{3x + 2}}$

3. Solve for x.

a. $e^x + 4e^{-x} = 5$

b. $e^x - 6e^{-x} = 1$

4. Starting from the graph of e^{-x^2} (see Example 3), sketch the graph of each function and find all intercepts.

a. $y = e^{-(x - 1)^2}$

b. $y = 4e^{-x^2} - 1$

c. $y = 1 - e^{-x^2}$

d. $y = 4 - e^{-x^2}$

5. Find the points of inflection on the graph of the function $f(x) = e^{-x^2}$ (refer to Example 3).

6. Find the equation of the tangent line to the graph of the function at the given point. By finding the second derivative, determine whether the graph lies above or below the tangent line.

a. $f(x) = e^{2x} + e^{-x}, \quad x = \ln 2$

b. $f(x) = xe^{\sin \pi x}, \quad x = \dfrac{1}{2}$

c. $f(x) = \ln(1 + e^{-x}), \quad x = 0$

7. Find the tangent line to the graph of $y = e^{-x}$ that is perpendicular to the line $2x - y = 5$.

8. Use the definition of the derivative to evaluate each limit.

a. $\lim\limits_{h \to 0} \dfrac{e^h - 1}{h}$

b. $\lim\limits_{h \to 0} \dfrac{e^{2h} - 1}{h}$

c. $\lim\limits_{h \to 0} \dfrac{e^{2 + h} - e^2}{h}$

9. Find the maximum and minimum values of each function on the given interval.

a. $f(x) = xe^{-\frac{1}{2}x}, \quad 1 \le x \le 2\ln 3$

b. $f(x) = 8x + e^{-2x}, \quad -1 \le x \le \ln 2$

c. $f(x) = \ln(e^x + 4e^{-x}), \quad -\ln 2 \le x \le \ln 4$

d. $f(x) = 3e^x + e^{2x}, \quad 0 \le x \le \ln 2$

e. $f(x) = e^{\sin x + \cos x}, \quad 0 \le x \le \pi$

10. If y is defined implicitly as a function of x by the given equation, find $\dfrac{dy}{dx}$ at the given point.

  a. $xe^y + y \ln x = 2$, $(1, \ln 2)$
  b. $y - e^{xy} = 0$, $(0, 1)$

  c. $e^{\sin 2y} + e^{\cos 2x} = 2$, $\left(\dfrac{\pi}{4}, \dfrac{\pi}{2}\right)$

  d. $e^{2x} = \sqrt{2} \sin(x + y)$, $\left(0, \dfrac{\pi}{4}\right)$

Problems 6.4

1. a. Show that the function $f(x) = Ce^x$, where C is a constant, has the property that its derivative is the same function.
  b. Can you think of a function whose derivative is the same function multiplied by 2? multiplied by the constant k?

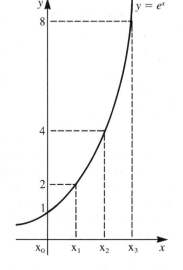

2. a. Consider the graph of $y = e^x$. Show that the x-values for which the corresponding y-values double are equally spaced.
  b. Show that this property also holds for the function

$$y = Ae^{kx}$$

for any positive constants k and A. That is, show that if $y_1 = Ae^{kx_1}$ and $2y_1 = Ae^{kx_2}$, then $x_2 - x_1$ does not depend on y_1.

3. For what values of m does $y = Ae^{mt}$ satisfy the following equation?

$$\frac{d^2y}{dt^2} + \frac{dy}{dt} - 6y = 0$$

4. Use the tangent approximation for $f(x) = e^x$ at $x = 0$ to show that

$$e^x \approx 1 + x$$

for x close to 0. Compare the values of e^x and $1 + x$ for x-values of -0.10, -0.05, 0, 0.05, and 0.10.

5. a. Use the tangent approximation to show that

$$\sin(\pi e^x) \approx -\pi x$$

for x close to 0.

b. Use part (a) to approximate $\sin(\pi e^{0.05})$. Check the accuracy of your answer with a calculator.

6. Let $f(x) = \dfrac{2 + 3e^x}{3 + 2e^x}$.

a. Show that $f(x)$ is increasing for all x.
b. Evaluate $\lim\limits_{x \to -\infty} f(x)$ and $\lim\limits_{x \to +\infty} f(x)$.
c. Sketch the graph of $f(x)$.

7. In Problem 2 of section 6.3 it was proved that

$$\lim_{t \to +\infty} \frac{\ln t}{t} = 0$$

By letting $t = e^x$, evaluate $\lim\limits_{x \to +\infty} \dfrac{x}{e^x}$.

8. Sketch the graph of $f(x) = \dfrac{x}{e^x}$.

6.5 Applications

In this section, we return to the applications of the derivative that were first discussed in Chapters 3 and 4. The examples emphasize curve sketching, since the presence of logarithm and exponential functions introduces some new features into the graphs. The exercises and problems, however, include other applications of the derivative, such as optimization problems, Newton's method, and velocity and acceleration. The functions $\ln x$ and e^x will also be important when we study differential equations in Chapter 7.

Example 1. Sketch the graph of the function

$$f(x) = xe^{-x}$$

by analyzing the sign of its first and second derivatives.

Solution. After using the Product Rule and simplifying (the reader should fill in the details), we obtain

$$f'(x) = -(x - 1)e^{-x}$$
$$f''(x) = (x - 2)e^{-x}$$

Since $e^{-x} > 0$ for all x, the following conclusions can be drawn.

	$x < 1$	$x = 1$	$x > 1$
$f'(x)$	+	0	−
$f(x)$	increasing	local maximum	decreasing

	$x < 2$	$x = 2$	$x > 2$
$f''(x)$	−	0	+
$f(x)$	concave down	point of inflection	concave up

In order to sketch the graph, observe that the only intercept is (0, 0) (since $e^{-x} > 0$ for all x). In addition, since $\lim_{x \to -\infty} e^{-x} = +\infty$, it follows that

$$\lim_{x \to -\infty} xe^{-x} = -\infty$$

The final piece of information that is needed is the behaviour of $f(x)$ as $x \to +\infty$. Since $xe^{-x} > 0$ for $x > 0$ and xe^{-x} is decreasing for $x > 1$, the graph of $f(x)$ must have a horizontal asymptote. Evaluating $f(x)$ for large positive values of x suggests that

$$\lim_{x \to +\infty} xe^{-x} = 0$$

(see also Problem 4). We thus obtain the following graph:

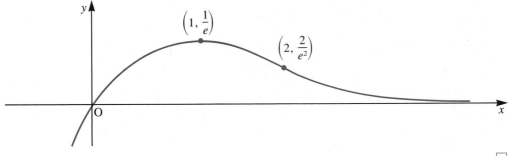

The result $\lim_{x \to +\infty} xe^{-x} = 0$ describes an important property of e^x. Since $xe^{-x} = \dfrac{x}{e^x}$, this limit shows that as $x \to +\infty$, e^x increases much more rapidly than x. In fact, e^x increases faster than any positive power of x as $x \to +\infty$:

$$\lim_{x \to +\infty} \frac{x^n}{e^x} = 0$$

for any **fixed** positive exponent n (see Problem 4).

Example 2. Sketch the graph of the function

$$f(x) = (\ln x)^2, \quad x > 0$$

by analyzing the signs of its first and second derivatives.

Solution. Differentiate $f(x)$, using the Chain Rule, to obtain

$$f'(x) = \frac{2 \ln x}{x}$$

On differentiating again, using the Quotient Rule, we obtain

$$f''(x) = \frac{2(1 - \ln x)}{x^2}$$

(The reader should verify this.) To find local maxima or local minima, let $f'(x) = 0$, which implies that $\ln x = 0$ and hence that $x = 1$. It follows from the graph of $\ln x$ that

$\ln x > 0$ is equivalent to $x > 1$

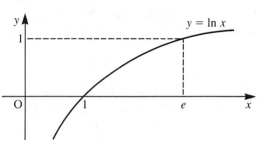

We summarize in the following table:

	$0 < x < 1$	$x = 1$	$x > 1$
$f'(x)$	$-$	0	$+$
$f(x)$	decreasing	local minimum	increasing

If we let $f''(x) = 0$, then $\ln x = 1$, and by exponentiating we obtain

$$x = e$$

It follows from the graph of $\ln x$ that

$\ln x < 1$ is equivalent to $x < e$

We summarize in the following table:

	$0 < x < e$	$x = e$	$x > e$
$f''(x)$	$+$	0	$-$
$f(x)$	concave up	point of inflection	concave down

The behaviour of $f(x)$ as $x \to 0$ is the only additional information that is needed. Since

$$\lim_{x \to 0^+} \ln x = -\infty$$

it follows that

$$\lim_{x \to 0^+} (\ln x)^2 = +\infty$$

Thus the y-axis is a vertical asymptote. We can now sketch the required graph.

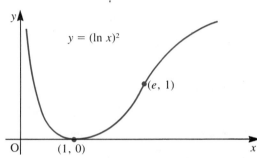

Example 3. Sketch the graph of

$$f(x) = e^{-x} \sin x, \quad x \geq 0$$

without using derivatives.

Solution. The graph has the same x-intercepts as $\sin x$:

$$x = 0, \ \pi, \ 2\pi, \ \ldots$$

Multiplying $\sin x$ by e^{-x} has the effect of reducing the amplitude of the oscillations of the sine function as x increases. We have

$$-1 \leq \sin x \leq 1$$

Multiplying by the positive quantity e^{-x} yields

$$-e^{-x} \leq e^{-x} \sin x \leq e^{-x}$$

Thus the graph of $f(x)$ oscillates between the curves $y = -e^{-x}$ and $y = e^{-x}$. In fact, when $\sin x = 1$, $f(x) = e^{-x}(1)$, and when $\sin x = -1$, $f(x) = e^{-x}(-1)$.
(The results of Exercise 2 will enable you to get a more accurate sketch.)

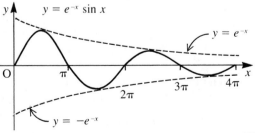

Functions of this type describe the behaviour of oscillatory systems that are damped, such as, for example, the vertical motion of a shock absorber.

Exercises 6.5

1. Sketch the graph of each function by studying the sign of its first and second derivatives.

   a. $f(x) = e^{-2x} - e^{-4x}$ **b.** $f(x) = xe^{-\left(\frac{x}{2}\right)}$
   c. $f(x) = e^x - 2x$ **d.** $f(x) = (\ln x)^2 - 2(\ln x)$
   e. $f(x) = \ln(x^2 + 2)$ **f.** $f(x) = (\ln x)^3$
   g. $f(x) = x^2 e^{-3x}$ **h.** $f(x) = e^{-x} + 3x$
   i. $f(x) = (\ln x)^3 - 3\ln x$ **j.** $f(x) = 2x^2 - \ln x$
   k. $f(x) = \dfrac{(x - 3)^2}{e^x}$

2. Find all local maxima and minima of the function

   $$f(x) = e^{-x}\sin x, \text{ for } 0 \le x \le 2\pi$$

   Refer to Example 3 in section 6.5.

3. Find the maximum value and minimum value of each function on the given interval.

   a. $f(x) = \dfrac{\ln x}{x}, \quad 1 \le x \le e^2$

   b. $f(x) = \ln(x^2 + x + 1), \quad -2 \le x \le 2$
   c. $f(x) = (x + 2)^3 e^{-x}, \quad 0 \le x \le 2$

   d. $f(x) = \dfrac{8e^x}{e^{2x} + 4}, \quad -\ln 2 \le x \le \ln 4$

4. A playground slide has the shape of the curve $y = 4e^{-\frac{x}{2}}$. If the horizontal component of the velocity for a person on the slide is $\dfrac{dx}{dt} = 2$ m/s when $x = 1$, find the vertical component of the velocity $\dfrac{dy}{dt}$ at that instant.

5. If y is defined implicitly as a function of x by the equation

   $$x + (\ln y)^2 - e^{xy} = 0$$

   find $\dfrac{dy}{dx}$ at the point $(0, e)$.

6. The tangent line to the curve $y = e^{-x}$ at the point (a, e^{-a}), where $a > 0$, intersects the x-axis at the point A and the y-axis at the point B. Find the area of the triangle AOB.

7. Sketch the graph of the function

   $$f(x) = e^{-x}\sin\left(x + \frac{\pi}{4}\right)$$

   without calculating derivatives.

8. The number N of bacteria in a culture at time t is

$$N = 2000[30 + te^{-\frac{t}{20}}]$$

Find the largest number of bacteria in the culture during the interval $0 \leq t \leq 50$, where t is measured in hours.

9. A mass suspended from a spring oscillates vertically. Its displacement from its equilibrium position as a function of time t is $h(t) = 5e^{-\frac{1}{10}t} \sin \pi t$, where t is measured in seconds and h is measured in centimetres. Find the velocity and acceleration of the mass at time $t = 1$ s.

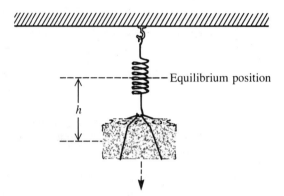

Equilibrium position

10. Referring to Exercise 6, find the triangle of largest area and the triangle of least area, subject to the restriction that the base of the triangle does not exceed 3 units.

11. A rectangle is inscribed under the curve $y = e^{-x^2}$, with its base along the x-axis. Find the rectangle of largest area, subject to the restriction that the base does not exceed 4 units.

12. The distance (in metres) fallen by a skydiver t seconds after jumping (and before his chute opens) is

$$s = 160\left(\frac{1}{4}t - 1 + e^{-\frac{t}{4}}\right)$$

a. Find the skydiver's velocity v at time t.

b. Show that the acceleration is given by $a = 10 - \frac{1}{4}v$.

c. Find $v_T = \lim_{t \to \infty} v$. This is the so-called terminal velocity, the constant velocity attained when the air resistance balances the force of gravity.

d. At what time is the skydiver's velocity 95% of the terminal velocity? How far has he fallen at that time?

13. The position function of a particle moving in a straight line is

$$s(t) = \frac{5}{2}e^{2t} - \frac{5}{2}$$

How far does the particle travel during the time when the velocity increases from 5 to 15 units?

14. The net monthly profit from the sale of a certain product is given (in dollars) by the formula

$$P(x) = 10^6[1 + (x - 1)e^{-0.001x}]$$

where x is the number of items sold.

   a. Find the number of items that yield the maximum profit. Assume that at most 2000 items can be produced per month.
   b. Repeat part (a) assuming that at most 500 items can be produced per month.

15. The concentrations of two medicines in the bloodstream t hours after injection are

$$c_1(t) = te^{-t} \quad \text{and} \quad c_2(t) = t^2e^{-t}$$

   a. Which medicine has the larger maximum concentration?
   b. Which medicine is slower in its action? Assume that the concentrations are monitored for 6 h.

16. The proportion of people who have responded to the advertisement of a new product after it has been marketed for t days is found to be

$$0.7(1 - e^{-0.2t})$$

The marketing area contains 10 million potential customers, and each response to the advertisement results in a profit to the company of $0.70 (on average), excluding the cost of advertising. The advertising costs $30 000 to produce and $5000 per day to run.

   a. Find $\lim_{t \to +\infty} 0.7(1 - e^{-0.2t})$ and interpret the result.
   b. What percentage of potential customers have responded after 7 days of advertising?
   c. Write the function $P(t)$ that represents the net profit after t days of advertising. What is the net profit after 28 days?
   d. For how many days should the advertising campaign be run in order to maximize profits? Assume an advertising budget of $180 000.

Problems 6.5

1. Sketch the graph of the function $f(x) = e^{x^3}$, using the first and second derivatives.

2. Show that

$$e^{2x} + 4e^{-4x} \geq 3, \text{ for all } x$$

(Hint: Find the minimum value of the function

$$f(x) = e^{2x} + 4e^{-4x}, \text{ for all real } x.)$$

3. a. Show graphically that the equation

$$e^{-x} = x$$

has only one solution.

b. Use Newton's method to approximate this solution and show that the recurrence relation can be written in the form

$$x_{n+1} = \frac{1 + x_n}{1 + e^{x_n}}$$

4. a. Using a calculator, evaluate $x^n e^{-x}$, when $n = 1, 2$, and 3, for large values of x, such as $10, 20, 50, 100$, and 200 and then make a conjecture concerning

$$\lim_{x \to +\infty} \frac{x^n}{e^x}$$

b. In Problem 5 of section 6.3 it was proved that

$$\lim_{t \to +\infty} \frac{(\ln t)^n}{t} = 0$$

for any positive number n. By letting $t = e^x$, evaluate

$$\lim_{x \to +\infty} \frac{x^n}{e^x}$$

5. In Example 3, we sketched the graph of $y = e^{-x} \sin x$. More generally, the graph of $y = g(x) \sin x$ oscillates between the graphs of $y = g(x)$ and $y = -g(x)$. Use this fact to sketch the graph of each function.

a. $y = x \sin x$

b. $y = \left(\dfrac{x}{1 + x} \right) \sin x, \quad x \geq 0$

c. $y = \dfrac{1}{x} \sin x, \quad x \neq 0$

d. $y = \cos(10x) \sin x$

6. In a telegraph cable, the speed of the signal is proportional to

$$v(x) = x^2 \ln \left(\frac{1}{x} \right)$$

where x is the ratio of the radius r of the cable's core to the overall radius R. Find the value of x that maximizes the speed of the signal. For technical reasons, it is required that $\dfrac{R}{10} \leq r \leq \dfrac{9R}{10}$.

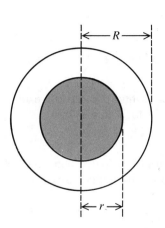

7. a. By graphing $\ln x$ and $2 - x$, show that the equation

$$\ln x + x = 2$$

has only one solution.

b. Use Newton's method to approximate this solution.

8. Sketch the graph of each function, using the first and second derivatives. You will have to write the function in two parts, in the form

$$f(x) = \begin{cases} \cdots , & x \geq 0 \\ \cdots , & x < 0 \end{cases}$$

a. $f(x) = |x|e^x$ **b.** $f(x) = xe^{-|x|}$ **c.** $f(x) = |x|e^{-x}$

9. A coaxial cable consists of two concentric conductors, as shown. An electrical signal being transmitted along a coaxial cable suffers a decrease in amplitude measured by the "attenuation factor"

$$d = \frac{C\left(\frac{1}{R} + \frac{1}{r}\right)}{\ln\left(\frac{R}{r}\right)}$$

where C is a constant. If R is fixed, determine r so as to minimize the attenuation. For technical reasons,

$$\frac{1}{10}R \leq r \leq \frac{9}{10}R$$

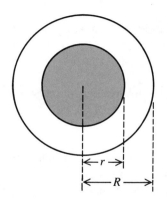

(*Suggestion:* Use $x = \frac{R}{r}$ as the variable. You will have to use Newton's method to solve $d'(x) = 0$.)

6.6 Logarithmic Differentiation

In order to find the derivative of $y = e^x$ in section 6.4, we first wrote the equation in the equivalent logarithmic form

$$\ln y = x$$

and then differentiated both sides of this equation with respect to x. This approach can also be used to differentiate **any** exponential function, as we shall now illustrate.

Example 1. Find the derivative of $f(x) = 5^x$.

Solution. **Write**

$$y = 5^x$$

and take the natural logarithm of both sides to obtain

$$\ln y = \ln(5^x)$$

Use the Property of Logarithms for Powers to simplify the right hand side, obtaining

$$\ln y = x \ln 5$$

To find $\dfrac{dy}{dx}$, differentiate the equation with respect to x, to get

$$\frac{d}{dx}(\ln y) = \ln 5$$

By the Chain Rule, this becomes

$$\frac{1}{y}\frac{dy}{dx} = \ln 5$$

On multiplying by y, and substituting 5^x for y, we obtain

$$\frac{dy}{dx} = (\ln 5)5^x \qquad\qquad \square$$

This procedure, namely, taking the natural logarithm of the equation $y = f(x)$, simplifying, and then differentiating, is called **logarithmic differentiation**.

We now show how the Power Rule of differentiation,

$$\frac{d}{dx}(x^r) = rx^{r-1}$$

which was proved earlier for integer and rational powers (see sections 2.1 and 2.4), can be extended to irrational powers, such as π. To find the derivative of $f(x) = x^r$, for any real number r, write

$$y = x^r$$

and hence obtain

$$\ln y = r \ln x$$

Differentiating with respect to x gives

$$\frac{1}{y}\frac{dy}{dx} = r\left(\frac{1}{x}\right)$$

Substituting x^r for y, we obtain

$$\frac{dy}{dx} = r\left(\frac{1}{x}\right)x^r$$
$$= rx^{r-1} \qquad\qquad \square$$

To summarize, we have shown that

$$\frac{d}{dx}(x^r) = rx^{r-1}$$

so that **the Power Rule of differentiation is valid for any real constant exponent** r. For example,

$$\frac{d}{dx}(x^\pi) = \pi x^{\pi - 1}$$

Keep in mind the difference between x^π and π^x. We can differentiate x^π using the Power Rule, since the exponent is constant. On the other hand, we have to use logarithmic differentiation in order to differentiate π^x since the exponent is not constant (see Exercise 1, part (b)).

Example 1 illustrated the use of logarithmic differentiation when the function to be differentiated has a variable exponent. This technique is also useful for differentiating functions that involve a product or quotient of factors, as in Example 2.

Example 2. If $y = \dfrac{(x + 1)^2(x + 3)}{\sqrt{x^2 + 1}}$, find $\dfrac{dy}{dx}$ when $x = 0$.

Solution. Taking the natural logarithm of both sides of the equation gives

$$\ln y = \ln\left[\frac{(x + 1)^2(x + 3)}{\sqrt{x^2 + 1}}\right]$$

$$= \ln(x + 1)^2 + \ln(x + 3) - \ln\sqrt{x^2 + 1}$$

$$= 2\ln(x + 1) + \ln(x + 3) - \frac{1}{2}\ln(x^2 + 1)$$

Differentiate this equation with respect to x, to obtain

$$\frac{1}{y}\frac{dy}{dx} = \frac{2}{x + 1} + \frac{1}{x + 3} - \frac{\frac{1}{2}(2x)}{x^2 + 1}$$

When $x = 0$, we have $y = \dfrac{(1)^2 3}{\sqrt{1}} = 3$, and hence

$$\frac{1}{3}\frac{dy}{dx} = 2 + \frac{1}{3} - 0$$

so that

$$\frac{dy}{dx} = 7 \text{ when } x = 0 \qquad \square$$

Exercises 6.6

1. Find $\dfrac{dy}{dx}$ in each case. Use the general Power Rule of differentiation where appropriate.

a. $y = 2^x$

b. $y = \pi^x$

c. $y = x^{\sqrt{2}}$

d. $y = e^x - x^e$

e. $y = x^{\pi^2}$

f. $y = 10^{x^2}$

g. $y = 2^{\sin x}$

h. $y = 3^{x^2 + 3x}$

2. If $f(x) = 5^{\sqrt{2x^2 - 1}}$, find $f'(1)$.

3. Find $\dfrac{dy}{dx}$ at the indicated x-value.

a. $y = \dfrac{(x - 1)(x - 2)^2}{(x - 3)^3}$, at $x = 4$

b. $y = \dfrac{(x + 2)^3 \sqrt{x^2 + 1}}{(x + 1)^3}$, at $x = 0$

c. $y = \dfrac{x^3 \sin^4 x}{\cos^3 x}$, at $x = \dfrac{\pi}{4}$

d. $y = \dfrac{1}{(x + b)(x + 2b)(x + 3b)}$, at $x = 0$

where b is a positive constant.

Problems 6.6

1. Find $\dfrac{dy}{dx}$ in each case.

a. $y = x^x$, $x > 0$ **b.** $y = x^{\frac{1}{x}}$, $x > 0$ **c.** $y = x^{\sin x}$, $x > 0$

2. If $f(x) = x^{\cos x}$, find $f'(\pi)$.

3. The position of a particle that moves on a straight line is given by

$$s(t) = t^{\frac{1}{t}}, \text{ for } t > 0$$

a. Find the velocity and acceleration.

b. At what time t is the velocity zero? What is the acceleration at that time?

4. Without using a calculator, determine which number is larger, e^π or π^e. (Hint: Problem 1, part (b) can help.)

6.7 The Function $f(x) = \ln|x|$

The table of powers of x and associated derivatives, given at the end of section 6.3, has been completed by the introduction of the function $\ln x$. However, whereas all other entries in the table are valid for all x (except $x = 0$ in the case of negative powers of x), the function $\ln x$ provides the missing entry **only for** $x > 0$. It is reasonable to ask (and this becomes important in some applications): "What function must be differentiated to give $\frac{1}{x}$, if $x < 0$?" We now answer this question by studying the function $\ln|x|$.

Since $\ln|-x| = \ln|x|$, the graph of $\ln|x|$ is symmetric about the y-axis, and hence can be obtained by reflecting the graph of $\ln x$ in the y-axis.

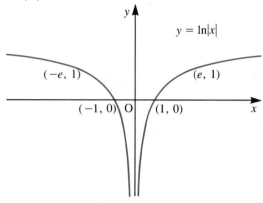

Example 1. Sketch the curve $y = \ln|2x - 3|$.

Solution. We write the function as

$$y = \ln\left|2\left(x - \frac{3}{2}\right)\right|$$

We can sketch this curve by translating the curve $y = \ln|2x|$ to the right by $\frac{3}{2}$ units. Furthermore, since

$$\ln|2x| = \ln(2|x|)$$
$$= \ln 2 + \ln|x|$$

by a property of logarithms, the graph of $\ln|2x|$ is simply the graph of $\ln|x|$ translated vertically by $\ln 2$ units. This changes the x-intercepts from $|x| = 1$ to $|2x| = 1$, i.e., from $x = \pm 1$ to $x = \pm\frac{1}{2}$.

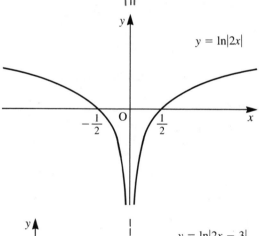

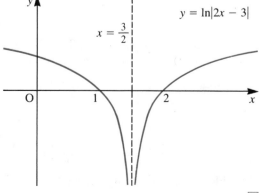

To determine the **derivative of the function** $y = \ln|x|$, we consider two cases.

If $x > 0$, then $\ln|x| = \ln x$, and hence

$$\frac{d}{dx}(\ln|x|) = \frac{1}{x}$$

If $x < 0$, then $|x| = -x$, and

$$y = \ln|x|$$
$$= \ln(-x)$$

To calculate $\dfrac{dy}{dx}$ in this case we use the Chain Rule, writing

$$y = \ln u \quad \text{and} \quad u = -x$$

Hence,

$$\frac{dy}{dx} = \frac{dy}{du}\frac{du}{dx}$$

$$= \left(\frac{1}{u}\right)(-1)$$

$$= -\frac{1}{u}$$

But since $u = -x$, we obtain

$$\frac{d}{dx}(\ln|x|) = \frac{1}{x} \text{ for } x < 0$$

Combine the two cases to obtain the result below.

$$\frac{d}{dx}(\ln|x|) = \frac{1}{x}, \text{ for } x \neq 0$$

The absence of an absolute value on the right hand side may be surprising at first. But note from the formula that $\dfrac{d}{dx}(\ln|x|)$ is positive if $x > 0$ and negative if $x < 0$, in agreement with the shape of the graph of $\ln|x|$.

Example 2. Find y' if $y = \ln|x^2 - 3|$.

Solution. We apply the Chain Rule, writing

$$y = \ln|u| \quad \text{and} \quad u = x^2 - 3$$

Then,

$$\frac{dy}{dx} = \frac{dy}{du}\frac{du}{dx}$$

$$= \left(\frac{1}{u}\right)(2x)$$

$$= \frac{2x}{x^2 - 3}$$

Hence,

$$y' = \frac{2x}{x^2 - 3} \qquad\qquad \square$$

Note that the domain of the function $\ln|x^2 - 3|$ is $\{x \epsilon R \mid |x^2 - 3| \neq 0\}$; i.e., $\{x \epsilon R \mid x \neq \pm\sqrt{3}\}$.

Example 3. Find the equation of the tangent line to the graph of

$$f(x) = \ln|\cos 2x|$$

when $x = \dfrac{3\pi}{8}$.

Solution. By the Chain Rule

$$f'(x) = \frac{d}{dx}\ln|\cos 2x|$$

$$= \frac{1}{\cos 2x}\frac{d}{dx}(\cos 2x)$$

$$= -2\tan 2x$$

The slope of the tangent line at $x = \dfrac{3\pi}{8}$ is

$$f'\left(\frac{3\pi}{8}\right) = -2\tan\left(\frac{3\pi}{4}\right)$$

$$= 2$$

and

$$f\left(\frac{3\pi}{8}\right) = \ln\left|\cos\frac{3\pi}{4}\right|$$

$$= \ln\left|-\frac{1}{\sqrt{2}}\right|$$

$$= \ln\left(2^{-\frac{1}{2}}\right)$$

$$= -\frac{1}{2}\ln 2$$

Therefore, the equation of the tangent line is

$$y + \frac{1}{2}\ln 2 = 2\left(x - \frac{3\pi}{8}\right)$$ $\square$

Exercises 6.7

1. Sketch the given logarithm curves.

   a. $y = \ln|3x|$ **b.** $y = \ln|x + 1|$
   c. $y = \ln|4x - 3|$ **d.** $y = \ln|2x + 5|$

2. Differentiate each function.

   a. $f(x) = \ln|x^2 - 1|$ **b.** $g(x) = \ln|x^3 - 7x + 1|$
   c. $f(x) = \cos x \ln|\cos x|$ **d.** $g(t) = (\ln|t|)^3$
   e. $h(u) = \left(\frac{\ln|u|}{u}\right)^2$ **f.** $p(t) = \ln|\tan t|$
   g. $h(y) = (\ln|3y - 1|)^2$ **h.** $p(y) = \sin(\ln|y|)$

3. Find the equation of the tangent line and the normal line to each curve at the given x-value.

   a. $y = \ln|3x - 5|, \quad x = 1$ **b.** $y = x\ln|x|, \quad x = -e^2$
   c. $y = \ln|1 - 2\sin x|, \quad x = \pi$ **d.** $y = \sin(\pi\ln|x|), \quad x = -\frac{1}{e}$

Problems 6.7

1. Let $f(x) = \ln(\ln|x|)$.

   a. Find the domain of $f(x)$.
   b. Find the derivative of $f(x)$.
   c. Sketch the graph of $f(x)$.

2. Repeat Problem 1 for the function $g(x) = \ln(|\ln|x||)$.

3. Sketch the graph of $f(x) = \ln|x^3 - x|$.

Review Exercises

1. Sketch the graph of each function.

    a. $f(x) = \ln(2x - 3)$ **b.** $f(x) = 3 - e^{-2x}$

2. Solve each equation for x.

    a. $e^{-2x} = 4$ **b.** $\ln\left(\dfrac{x+1}{x}\right) = 1$

    c. $e^x - 2e^{-x} = 1$ **d.** $\ln(x^2 + e) - \ln(x + 1) = 1$

3. Find $\dfrac{dy}{dx}$.

    a. $y = \ln(2x - 3)$ **b.** $y = x(\ln x)^2$

    c. $y = e^{-3x^2 + 2x}$ **d.** $y = e^{2\cos \pi x}$

    e. $y = \ln(e^{\pi x} - e^{-\pi x})$ **f.** $y = e^{\sqrt{x} - \frac{1}{x}}$

    g. $y = \dfrac{e^{x^3}}{x}$ **h.** $y = \dfrac{xe^x - 5}{x + 1}$

    i. $\ln(x + y) = y$ **j.** $e^{xy} = x + y$

4. The world's population was 2.5 billion in 1950 and reached 5 billion in 1987. Assume that the world's population grows exponentially, so that at time t (measured in years) the population is

$$N = 2.5e^{kt}$$

where $t = 0$ corresponds to the year 1950, and N is measured in billions of people.

    a. Find the constant k.
    b. Find the rate of growth of the population in 1987.
    c. According to this model, when will the population reach 10 billion?

5. If $y = \dfrac{e^{2x} - 1}{e^{2x} + 1}$, show that $\dfrac{dy}{dx} = 1 - y^2$.

6. Find the slope of the tangent line to the curve

$$e^{x+y} = \cos x - \cos y + 1$$

at the point $\left(\dfrac{\pi}{6}, -\dfrac{\pi}{6}\right)$.

7. Find an equation for the normal line to the curve

$$y = \dfrac{e^x}{1 + \ln x}$$

at the point where $x = 1$.

8. Let $y = Ae^{kx} + Be^{-kx}$, where A, B, and k are constants. Show that $y'' = k^2 y$.

9. a. Sketch the graph of $f(x) = \dfrac{(x + 3)^2}{e^{2x}}$.

b. Show that the graph has two points of inflection, which are symmetrically placed on either side of a local maximum.

c. Find $\lim\limits_{x \to +\infty} f(x)$ (see Problem 4, section 6.5).

10. The graph of $f(x) = (x + 2)e^{-kx}$ has a turning point when $x = 0$.
a. Find the constant k. Is the turning point a local maximum or a local minimum?
b. Sketch the graph of $f(x)$.

11. Evaluate each limit.

a. $\lim\limits_{h \to 0} \dfrac{e^{3h} - 1}{h}$

b. $\lim\limits_{h \to 0} \dfrac{\ln(2 + h) - \ln 2}{h}$

12. The concentration of a certain medicine t hours after injection into the bloodstream is given by

$$c(t) = e^{-t} - e^{-3t}, \quad t \geq 0$$

Sketch the graph of $c(t)$ and determine when the maximum concentration occurs.

13. The graph of $f(x) = (\ln x)^n$ has a point of inflection when $x = e$.

a. Find the constant n.
b. Sketch the graph of $f(x)$, for $x > 0$.

14. A cable hangs in a curve that is symmetric with respect to the y-axis. The tension T (in newtons) in the cable at a point x metres from the y-axis is given by

$$T = 200\left(e^{\frac{x}{10}} + e^{-\frac{x}{10}}\right)$$

Find the maximum and minimum tension if the cable extends from $x = -10$ to $x = 10$.

15. Solve the equation $x = \ln(y + \sqrt{y^2 - 1})$ for y, where $y > 1$. Find $\dfrac{dy}{dx}$.

16. The number of trout in a lake t years after restocking, is given by

$$N = \frac{10N_0}{1 + 9e^{-\frac{t}{5}}}, \quad t \geq 0$$

where N_0 is the initial number of trout.

a. How long will the population take to double, starting at $t = 0$?
b. When is the population increasing most rapidly?
c. Sketch the graph of N versus t.

17. a. By sketching the graphs of $y = \ln x$ and $y = -x$ show that the equation

$$\ln x + x = 0$$

has one solution.
b. Use Newton's method to find the solution to four decimal places.

18. Show that $y = e^{2x} \sin 3x$ satisfies the equation $y'' - 4y' + 13y = 0$.

19. Let $f(x) = e^{2x} - 6e^x + 4x$. Do a complete analysis of all properties that are required to give a detailed sketch of the graph.

20. Suppose that y depends on two variables p and q according to the relation

$$y = pe^q$$

At a certain instant, p has the value 3 and is **decreasing** at the rate of 2 units per second, while q has the value 4 and is **increasing** at the rate of 1 unit per second. Is y increasing or decreasing at this instant?

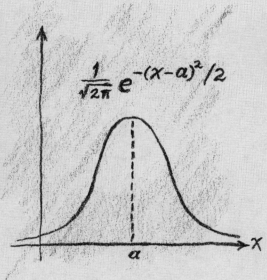

$$\frac{1}{\sqrt{2\pi}}\, e^{-(x-a)^2/2}$$

Carl Friedrich Gauss *(1777–1855), born in Brunswick, Germany, is usually regarded as the greatest mathematician who ever lived. Before he was fifteen he conceived the Gaussian law in the theory of probability and the prime number theorem ("If* P(n) *is the number of primes less than* n, *then*

$$\lim_{n\to\infty} \frac{P(n)}{n/ln\,(n)} = 1",\ \textit{making}\ n/ln\,(n)\ \textit{a good approximation to}\ P(n),\ \textit{for large}\ n).\ \textit{At age twenty-two he}$$

gave the first satisfactory proof of the fundamental theorem of algebra ("Every polynomial equation with real or complex coefficients has at least one real or complex root"). Gauss never left the University of Göttingen in Germany, making it the world centre of excellence in mathematical thought. While there he worked on problems in mathematics, astronomy, physics and geodesy (wherein he was concerned with the precise measurement of triangles on the earth's surface, leading to important discoveries in the theory of surfaces). Gauss was often occupied with very practical applications, undertaking, for example, to survey the district around his home town, Brunswick. He was also as a perfectionist, insisting upon the greatest mathematical rigour. He refused to publish his discoveries until they were highly polished and concise (often making them exceedingly difficult to read!). Many ideas attributed to other mathematicians originated with Gauss. (A diary of his, containing a wealth of information concerning his investigations over an eighteen-year period, was discovered thirty-five years after his death.)

Antiderivatives and Differential Equations

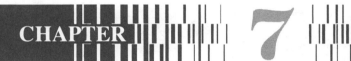

CHAPTER 7

In the previous chapters we considered applications of the derivative to problems involving velocity and acceleration. We showed that if the position function $s(t)$ of an object is known, then its velocity $v(t)$ and acceleration $a(t)$ can be found by differentiation.

$$v(t) = s'(t), \quad a(t) = v'(t)$$

On the other hand, when physicists and engineers study problems of motion, it is often the acceleration of the object that is known and they want to calculate the velocity and position. In other words, one wants to perform the "inverse" of the operation of differentiation. For example, the thrust of a rocket engine determines the acceleration, from which one wants to calculate (and hence control) the rocket's velocity and position.

Consider, then, the following problem: given a function $f(x)$, find a function $F(x)$ such that $F'(x) = f(x)$. The unknown function $F(x)$ is called an antiderivative of the given function $f(x)$. Antiderivatives have many applications, some of which are discussed in this chapter and in Chapter 8.

7.1 Antiderivatives

We shall begin our study of antiderivatives with a simple example.

Example 1. Find a function whose derivative is $9x^2 + 4x$.

Solution. A suitable function can be constructed by using the rules of differentiation. From the Power Rule of differentiation, it follows that

$$\frac{d}{dx}(x^3) = 3x^2 \quad \text{and} \quad \frac{d}{dx}(x^2) = 2x$$

and hence

$$\frac{d}{dx}(3x^3) = 9x^2, \quad \frac{d}{dx}(2x^2) = 4x$$

Add the last two equations to obtain

$$\frac{d}{dx}(3x^3 + 2x^2) = 9x^2 + 4x$$

A suitable function is thus

$$F(x) = 3x^3 + 2x^2 \qquad\qquad \Box$$

The function $F(x) = 3x^3 + 2x^2$, which has the property that

$$F'(x) = 9x^2 + 4x$$

is said to be an **antiderivative** of $f(x) = 9x^2 + 4x$.

An **antiderivative of the function** $f(x)$ is a function $F(x)$ that satisfies

$$F'(x) = f(x)$$

Example 2. Find an antiderivative of $f(x) = 3\cos 2x$.

Solution. As in Example 1, we obtain an antiderivative by using the rules of differentiation. The derivative of the sine function is

$$\frac{d}{dx}(\sin x) = \cos x$$

or, more generally,

$$\frac{d}{dx}(\sin u) = (\cos u)\frac{du}{dx}$$

by the Chain Rule. The form of $f(x)$ suggests that we choose $u = 2x$. Then the previous equation becomes

$$\frac{d}{dx}[\sin 2x] = 2\cos 2x$$

On multiplying by $\frac{3}{2}$ we finally obtain

$$\frac{d}{dx}\left[\frac{3}{2}\sin 2x\right] = f(x)$$

Thus, $F(x) = \frac{3}{2}\sin 2x$ is an antiderivative of $f(x)$.

It is important to note that $\frac{3}{2}\sin 2x$ is **not** the only antiderivative of $3\cos 2x$. Since the derivative of a constant function is zero, it follows that

$$\frac{d}{dx}\left[\frac{3}{2}\sin 2x + C\right] = 2\cos 2x$$

for any constant C. Thus $\frac{3}{2}\sin 2x + C$ is an antiderivative of $3\cos 2x$, for any constant C. For example, $\frac{3}{2}\sin 2x + 5$ and $\frac{3}{2}\sin 2x - \pi$ are antiderivatives of $3\cos 2x$.

In general, if $F(x)$ is an antiderivative of $f(x)$, then so is $F(x) + C$, for any constant C. It is natural to ask whether there are antiderivatives of $f(x)$ other than those of the form $F(x) + C$. The answer is "NO," and this can be shown as follows. Suppose that $F(x)$ is an antiderivative of $f(x)$, so that

$$F'(x) = f(x)$$

and suppose that $G(x)$ is any other antiderivative of $f(x)$, so that

$$G'(x) = f(x)$$

On subtracting the last two equations we obtain

$$G'(x) - F'(x) = 0$$

and hence

$$[G(x) - F(x)]' = 0$$

Since any function whose derivative is zero (on some interval) is a constant function (on that interval), we obtain

$$G(x) - F(x) = C$$

or

$$G(x) = F(x) + C$$

where C is a constant. In other words, **any** antiderivative $G(x)$ equals $F(x)$ plus a constant.

If $F'(x) = f(x)$, then the general antiderivative of $f(x)$ is $F(x) + C$, where C is an arbitrary constant.

In order to appreciate the geometrical significance of the antiderivative, consider the function $f(x) = 2x$, which has the general antiderivative

$$F(x) = x^2 + C$$

The curves $y = x^2 + C$ are simply vertical translations of $y = x^2$, and hence they all have the same slope at the position x, namely,

$$\frac{dy}{dx} = 2x.$$

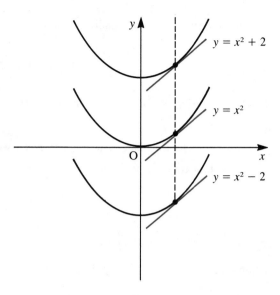

Example 3. Find the general anti-derivative of the function

$$f(x) = 6e^{3x} + 5e^{-x}$$

Solution. The derivative of a general exponential function is

$$\frac{d}{dx}(e^{kx}) = ke^{kx}$$

for any constant k. In particular, with $k = 3$ and $k = -1$, we obtain

$$\frac{d}{dx}(e^{3x}) = 3e^{3x}, \quad \frac{d}{dx}(e^{-x}) = -e^{-x}$$

On multiplying these equations by 2 and -5 respectively, and adding, we obtain

$$\frac{d}{dx}(2e^{3x} - 5e^{-x}) = 6e^{3x} + 5e^{-x}$$

Thus $G(x) = 2e^{3x} - 5e^{-x}$ is an antiderivative of $f(x)$. It follows that the general antiderivative of $f(x)$ is

$$F(x) = 2e^{3x} - 5e^{-x} + C$$

where C is an arbitrary constant. $\qquad\qquad\qquad\qquad\qquad\qquad\qquad$ □

We have seen that a function has **infinitely many** antiderivatives, differing only by an arbitrary constant C. In applications one is usually given additional information that determines a value for C, thereby specifying the **unique** antiderivative that solves the problem. This is illustrated in the next example.

Example 4. The population of Lynchburg grows at a rate of

$$r(t) = 2 + 10t^{\frac{3}{2}}$$

where t is the time in years measured from 1960, and the rate r is measured in people per year. If the population in 1969 was 2010, find the population in 1996.

Solution. Let $n(t)$ be the number of people at time t, so that

$$\begin{aligned} n'(t) &= r(t) \\ &= 2 + 10t^{\frac{3}{2}} \end{aligned} \tag{1}$$

and

$$n(9) = 2010$$

We are required to calculate $n(36)$.

According to equation (1), $n(t)$ is an antiderivative of $2 + 10t^{\frac{3}{2}}$. Using the rules of differentiation, as in the previous examples, we find that

$$\frac{d}{dt}(2t + 4t^{\frac{5}{2}}) = 2 + 10t^{\frac{3}{2}}$$

Thus, the general antiderivative of $r(t)$ is

$$n(t) = 2t + 4t^{\frac{5}{2}} + C$$

for some choice of the constant C.

The value of C is determined by the condition $n(9) = 2010$. Set $t = 9$ in the equation for $n(t)$ to obtain

$$2010 = 18 + 4(9)^{\frac{5}{2}} + C$$

It follows that $C = 1020$, and hence

$$n(t) = 2t + 4t^{\frac{5}{2}} + 1020$$

Now substitute $t = 36$ to find $n(36) = 32\ 196$. Thus the population in 1996 (when $t = 36$) is 32 196. □

The formula $n(t) = 2t + 4t^{\frac{5}{2}} + C$, obtained in Example 4, describes **all** populations that have the given growth rate $r(t) = 2 + 10t^{\frac{3}{2}}$. A change in the constant C simply changes the initial population and corresponds graphically to a vertical translation of the graph of $n(t)$. The given value $n(9) = 2010$ fixes the constant C, thereby determining a specific curve.

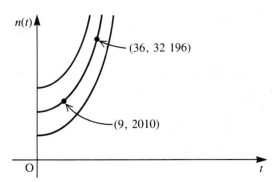

The problem of finding an antiderivative of a function $f(x)$ can be thought of symbolically as follows: find an unknown function (?) that satisfies the equation

$$\frac{d}{dx}(?) = f(x)$$

This is the inverse problem of differentiation and is much more difficult, since there is no complete set of rules for finding antiderivatives. In this book we shall find antiderivatives only for a special class of functions, namely, functions that are formed by taking constant multiples and sums of the basic functions

$$x^r, \quad \sin x, \quad \cos x, \quad e^x$$

We shall also permit x to be replaced by $kx + b$, where k and b are constants.

We do not recommend that you memorize formulas for finding the antiderivatives of this class of functions. If you know the derivatives of the basic functions, and the Chain Rule, you can always "work backwards," as in the examples of this section. Better still, after sufficient practice you can simply write the answer to such antiderivative problems by inspection; we urge you to make this your goal. Keep in mind that the answer to any antiderivative problem can be checked by differentiation: the derivative of your answer should be the given function. We strongly suggest that you always check your answers this way.

Finally, here are three examples that illustrate this approach to antiderivatives.

1. The general antiderivative of $\sin \pi x$ is $-\dfrac{1}{\pi}\cos \pi x + C$, since

$$\frac{d}{dx}\left(-\frac{1}{\pi}\cos \pi x + C\right) = \sin \pi x$$

Note that the factor of $\dfrac{1}{\pi}$ is needed to combine with the factor of π that arises from the Chain Rule to produce the coefficient 1.

2. If $\dfrac{dy}{dx} = (2x + 5)^4$, then

$$y = \tfrac{1}{10}(2x + 5)^5 + C$$

Note that the factor of $\dfrac{1}{10}$ is needed to combine with the factor of 5 that arises from the Power Rule and the factor of 2 that arises from the Chain Rule, to produce the desired coefficient.

3. If $\dfrac{dy}{dx} = \dfrac{1}{3x - 2}$ and $3x - 2 > 0$, then

$$y = \tfrac{1}{3}\ln(3x - 2) + C$$

Exercises 7.1

1. Find the general antiderivative of each function and verify your results by differentiation.

   a. $2x^2 - 8x$

   b. $3x^5 + 4x^3 - 7$

   c. $5x^9 + 4x^7 + 3x^5$

   d. $x^4 + \dfrac{1}{x^4}$

   e. $\dfrac{3}{x^5}$

   f. $\dfrac{10}{x}$

   g. $x^{\frac{2}{3}} - x^3$

   h. $2x^{-\frac{1}{5}} + x^{\frac{2}{5}}$

   i. $2\cos x - 3$

   j. $\cos(2x) + 2x$

   k. $3\sqrt{x} - \dfrac{1}{\sqrt{x}}$

   l. $2\sin(\pi x) - \cos(\pi x)$

   m. $10e^{5x} - 2e^{-3x}$

   n. $\dfrac{3}{x} - \dfrac{4}{x^2} + 2\pi$

   o. $3x^4 - 1 + e^{\pi x}$

   p. $3\sin(\sqrt{3}x) - e^{\sqrt{3}x}$

2. Complete each statement.

   a. If $\dfrac{dy}{dx} = 7e^{-2x}$, then $y = ?$

   b. If $\dfrac{du}{dt} = 3t^2 + 5t - 2$, then $u = ?$

   c. If $\dfrac{dx}{dt} = \sin t + \sin 2t + \sin 3t$, then $x = ?$

   d. If $\dfrac{dy}{dt} = e^{-t} + 2e^{-2t} + 3e^{-3t}$, then $y = ?$

   e. If $\dfrac{dy}{du} = \dfrac{1}{u} - \dfrac{1}{u-1}$, then $y = ?$

   f. If $\dfrac{du}{dv} = v^4 - (1 - v)^4$, then $u = ?$

   g. If $\dfrac{du}{dx} = \cos\left(5x - \dfrac{\pi}{5}\right)$, then $u = ?$

   h. If $\dfrac{dy}{dx} = e^x + x^e$, then $y = ?$

   i. If $\dfrac{du}{dv} = \dfrac{1}{3}\sin(\pi v + 3)$, then $u = ?$

   j. If $\dfrac{dy}{dx} = 5\sec^2 3x$, then $y = ?$

3. Find the general antiderivative of each function. You may have to rearrange the function in some way before you can find the antiderivative by inspection.

a. $x^2(\sqrt{x} + 3)$

b. $e^{-x}(e^{3x} + \pi)$

c. $(e^{2x} + e^{-2x})^2$

d. $\left(\sqrt{x} - \dfrac{1}{\sqrt{x}}\right)^2$

e. $\dfrac{7x^3 + 3}{x}$

f. $\dfrac{(x + 2)^2}{\sqrt{x}}$

g. $\sin x \cos x$

h. $\dfrac{\sec x}{1 + \tan^2 x}$

i. $\dfrac{\sin^2 x}{1 - \cos x}$

j. $(\sin x + \cos x)^2$

k. $\tan^2 x + \sec^2 x$

l. $\dfrac{x^2 + 2x + 2}{x + 1}$

4. Complete the following statements. Letters other than x and y represent constants.

a. If $\dfrac{dy}{dx} = ax^n$, where $n \neq -1$, then $y = \,?$

b. If $\dfrac{dy}{dx} = \dfrac{1}{kx + b}$, then $y = \,?$

c. If $\dfrac{dy}{dx} = A \sin(kx + b)$, then $y = \,?$

d. If $\dfrac{dy}{dx} = (ax + b)^{-3}$, then $y = \,?$

e. If $\dfrac{dy}{dx} = Be^{-kx}$, then $y = \,?$

f. If $\dfrac{dy}{dx} = \sqrt{cx + d}$, then $y = \,?$

5. By using the trigonometric identities

$$\cos 2x = 2\cos^2 x - 1 = 1 - 2\sin^2 x$$

find the general antiderivative of

a. $\sin^2 x$

b. $\cos^2 x$

6. If $y' = x^2 - 2x + 8$, and $y = 1$ when $x = 1$, find y as a function of x and calculate its maximum and minimum value on the interval $-3 \leq x \leq 5$.

7. A sunflower plant grows at the following rate in centimetres per day

$$r(t) = 2 + \frac{1}{30}t$$

where t denotes the time in days since the seed germinated. If the height of the sunflower is 75 cm after 30 days, what will its height be after 60 days?

8. Water leaks out of a tank at a rate of $\dfrac{t}{50}$ L/min. If the tank contains 400 L at time $t = 0$, when will the tank be empty?

9. If the water supply in a house is unsoftened, calcium compounds are deposited on the inner walls of water pipes, thereby reducing the flow of water. Suppose that the inner radius of a water pipe decreases at a rate of $0.02e^{-0.002t}$ cm per year owing to this process.
   a. Find the inner radius at time t of a pipe whose inner radius is initially (at $t = 0$) 1 cm.
   b. Find the inner radius of this pipe after 5 years.
   c. When will the pipe be completely blocked?

10. A pine tree grows at a rate of $\dfrac{20}{t + 30}$ m per year starting from when it has a height of 3 m. Find its height 30 years later.

Problems 7.1

1. Sometimes the product rule for differentiation can be used to find an antiderivative that is not obvious by inspection.
   a. By differentiating $x \ln x$, find an antiderivative of $\ln x$.
   b. By differentiating xe^x, find an antiderivative of xe^x.
   c. By differentiating $x \sin x$, find an antiderivative of $x \cos x$.

2. At each point (x_0, y_0) of a curve $y = f(x)$, the tangent line has the equation $y = 2x_0 x - y_0$. Find $f(x)$.

3. Find a function f that satisfies the equation $\dfrac{d}{dx} [\ln f(x)] = \dfrac{4}{x}$.

4. Let f be a function defined for all $x > -5$ and having the following properties:
   (i) $f''(x) = \dfrac{1}{3\sqrt{x + 5}}$ for all x in the domain of f.
   (ii) The tangent to the graph of f at $(4, 2)$ has an angle of inclination of 45 degrees. Find an expression for $f(x)$.

5. One can sometimes find antiderivatives of more complicated functions by using the Chain Rule. For example, since

$$\frac{d}{dx} \sin (x^2) = 2x \cos (x^2)$$

it follows that $\dfrac{1}{2} \sin (x^2)$ is an antiderivative of $x \cos (x^2)$. Find an antiderivative of each of the following functions.

a. xe^{-x^2}

b. $x\sqrt{x^2 + 1}$

c. $\dfrac{x}{x^2 + 1}$

d. $\sin x \cos^2 x$

e. $\dfrac{\sin x}{1 + \cos x}$

f. $\dfrac{e^x}{1 + e^x}$

7.2 Motion with Given Velocity or Acceleration

In this section we shall illustrate the use of antiderivatives for solving motion problems. Recall that if $s(t)$ is the position function of an object that moves in a straight line, then the velocity $v(t)$ and acceleration $a(t)$ are given by

$$v(t) = s'(t) \quad \text{and} \quad a(t) = v'(t)$$

This section deals with problems in which one has to find the position function when the velocity or the acceleration is given.

Example 1. The velocity of a car moving in heavy traffic is $v(t) = 30 + 20\sin(10\pi t)$ km/h, starting at $t = 0$. How far does the car travel in the first 30 min?

Solution. Let $s(t)$ denote the position function of the car. Observe that $v(t)$ is always positive (in fact, $v(t) \geq 10$). This means that $s(t)$ increases with time and the car always moves in the same direction. Thus the distance travelled in the first 30 min is $s\left(\frac{1}{2}\right) - s(0)$, since t is measured in hours.

Since $s'(t) = v(t)$,

$$s'(t) = 30 + 20\sin(10\pi t)$$

Observe that

$$\frac{d}{dt}\left[30t - \frac{2}{\pi}\cos(10\pi t)\right] = 30 + 20\sin(10\pi t)$$

It follows that

$$s(t) = 30t - \frac{2}{\pi}\cos(10\pi t) + C \tag{1}$$

for some constant C. It is not necessary to find C, however, since when the difference $s\left(\frac{1}{2}\right) - s(0)$ is calculated using equation (1), the constant C will cancel. Therefore,

$$s\left(\frac{1}{2}\right) - s(0) = (15 - \frac{2}{\pi}\cos 5\pi + C) - (0 - \frac{2}{\pi}\cos 0 + C)$$

$$= 15 + \frac{4}{\pi}$$

Thus the car travels $15 + \frac{4}{\pi}$ km in the first 30 min. $\square$

The next example concerns motion under the influence of gravity. The motion of any material object close to the earth is influenced by the gravitational attraction between that object and the earth. According to Newton's theory of gravity, if gravity is the only force acting on a moving object, then its acceleration is independent of the composition and mass of the object but varies inversely as the square of the distance of the object from the centre of the earth.

For objects that remain close to the earth's surface (e.g., a baseball or a pebble dropped from a cliff), it is a reasonable approximation to treat the acceleration due to gravity as a constant, usually denoted by g. In this section we shall restrict our attention to this situation and, for simplicity, we shall use a value of $g = 10$ m/s^2, although $g = 9.8$ m/s^2 is a better approximation. (You should also keep in mind that the value of g is greater at the poles than at the equator, since the earth is flattened at the poles.) On the other hand, when one is studying the motion of rockets and spacecraft, the acceleration due to gravity cannot be treated as a constant, and this leads to more difficult mathematical problems (see section 7.5, Problem 4).

Example 2. A model rocket is fired vertically upward. When its fuel is exhausted it has a velocity of 30 m/s and has reached a height of 80 m. Assume that the acceleration due to gravity is 10 m/s^2 and neglect the effects of air resistance.

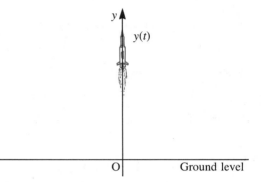

a. For how long will the rocket continue to rise?

b. Find the maximum height attained.

c. When will the rocket strike the ground?

Solution. **a.** Choose the vertically upward direction to be positive, with the origin at ground level. Let $v(t)$ denote the velocity at time t. When the fuel is exhausted the acceleration of the rocket is due solely to gravity, so

$$\frac{dv}{dt} = -10$$

The minus sign is due to the fact that gravity acts downward, with the effect of decreasing the upward velocity.

It follows by inspection that

$$v(t) = -10t + C_1 \tag{2}$$

where C_1 is a constant. Choose $t = 0$ to be the time when the fuel is exhausted, so that equation (2) is valid for $t \geq 0$. We also have

$$v(0) = 30$$

On setting $t = 0$ in equation (2), we obtain

$$30 = 0 + C_1$$

Hence,

$$v(t) = -10t + 30 \tag{3}$$

The rocket will continue to rise ($v \geq 0$) until $v = -10t + 30 = 0$, which occurs when $t = 3$. Thus the rocket will continue to rise for 3 s after its fuel is exhausted.

b. Now determine the position function $y(t)$. By equation (3),

$$\frac{dy}{dt} = -10t + 30$$

It follows by inspection that

$$y(t) = -5t^2 + 30t + C_2 \tag{4}$$

where C_2 is a constant. Since

$$y(0) = 80$$

we can set $t = 0$ in equation (4) to obtain

$$80 = 0 + 0 + C_2$$

Hence,

$$y(t) = -5t^2 + 30t + 80 \tag{5}$$

By part (a), the maximum height will occur when $t = 3$. From equation (5) we obtain

$$y(3) = 125$$

Thus the maximum height is 125 m.

c. The rocket will strike the ground when $y(t) = -5t^2 + 30t + 80 = 0$. On solving for t we obtain $t = 8$ or $t = -2$ (which is an inadmissible solution). Thus the rocket strikes the ground 8 s after the fuel runs out.   □

In Example 2, note the essential role that is played by the constant that appears in the general antiderivative. In equation (2) the constant C_1 is the initial velocity. In equation (4) the constant C_2 is the initial elevation.

Example 3.

A jet-propelled sled starts a run at time $t = 0$, with a velocity of 11 m/s. Its acceleration at time $t \geq 0$ is given by $a(t) = 10 - 2t$.
a. When does the sled come to rest?
b. How far will the sled have travelled at this time?

Solution. **a.** Let $v(t)$ be the velocity at time t. Since $\dfrac{dv}{dt} = a$, then

$$\frac{dv}{dt} = 10 - 2t$$

for $t \geq 0$. It follows by inspection that

$$v(t) = 10t - t^2 + C_1 \tag{6}$$

where C_1 is a constant. Since

$$v(0) = 11$$

we can set $t = 0$ in equation (6) to obtain

$$11 = 0 - 0 + C_1$$

Hence,

$$v(t) = -t^2 + 10t + 11 \tag{7}$$

The sled will come to rest when $v(t) = 0$. On solving the equation $-t^2 + 10t + 11 = 0$, we obtain $t = 11$ or $t = -1$ (which is an inadmissible solution). Hence the sled comes to rest after 11 s.

b. Now determine the position function $s(t)$. By equation (7),

$$\frac{ds}{dt} = -t^2 + 10t + 11$$

for $t \geq 0$. It follows by inspection that

$$s(t) = -\frac{1}{3}t^3 + 5t^2 + 11t + C_2 \tag{8}$$

where C_2 is a constant. The distance travelled between times $t = 0$ and $t = 11$ will be $s(11) - s(0)$, since the sled does not change direction during this interval (the velocity is positive for $0 \leq t < 11$). It follows from equation (8) that

$$s(11) - s(0) = \left[-\frac{1}{3}(11)^3 + 5(11)^2 + 11(11) + C_2 \right] - [C_2]$$

$$= \frac{847}{3}$$

Thus, the sled travels a distance of $\frac{847}{3}$ m. ☐

Exercises 7.2

1. Find the position function $s(t)$ for an object with velocity function $v(t)$ and initial position $s(0)$.

a. $v(t) = 3t - t^2, \quad s(0) = 5$

b. $v(t) = 4 \sin \pi t, \quad s(0) = 0$

c. $v(t) = \sqrt{1 + 3t}, \quad s(0) = 0$

d. $v(t) = 10 \left[1 - \frac{1}{(1 + t)^2} \right], \quad s(0) = 0$

e. $v(t) = 5 - e^{-2t}, \quad s(0) = \frac{3}{2}$

2. A submersible robot descends to the ocean floor at a rate of

$$2 - \frac{8}{(t + 2)^2} \text{ m/s}$$

where t is the time after it initially submerges. If the ocean depth is 1 km, how long does the descent take?

3. Find the position function $s(t)$ for an object with acceleration function $a(t)$, initial velocity $v(0)$, and initial position $s(0)$.

    a. $a(t) = 5$, $v(0) = 10$, $s(0) = 20$

    b. $a(t) = t - 1$, $v(0) = 1$, $s(0) = 0$

    c. $a(t) = t^2 + t$, $v(0) = 0$, $s(0) = 0$

    d. $a(t) = 4\cos 2t$, $v(0) = -3$, $s(0) = 0$

    e. $a(t) = \sqrt{4 + 5t}$, $v(0) = 0$, $s(0) = 0$

    f. $a(t) = e^{-\frac{t}{3}}$, $v(0) = 0$, $s(0) = 7$

    g. $a(t) = \dfrac{4}{(1 + 2t)^2}$, $v(0) = 0$, $s(0) = 5$

4. A particle moves along the x-axis with acceleration $a(t) = -2t + 10 - \dfrac{12}{t}$, for $t \geq 1$.

    a. Find the velocity function $v(t)$, given that $v(1) = 9$.
    b. Find the maximum velocity on the interval $1 \leq t \leq 3$.

5. If the velocity of a rocket, in metres per second, is given by $v = 8t + 10\sqrt{t}$, where t is time in seconds after lift-off, find the distance travelled by the rocket in the first 4 min.

6. A pebble is dropped from the 15th floor of a skyscraper (45 m above the ground). At the same instant a pebble is thrown downwards with a velocity of 20 m/s from the 20th floor (60 m above the ground). Which pebble strikes the ground first? Assume that the acceleration due to gravity is 10 m/s², and neglect the effect of air resistance.

7. A woman throws a ball vertically upwards so that 4 s elapse before it strikes the ground. Determine
    a. the maximum height of the ball.
    b. the velocity with which the ball was thrown.
Assume that the acceleration due to gravity is 10 m/s², and neglect the effect of air resistance.

8. Repeat Exercise 7, assuming that the ball stays aloft for T s and that the acceleration due to gravity is g m/s².

9. If the woman in Exercise 7 performs her throwing feat on the moon, how high would the ball rise, and how long would it stay aloft? Assume the existence of an ideal spacesuit that does not adversely affect athletic performance. The acceleration due to gravity on the moon is 1.6 m/s².

10. The world high-jump record for men, as of 1985, was 2.41 m. What would you expect the record to be on the moon? Assume the existence of an ideal spacesuit that does not adversely affect athletic performance. The acceleration due to gravity on the moon is 1.6 m/s².

11. A dragster starts from rest and steadily increases its velocity. It covers a fixed distance in 6 s. If its final velocity is 420 km/h, find the distance covered.

12. A dragster has an acceleration of $20\,e^{-\frac{t}{4}}$ m/s², t seconds after starting from rest. If it completes the run with a velocity of 252 km/h, find the distance covered.

Problems 7.2

1. Referring to Exercise 12, how long will the dragster take to cover 400 m? (Hint: Use Newton's method to solve for t.)

2. As of 1985, the highest final velocity for a one-quarter-mile (0.4 km) run using a piston-engined dragster is 419.2 km/h, and the lowest elapsed time is 5.48 s, but not during the same run. For each case, determine the acceleration (assuming it to be constant).

7.3 Differential Equations and Families of Curves

In this chapter we have considered equations of the form

$$\frac{dy}{dt} = f(t)$$

where $f(t)$ is given and y is an unknown function of t. This type of equation is a simple example of a **differential equation**. More generally, a differential equation is any equation that involves an unknown function and its derivatives. For example,

$$\frac{dy}{dt} = ky$$

where k is a constant is a common form of differential equation, with y denoting the unknown function. This particular differential equation can be used to model radioactive decay and population growth (see section 7.4). Many other natural phenomena can also be modelled by using differential equations, and this topic has become an important branch of mathematics. We shall henceforth use the standard abbreviation "DE" for differential equation.

In order to predict the behaviour of a system that is modelled by a DE, one needs to find the unknown function. The process of finding the unknown function is referred to as **solving the DE**. Any function that when substituted for the unknown function, reduces the DE to an identity is said to be a **solution of the DE**. It is usually difficult to solve all but the simplest of DE's. However, it is straightforward to verify that a given function is a solution of a DE, as is illustrated in Example 1.

Example 1. Verify that $y = e^{-t} + Ce^{-2t}$, where C is an arbitrary constant, is a solution of the DE

$$\frac{dy}{dt} + 2y = e^{-t}$$

Solution. Differentiate the given function to obtain

$$\frac{dy}{dt} = -e^{-t} - 2Ce^{-2t}$$

On substituting for y and $\frac{dy}{dt}$ in the left side of the DE, we get

$$(-e^{-t} - 2Ce^{-2t}) + 2(e^{-t} + Ce^{-2t}) = e^{-t}$$

which verifies that we have a solution. ☐

The examples in section 7.2 essentially required us to solve a DE of the form

$$\frac{dy}{dt} = f(t)$$

where $f(t)$ is a given function. As we have seen, this is a simple matter provided that we can find an antiderivative $F(t)$ of $f(t)$—all solutions can then be written in the form

$$y = F(t) + C$$

where C is an arbitrary constant. In other words, the DE $\frac{dy}{dt} = f(t)$ has infinitely many solutions.

Each of the solutions can be represented as a curve in the t-y plane, called a **solution curve of the DE**. We say that the set of all solutions of the form $y = F(t) + C$ is a **one-parameter family of solution curves**, with C being the parameter.

Example 2. Find the one-parameter family of solution curves of the DE

$$\frac{dy}{dx} = 4x - 4$$

Sketch some typical solution curves. Find the unique solution such that $y = -1$ when $x = 1$.

Solution. **Since**

$$\frac{d}{dx}(2x^2 - 4x) = 4x - 4$$

it follows that the one-parameter family of solution curves is

$$y = 2x^2 - 4x + C \tag{1}$$

These curves are all parabolas with axis $x = 1$. Some typical curves are shown in the diagram.

The unique solution that satisfies $y(1) = -1$ is the solution curve that passes through the point $(1, -1)$. Substitute $x = 1$ and $y = -1$ in equation (1) to get

$$-1 = 2 - 4 + C$$

Hence, $C = 1$ and the unique solution that passes through $(1, -1)$ is

$$y = 2x^2 - 4x + 1$$

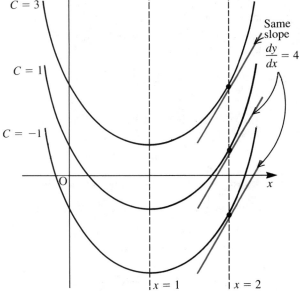

The problem in Example 2 is equivalent to finding all curves whose slope at position (x, y) is given by

$$\frac{dy}{dx} = 4x - 4$$

Since the slope $\frac{dy}{dx}$ depends on x but not on y, the resulting family of curves are vertical translations of one another (as shown in the diagram). This geometric interpretation also follows directly from equation (1).

The following example illustrates a geometrical application of DE's and families of curves.

Example 3. Find the family of curves that intersects the family

$$y = -\tfrac{1}{2}x^2 + C, \text{ where } C \text{ is constant,}$$

at right angles. Sketch typical members of both families on the same axes.

Solution. The given family has slope

$$\frac{dy}{dx} = -x$$

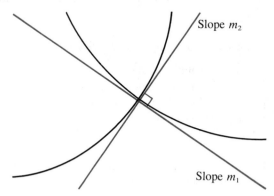

Recall that if two curves intersect at right angles, the slopes of their tangent lines, m_1 and m_2, satisfy the relation $m_1 m_2 = -1$. It follows that the desired family of curves must have slope

$$\frac{dy}{dx} = \frac{1}{x}$$

If $x > 0$, this DE can be solved to obtain the family of curves

$$y = \ln x + K$$

where K is a constant (recall that $\dfrac{d}{dx} \ln x = \dfrac{1}{x}$ if $x > 0$). On the other hand, if $x < 0$, $\ln x$ is undefined. In this case, however, $\ln(-x)$ is defined, and

$$\frac{d}{dx} \ln(-x) = \frac{1}{(-x)}(-1) = \frac{1}{x}$$

Thus, if $x < 0$, the solutions of the DE $\dfrac{dy}{dx} = \dfrac{1}{x}$ are the family of curves

$$y = \ln(-x) + K$$

Since

$$|x| = \begin{cases} x, & \text{if } x > 0 \\ -x, & \text{if } x < 0 \end{cases}$$

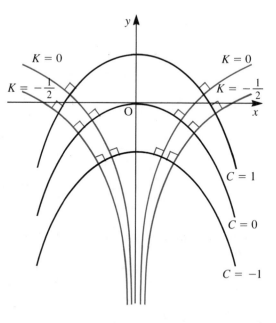

we may combine the two cases by writing

$$y = \ln|x| + K$$

Typical members of both families are shown in the sketch. Note that all intersections occur at right angles.   □

Two families of curves that intersect each other at right angles are called **orthogonal trajectories of each other**. In Example 3, the families $y = -\frac{1}{2}x^2 + C$ and $y = \ln|x| + K$ are orthogonal trajectories of each other. Orthogonal trajectories occur in a variety of areas in science and engineering. For example, the curves of constant elevation on a contour map of a

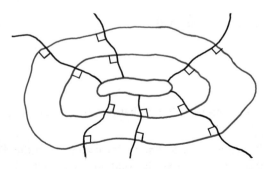

mountain and the curves of steepest descent are orthogonal trajectories of each other. Problems 1 and 2 discuss examples of orthogonal trajectories.

Examples 2 and 3 of this section and the examples of section 7.2, involved the simplest type of DE, $\frac{dy}{dx} = f(x)$. In contrast, the final example in this section shows a DE whose right side depends on the unknown function.

Example 4. Find all curves whose slope at the point (x, y) is given by

$$\frac{dy}{dx} = -2y \qquad (2)$$

Sketch some members of this family of curves. Find the unique solution of the DE that satisfies

$$y(0) = \frac{1}{2}$$

Solution. A solution of the DE is a function whose derivative equals -2 times the function. This is reminiscent of the exponential function, since

$$\frac{d}{dx}(Ce^{kx}) = kCe^{kx}$$

It follows that

$$y = Ce^{-2x} \qquad (3)$$

is a solution of the DE for any constant C (as can be verified by substituting in equation (2)). This equation describes the required family of curves (see sketch).

To find the unique solution of the DE that satisfies $y(0) = \frac{1}{2}$, set $x = 0$, $y = \frac{1}{2}$ in equation (3) to obtain

$$\frac{1}{2} = Ce^0$$

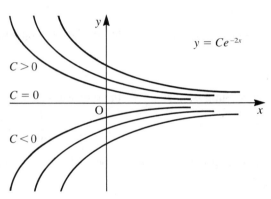

Hence, $C = \frac{1}{2}$, and

$$y = \frac{1}{2}e^{-2x}$$

is the unique solution that passes through the point $\left(0, \frac{1}{2}\right)$.   □

It is important to know (for example, in the applications of section 7.4) that equation (3) represents all possible solutions of the DE of Example 4. To prove that this is the case we shall derive these solutions systematically. Consider the more general DE

$$\frac{dy}{dx} = ky, \text{ where } k \text{ is a constant}$$

Write the DE in the form

$$\frac{1}{y}\frac{dy}{dx} = k$$

The idea is to express the left side as a derivative. First suppose that $y > 0$ and observe that

$$\frac{d}{dy}\ln y = \frac{1}{y}$$

Hence, by the Chain Rule,

$$\frac{d}{dx}\ln y = \frac{1}{y}\frac{dy}{dx}$$

The DE thus assumes the form

$$\frac{d}{dx}\ln y = k$$

In other words, $\ln y$ must equal the general antiderivative of the constant function k. Thus

$$\ln y = kx + B$$

where B is an arbitrary constant. On solving for y we obtain

$$y = e^{kx+B}$$
$$= e^B e^{kx}$$

Now, suppose that $y < 0$. In this case we have

$$\frac{d}{dy}\ln(-y) = \frac{1}{y}$$

Repeating the derivation of the first case, we obtain

$$-y = e^B e^{kx}$$

Summarizing, we have

$$y = e^B e^{kx}, \text{ with } y > 0 \text{ for all } x, \text{ and}$$
$$y = -e^B e^{kx}, \text{ with } y < 0 \text{ for all } x.$$

These cases can be combined into a single equation

$$y = Ce^{kx}$$

where C is a constant that can be positive or negative. Finally, note that C can also be zero, since by inspection, $y = 0$ is also a solution of the DE.

All solutions of the DE

$$\frac{dy}{dx} = ky, \text{ where } k \text{ is a constant}$$

are of the form

$$y = Ce^{kx}$$

where C can be any real number.

For this family of solution curves the slope depends on y but not on x. The curves are thus **horizontal translations** of one another. The diagram illustrates typical curves in the case $k > 0$.

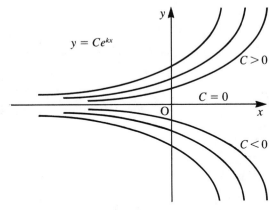

Initial Conditions

In applications, when one uses a DE to model a physical system, the unknown function y is usually specified at the initial value of t (or x); that is,

$$y(t_0) = y_0$$

For example, in order to determine the position of an object, given its velocity at time t, one needs to know the position of the object at some time t_0. A restriction of this form is called an **initial condition**. The use of the initial condition determines a value for the arbitrary constant C that arises when one solves the DE and results in a unique solution. In geometrical terms, the initial condition $y(t_0) = y_0$ specifies the particular solution curve that passes through the point (t_0, y_0) in the t-y plane. The importance of initial conditions in applications will be discussed further in the next section.

Exercises 7.3

1. Verify that the given function is a solution of the DE, where C, C_1, and C_2 are constants.

   a. $\dfrac{dy}{dt} = -3y, \quad y = Ce^{-3t}$

   b. $\dfrac{dy}{dt} = y + 1, \quad y = Ce^t - 1$

   c. $\dfrac{dy}{dt} = y^2, \quad y = \dfrac{1}{C - t}$

   d. $\dfrac{dy}{dt} = 2y + t^2 e^{2t}, \quad y = Ce^{2t} + \dfrac{1}{3} t^3 t^{2t}$

   e. $\dfrac{d^2y}{dt^2} + 4y = 0, \quad y = C_1 \sin 2t + C_2 \cos 2t$

   f. $\dfrac{d^2y}{dx^2} - 9y = 0, \quad y = C_1 e^{3x} + C_2 e^{-3x}$

   g. $\dfrac{d^2y}{dx^2} - 4\dfrac{dy}{dx} + 13y = 0, \quad y = e^{2x}(C_1 \cos 3x + C_2 \sin 3x)$

   h. $x\left(\dfrac{dy}{dx}\right)^2 - y\dfrac{dy}{dx} + 1 = 0, \quad y = Cx + \dfrac{1}{C}$

2. Find and sketch the family of curves whose slope $\dfrac{dy}{dx}$ is given. Find the curve that passes through the given point and illustrate this in your sketch.

   a. $\dfrac{dy}{dx} = 3, \quad (2, 1)$

   b. $\dfrac{dy}{dx} = -2x, \quad (1, -1)$

   c. $\dfrac{dy}{dx} = 4x - 1, \quad (0, 1)$

   d. $\dfrac{dy}{dx} = 6x^2, \quad (1, -2)$

   e. $\dfrac{dy}{dx} = 4e^{-2x}, \quad (\ln 2, \tfrac{3}{2})$

   f. $\dfrac{dy}{dx} = 3 \sin 2x, \quad \left(\dfrac{\pi}{2}, 0\right)$

   g. $\dfrac{dy}{dx} = 3x^2 - 3, \quad (1, 1)$

   h. $\dfrac{dy}{dx} = \dfrac{1}{x - 3}, \quad (2, 1)$

   i. $\dfrac{dy}{dx} = \dfrac{4}{1 - 2x}, \quad (0, 3)$

3. Find all solutions of each differential equation. Find the unique solution that satisfies the given initial condition.

   a. $\dfrac{dy}{dx} = 3\sqrt{x} - \dfrac{1}{x}, \quad y(e^2) = -1$

   b. $\dfrac{dy}{dt} = 3 \sin t + \sin 3t, \quad y(0) = \dfrac{2}{3}$

   c. $\dfrac{dx}{dt} = (3 - 2t)^5, \quad x(2) = 1$

   d. $\dfrac{dy}{dx} = \dfrac{12}{(2 - 3x)^3}, \quad y(1) = 0$

   e. $\dfrac{dv}{dt} = \dfrac{1}{2}e^{2t} + 8e^{-3t}, \quad v(\ln 2) = 1$

   f. $\dfrac{ds}{dt} = (e^t - e^{-t})^2, \quad s(0) = 5$

4. Find the equation of the curve $y = f(x)$ whose tangent line has a slope of
$$f'(x) = x^{\frac{2}{3}}$$
given that the point $\left(1, \frac{3}{5}\right)$ is on the curve.

5. If $\dfrac{dy}{dx} = 3 + e^{-x}$ and $y(0) = -2$, find $y(\ln 2)$.

6. If $\dfrac{du}{dt} = \dfrac{1}{(2 + \pi t)^2}$ and $u\left(\dfrac{1}{\pi}\right) = \dfrac{2}{3\pi}$, find $u\left(\dfrac{2}{\pi}\right)$.

7. Find the family of curves that intersects the given family of curves at right angles. Sketch typical members of both families on the same set of axes.

   a. $y = 3x + C$ **b.** $y = x^3 + C$
   c. $y = e^x + C$ **d.** $y = \ln|x - 1| + C$

8. If $\dfrac{dy}{dt} = 3y$ and $y(0) = -\dfrac{1}{2}$, find $y(\ln 2)$. Sketch the graph of y as a function of t.

9. If $\dfrac{du}{dx} = -2u$ and $u(0) = 18$, find $u(\ln 3)$. Sketch the graph of u as a function of x.

10. Sketch the family of solution curves of the DE $\dfrac{dv}{dx} = -\pi v$. Find the unique solution that satisfies the initial condition $v\left(\dfrac{1}{\pi}\right) = \dfrac{\pi}{e}$.

Problems 7.3

1. The contour lines (curves of constant elevation C) on the map of a mountain are described by the equation
$$x^2 + 2y^2 = C$$

   Determine the orthogonal trajectories and identify the curve of steepest descent that passes through the point $(1, 1)$. Illustrate with a sketch.

2. Suppose that the temperature T at the point (x, y) in a metal sheet is given by
$$T = y^2 - x^2 + 50$$

   The curves
$$y^2 - x^2 + 50 = C$$

   are the curves of constant temperature (called isothermals). The orthogonal trajectories of the isothermals represent the direction of heat flow.

   a. Find the orthogonal trajectories.
   b. Sketch both families of curves and, using an arrow, show the direction of heat flow at $(1, 1)$ on your diagram.

3. On a certain day it began to snow early in the morning and the snow continued to fall at a constant rate. The velocity at which a snowplow is able to clear a road is inversely proportional to the height of the accumulated snow. The snowplow started at 11 a.m. and had cleared 4 km by 2 p.m. By 5 p.m. it had cleared another 2 km. When did it start snowing?

7.4 Exponential Growth and Decay

In certain circumstances, quantities such as the size of a population, the mass of a radioactive substance, and the difference between the temperature of an object and its surroundings, change at a rate that is proportional to the quantity itself. Let y denote the quantity at time t. Then a mathematical model for the above behaviour is given by the differential equation (DE)

$$\frac{dy}{dt} = ky$$

where k is a constant.

We showed in section 7.3 that all solutions of this DE are of the form

$$y = Ce^{kt}$$

where C is any constant. Thus if $k > 0$, the quantity described by y undergoes **exponential growth**, and if $k < 0$, y undergoes **exponential decay**.

The examples in this section illustrate the use of this mathematical model.

Example 1. The growth rate of a population of bacteria is proportional to the number of bacteria. If the number of bacteria in a culture grew from 100 to 900 in 24 h, what was the population after the first 12 h?

Solution. Let $N(t)$ denote the number of bacteria at time t. It follows from the given growth rate that

$$\frac{dN}{dt} = kN \tag{1}$$

where k is, as yet, an unknown constant. We measure time t in hours, with $t = 0$ initially. The given data imply that

$$N(0) = 100 \tag{2}$$

and

$$N(24) = 900 \tag{3}$$

The solution of the DE (1) is

$$N(t) = Ce^{kt} \tag{4}$$

where C is a constant. On setting $t = 0$ in equation (4), the initial condition (2) implies that

$$100 = Ce^0$$
$$= C$$

Using this result, equations (3) and (4) imply that

$$900 = 100\, e^{24k}$$

To solve for k, we write

$$e^{24k} = 9$$

and hence

$$24\,k = \ln 9$$
$$= 2\ln 3$$

giving

$$k = \frac{1}{12}\ln 3$$

Thus the population at time t is

$$N(t) = 100\, e^{\frac{t \ln 3}{12}}$$

In particular,

$$N(12) = 100\, e^{\ln 3}$$
$$= 300$$

Thus, after the first 12 h there are 300 bacteria. $\qquad\square$

Equation (2) is the initial condition in this problem and determines the constant C in the solution. Equation (3) is a subsidiary condition and serves to determine the constant k, which is called the **intrinsic rate of growth**.

Radioactive Decay

The atoms of certain radioactive elements, for example radium, are unstable, and disintegrate spontaneously to form other elements. It is observed that the amount of a radioactive substance decreases at a rate proportional to the amount present. Thus if $M(t)$ is the amount present at time t, then

$$\frac{dM}{dt} = -kM$$

where k is a positive constant called **the decay constant**. The negative sign indicates that M decreases with time t.

Example 2. Radioactive carbon 14 decays at a rate proportional to the amount present. After 10 years it is found that 1.25 mg in a sample of 1000 mg has decayed. Determine how long it will take for half of the sample to decay.

Solution. Let M denote the mass of carbon 14 at time t. By the law of radioactive decay,

$$\frac{dM}{dt} = -kM$$

where k is a constant. The data imply that

$$M(0) = 1000 \tag{5}$$

and

$$M(10) = 998.75 \tag{6}$$

All solutions of the DE are of the form

$$M(t) = Ce^{-kt} \tag{7}$$

where C is a constant. On setting $t = 0$ in equation (7), the initial condition (5) implies that

$$1000 = Ce^0$$
$$= C$$

Using this result, equations (6) and (7) imply that

$$998.75 = 1000\,e^{-10k}$$

To solve for k, write

$$e^{-10k} = \frac{998.75}{1000}$$
$$= 0.998\ 75$$

Therefore,

$$-10k = \ln(0.998\ 75)$$
$$= -0.001\ 25$$

giving

$$k = 0.000\ 125$$

Equation (7) yields

$$M(t) = 1000\,e^{-0.000\ 125t}$$

To find t when $M = 500$, solve the equation

$$500 = 1000\,e^{-0.000\ 125t}$$

Hence

$$e^{0.000\ 125t} = 2$$

and

$$t = \frac{\ln 2}{0.000\ 125}$$
$$= 5545$$

Thus it will take 5545 years for half the sample to decay. □

For any radioactive element, it can be shown that the time taken for half of a sample to decay is independent of the initial amount (see Problem 2). This time is called the **half-life** of the element. In Example 2, we calculated the half-life of carbon 14.

Living organisms contain a fixed ratio of radioactive carbon 14 to carbon 12. When an organism dies, it ceases to take in new carbon, and the amount of carbon 14 decreases owing to radioactive decay. By measuring the ratio of carbon 14 to carbon 12 in fossils and using the equations in Example 2, one can estimate the age of the fossils. (See Exercise 8.)

The next example applies the decay model to changing temperatures.

Example 3. According to Newton's law of temperature change, the rate of cooling of an object in air is proportional to the difference between the temperature of the object and the air temperature. If the air temperature is 20°C and boiling water cools from 100°C to 60°C in 10 min, how long will it take the water to reach 30°C?

Solution. Let $T(t)$ denote the temperature of the water at time t. According to Newton's law,

$$\frac{dT}{dt} = -k(T - 20) \tag{8}$$

where k is a positive constant. The data imply that

$$T(0) = 100 \tag{9}$$

and

$$T(10) = 60 \tag{10}$$

In order to solve the DE (8) we transform it into the standard form by letting

$$y = T - 20 \tag{11}$$

Since

$$\frac{dy}{dt} = \frac{dT}{dt}$$

the DE (8) assumes the form

$$\frac{dy}{dt} = -ky$$

It follows that

$$y = Ce^{-kt}$$

where C is a constant, and hence, by equation (11),

$$T - 20 = Ce^{-kt}$$

or

$$T = 20 + Ce^{-kt} \qquad (12)$$

On setting $t = 0$ in equation (12), the initial condition (9) implies that

$$100 = 20 + Ce^0$$

so that $C = 80$. Using this value for C, equations (10) and (12) imply that

$$60 = 20 + 80\,e^{-10k}$$

To solve for k, write

$$e^{-10k} = \frac{60 - 20}{80}$$

$$= \frac{1}{2}$$

and hence

$$-10k = \ln\left(\frac{1}{2}\right)$$

$$= -\ln 2$$

or

$$k = \frac{1}{10}\ln 2$$

Thus,

$$T(t) = 20 + 80\,e^{-\left(\frac{\ln 2}{10}\right)t}$$

To find the time when $T = 30$, solve the equation

$$30 = 20 + 80\,e^{-\left(\frac{\ln 2}{10}\right)t}$$

to obtain

$$-\left(\frac{\ln 2}{10}\right)t = \ln\left(\frac{10}{80}\right)$$

$$= -3\ln 2$$

and so $t = 30$. Thus the water will have cooled to 30°C after 30 min.   □

Exercises 7.4

1. The mass W, in grams, of a young animal is

$$W(t) = 500 \, e^{0.08t}$$

where t is the time in days after the animal's birth and $0 \le t \le 14$.

   a. What is the mass at birth?
   b. How many days will it take to triple the birth mass?
   c. Calculate the ratio

$$\frac{\text{rate of change of mass}}{\text{mass}}$$

   for $t = 1, 3, 5$.
   d. Find the DE satisfied by $W(t)$.

2. The power supply of a satellite is a radioisotope. The power output P, in watts, decreases at a rate proportional to the amount present, so that

$$P(t) = 50e^{-0.004t}$$

where t is the time in days.

   a. What was the power output of the satellite initially?
   b. What is the half-life of the power supply?
   c. The satellite's equipment cannot operate on less than 10 W of power. How long can the satellite stay in operation?
   d. Find the DE satisfied by $P(t)$.

3. The number of bacteria in a culture increases at a rate proportional to the number present. Consider the following situations:

   a. If there were 1000 bacteria at 1 p.m. and 1200 at 3 p.m., how many would there be at 8 p.m.?
   b. The number of bacteria doubles after 10 min. If there were 100 bacteria initially, when will the number have increased to 3000?
   c. If the original number increases by 20% in 3 h, when will it double?

4. The world's population has been estimated as 0.8 billion in 1750 and 1 billion in 1800. Find the population in 1950, assuming that the rate of change is proportional to the population. (This simple model underestimates the actual value, which was 2.5 billion.)

5. a. The half-life of polonium is 3 min. What is its decay constant?
   b. Of an initial amount of 100 g of polonium, how much will remain after 20 min?

6. The growth rate of the population of Central America is 3.5% per year (one of the highest in the world). What is the doubling time?

7. Polonium 210 decays into lead with a half-life of 138 days. How long will it take for 90% of the radioactivity in a sample of polonium 210 to dissipate?

8. Fragments of a human skeleton found in a cave are brought to a laboratory for carbon dating. Analysis shows that the ratio of radioactive carbon 14 to carbon 12 is only 6.24% of the value in living tissue. Determine how long ago the person lived. The decay constant for carbon 14 is $\frac{1}{8000}$ per year.

9. Pizza Unlimited, a national pizza firm, is selling franchises throughout the country. The president estimates that the number of franchises N will increase at a rate of 15% per year; that is

$$\frac{dN}{dt} = 0.15N$$

   a. Find the solution of the differential equation, assuming that the number of franchises when $t = 0$ is 40.
   b. How many franchises will there be in 20 years?
   c. After what period of time will the initial number of 40 franchises double?

10. The population of the USSR was 209 million in 1959. It is estimated that the population P is growing exponentially at the rate of 1% per year; that is,

$$\frac{dP}{dt} = 0.01P$$

   a. Estimate the population of the USSR in 1999.
   b. After what period of time will the population be double that of 1959?

11. The current $I(t)$ in a coil of wire satisfies the DE

$$\frac{dI}{dt} + 2I = 0$$

   If the initial current is 3 A, find the current after 1 s.

12. Extensive research has provided data relating the risk R(%) of having an automobile accident to the blood alcohol level b(%). This relationship is best described by the model $\frac{dR}{db} = kR$. The risk is 1% if the blood alcohol level is 0 and the risk is 20% when the blood alcohol level is 0.14. At what blood alcohol level will the risk of having an accident be 80%?

13. A bowl of porridge initially at 80°C cools to 40°C in 15 min when the room temperature is 20°C. James refuses to eat his porridge if it cools to a temperature below 50°C. How long does he have to come to the table? Assume Newton's law of temperature change.

14. An indoor thermometer reading 20°C is put outdoors. In 10 min it reads 25°C and in another 10 min it reads 27°C. Use Newton's law of temperature change to calculate the outdoor temperature.

15. When a coil of steel is removed from an annealing furnace its temperature is 684°C. Four minutes later its temperature is 246°C. How long will it take to reach 100°C? Assume Newton's law of cooling, with the surrounding temperature equal to 27°C.

Problems 7.4

1. A cook monitors the temperature of a roast that is in a 200°C oven. At 2 p.m., the temperature of the roast is 80°C and at 3 p.m. the temperature of the roast is 156°C. If the temperature of the roast was initially 20°C, at what time was the roast put in the oven?

2. For any radioactive decay process, show that the time taken for half a sample to decay is independent of the initial amount.

3. Let y be any non-zero solution of the DE

$$\frac{dy}{dt} = ky$$

and let Δt be a fixed time interval. Show that

$$\frac{y(t + \Delta t) - y(t)}{y(t)}$$

is independent of t. This means that the percentage increase (or decrease) in y over a fixed time interval Δt is independent of when the time interval begins.

4. If a bank advertises that its interest rate is r% per annum "compounded continuously," it means that the amount of money you deposit will increase at a rate proportional to the current balance, with the constant of proportionality being the interest rate. If $1000 is deposited at an interest rate of 10% compounded continuously, how much money will be in the account after 10 years? Compare this to the amount if the interest is only compounded annually.

5. What annual rate of interest compounded annually is equivalent to an annual rate of 6% compounded continuously?

6. A radioactive substance decays, so that after H years, one half the original amount remains.

   a. Show that the amount $M(t)$ left after t years can be expressed as

   $$M(t) = M(0)\left(\frac{1}{2}\right)^{\frac{t}{H}}$$

   b. Relate the decay constant k to the half-life H.

7.5 Separable Differential Equations

In this section we shall extend our range of applications by considering DE's of the form

$$\frac{dy}{dx} = f(y)\, g(x)$$

where y is an unknown function of x, and $f(y)$ and $g(x)$ are given functions.

Example 1. Find and sketch the family of solution curves of the DE

$$\frac{dy}{dx} = -\frac{9x}{16y}$$

Solution. Rearrange the DE so that the unknown function and its derivative appear only on the left side:

$$y\frac{dy}{dx} = -\frac{9}{16}x$$

Now try to express the left side as the derivative of an expression involving y. Since

$$\frac{d}{dy}\left(\frac{1}{2}y^2\right) = y$$

it follows from the Chain Rule that

$$y\frac{dy}{dx} = \frac{d}{dy}\left(\frac{1}{2}y^2\right)\frac{dy}{dx}$$

$$= \frac{d}{dx}\left(\frac{1}{2}y^2\right)$$

Thus, the original DE can be written as

$$\frac{d}{dx}\left(\frac{1}{2}y^2\right) = -\frac{9}{16}x$$

It follows that $\frac{1}{2}y^2$ must equal the general antiderivative of $-\frac{9}{16}x$:

$$\frac{1}{2}y^2 = -\frac{9}{16}\left(\frac{1}{2}x^2\right) + C$$

On rearranging, we obtain

$$\frac{x^2}{16} + \frac{y^2}{9} = K$$

where $K = \dfrac{2C}{9}$ is a new constant. The solution curves thus form a family of ellipses.

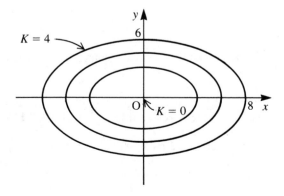

Example 1 illustrates the technique for solving DE's of the form

$$\frac{dy}{dx} = f(y)\, g(x) \tag{1}$$

Rearrange the DE by dividing by $f(y)$ to get

$$\frac{1}{f(y)}\frac{dy}{dx} = g(x)$$

If $F(y)$ is an antiderivative of $\dfrac{1}{f(y)}$, then, by the Chain Rule,

$$\frac{1}{f(y)}\frac{dy}{dx} = \frac{dF(y)}{dy}\frac{dy}{dx}$$
$$= \frac{d}{dx}[F(y)]$$

The original DE can thus be written in the form

$$\frac{d}{dx}[F(y)] = g(x) \tag{2}$$

If we think of $F(y)$ as the unknown function, say u, then the DE (2) is the same as the DE's that were discussed in section 7.3:

$$\frac{du}{dx} = g(x)$$

The DE (2) can be solved to give

$$F(y) = G(x) + C$$

where $G(x)$ is an antiderivative of $g(x)$. A DE of the form (1) is called a **separable DE**. A DE like $\dfrac{dy}{dx} = x^2 + y^2$ is not separable, since the right side cannot be factored as in equation (1).

Example 2. Solve the DE

$$\frac{dy}{dt} = y^2 e^{-t}$$

subject to the initial condition $y(0) = \frac{1}{4}$. Show that the solution satisfies

$$\lim_{t \to +\infty} y(t) = \frac{1}{3}$$

and graph the solution.

Solution. Since the DE is separable, it can be rearranged in the usual way to obtain

$$\frac{1}{y^2} \frac{dy}{dt} = e^{-t}$$

Since $\frac{d}{dy}\left(-\frac{1}{y}\right) = \frac{1}{y^2}$, the DE assumes the form

$$\frac{d}{dt}\left(-\frac{1}{y}\right) = e^{-t}$$

Hence,

$$-\frac{1}{y} = -e^{-t} + C$$

so that

$$y = \frac{1}{e^{-t} - C}$$

On setting $t = 0$, the initial condition implies that

$$\frac{1}{4} = \frac{1}{1 - C}$$

so that $C = -3$. The solution is therefore

$$y = \frac{1}{e^{-t} + 3}$$

Also note that

$$\lim_{t \to +\infty} y = \frac{1}{\lim_{t \to +\infty} (e^{-t} + 3)}$$

$$= \frac{1}{3}$$

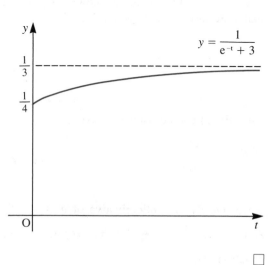

The Logistic Differential Equation

The model of population growth that is provided by the DE

$$\frac{dN}{dt} = kN$$

gives reasonable agreement with observations of population growth for a single species, provided that there is no competition for food, water, or living space. In order to incorporate competition into the model, one assumes that the environment can support a maximum population M, called the **carrying capacity**. The modified DE should have $\frac{dN}{dt} < 0$ when $N > M$ (a decrease in population due to overpopulation) and $\frac{dN}{dt} > 0$ when $N < M$ (an increase in population if the population is less than the carrying capacity). A DE that incorporates these features is

$$\frac{dN}{dt} = kN\left[1 - \frac{N}{M}\right] \tag{3}$$

where k and M are constants. When N approaches the fixed carrying capacity M, $\frac{dN}{dt}$ tends to zero as one would expect. Equation (3) is called the **logistic DE**.

Example 3. A lake is estimated to have a carrying capacity of 10 000 trout. In 1983, 2000 trout were introduced into the lake, and in 1986 it was observed that the population had increased to 4000. Assuming that the growth is governed by the logistic equation, determine the population in 1989.

Solution. Let $N(t)$ denote the number of trout at time t, where t is in years, and $t = 0$ corresponds to the year 1983. Since carrying capacity is 10 000, the logistic DE (3) assumes the form

$$\frac{dN}{dt} = kN\left[1 - \frac{N}{10\ 000}\right] \tag{4}$$

It is convenient to define a new variable by

$$y = \frac{N}{10\ 000} \tag{5}$$

Since

$$\frac{dy}{dt} = \frac{1}{10\ 000}\frac{dN}{dt}$$

the DE (4) can be written as

$$\frac{dy}{dt} = ky(1 - y)$$

Now arrange the DE in the usual way to get

$$\frac{1}{y(1-y)}\frac{dy}{dt} = k \tag{6}$$

The next step, finding an antiderivative of $\dfrac{1}{y(1-y)}$, requires a new approach. Observe that

$$\frac{1}{y(1-y)} = \frac{1}{y} + \frac{1}{1-y}$$

On taking antiderivatives, we get

$$\frac{1}{y} + \frac{1}{1-y} = \frac{d}{dy}[\ln y - \ln(1-y)]$$
$$= \frac{d}{dy}\left[\ln\left(\frac{y}{1-y}\right)\right]$$

Note that since $0 < N < 10\ 000$, it follows that $0 < y < 1$, and hence $\ln y$ and $\ln(1-y)$ are both defined. The DE (6) can now be written as

$$\frac{d}{dy}\left[\ln\left(\frac{y}{1-y}\right)\right]\frac{dy}{dt} = k$$

or, equivalently,

$$\frac{d}{dt}\left[\ln\left(\frac{y}{1-y}\right)\right] = k$$

Hence,

$$\ln\left(\frac{y}{1-y}\right) = kt + C$$

On exponentiating, we obtain

$$\frac{y}{1-y} = e^C e^{kt}$$

If we take the reciprocals of both sides at this point, the expression for N as a function of t will take a simpler form. Hence,

$$\frac{1-y}{y} = e^{-C}e^{-kt} \tag{7}$$

It is preferable to determine the constants C and k before solving for y. The initial condition is $N(0) = 2000$, so that from equation (5)

$$y(0) = 0.2$$

Equation (7) implies that

$$\frac{1 - 0.2}{0.2} = e^{-C}$$

Hence $e^{-C} = 4$, and

$$\frac{1 - y}{y} = 4\,e^{-kt} \tag{8}$$

Since $N(3) = 4000$, it follows from equation (5) that

$$y(3) = 0.4$$

Equation (8) implies that

$$\frac{1 - 0.4}{0.4} = 4\,e^{-3k}$$

Hence, $e^{-k} = \left(\frac{3}{8}\right)^{\frac{1}{3}}$, and equation (8) becomes

$$\frac{1 - y}{y} = 4\left(\frac{3}{8}\right)^{\frac{t}{3}}$$

On solving for y and with the use of equation (5), we find that

$$N(t) = \frac{10\ 000}{1 + 4\left(\frac{3}{8}\right)^{\frac{t}{3}}}$$

Finally, when $t = 6$,

$$N(6) = \frac{10\ 000}{1 + \frac{9}{16}}$$
$$= 6400$$

Thus the population will be 6400 in 1989.

Exercises 7.5

1. Find and sketch the family of curves defined by each DE. Find the member of the family that passes through the given point.

a. $\dfrac{dy}{dx} = \dfrac{x}{4y}$, $(3, 1)$

b. $\dfrac{dy}{dx} = -xy$, $(0, 3)$

c. $\dfrac{dy}{dx} = \dfrac{-y}{x}$, $(1, 2)$

d. $\dfrac{dy}{dx} = \dfrac{9x}{y - 3}$, $(1, 4)$

2. Solve each DE subject to the initial condition.

a. $\dfrac{dy}{dt} = y^3 \sin t, \quad y(0) = 1$

b. $v\dfrac{dv}{dr} = -\dfrac{1}{r^2}, \quad v(1) = 2$

c. $\dfrac{ds}{dt} = s^2 e^{-t}, \quad s(0) = \dfrac{1}{2}$

d. $\dfrac{dN}{dt} = 2N - 5, \quad N(0) = 10$

e. $\dfrac{dy}{dx} = 4e^{x+y}, \quad y(-\ln 2) = 0$

f. $\dfrac{dy}{dt} = \sqrt{y}\,(\sin t + \cos t), \quad y\left(\dfrac{\pi}{2}\right) = 1$

3. Find the curve $y = f(x)$ that passes through the point $(0,\, e^2)$ and satisfies the condition

$$\frac{dy}{dx} = -2xy$$

4. Find the curve $y = f(x)$ that passes through the point $\left(\dfrac{\pi}{2},\, \ln 2\right)$ and satisfies the equation

$$\frac{dy}{dx} = e^{-2y} \sin x$$

5. Find the family of curves that intersects each given family at right angles. Sketch members of both families on the same axes.

a. $y = C e^x$

b. $x = C y^2$

6. Consider the DE $\dfrac{dy}{dt} = y^2$. Show that if $y(0) = \dfrac{1}{b}$, where $b > 0$, then the solution $y(t)$ satisfies

$$\lim_{t \to b^-} y(t) = +\infty$$

Sketch the solution for $b = 2$.

7. Consider the DE $\dfrac{dv}{dt} = \dfrac{e^{2t}}{v}$.

a. If $v(0) = 3$, find $v(\ln 2)$.

b. If $v(1) = -2$, find $v(\ln 3)$.

Problems 7.5

1. If an object moves through a liquid that provides a resistance proportional to the square of the object's velocity v, the velocity satisfies the DE

$$\frac{dv}{dt} = -kv^2$$

where k is a constant. If the velocity decreases from 2 m/s to 1 m/s in 10 s, when will the velocity be $\dfrac{1}{2}$ m/s?

2. The velocity v of a skydiver satisfies the DE

$$\frac{dv}{dt} = g - kv$$

where k is a constant and $g = 10$ m/s^2 is the acceleration due to gravity. The term $-kv$ represents the air resistance.

a. Find v as a function of time, assuming that the skydiver jumps at time $t = 0$.
b. Show that

$$\lim_{t \to +\infty} v(t) = \frac{g}{k}$$

(This is the so-called terminal velocity.)

c. If $k = \frac{1}{4}$ (a typical value) how long will it take for the skydiver to reach 90% of her terminal velocity?

3. A species of rodent that inhabits a remote Pacific Island is limited to a steady population of 3000 owing to restrictions in food supply. One year a disease kills 2000 rodents. It is observed that it takes 5 years for the population to rise to 1500 rodents again. Assuming that the population satisfies the logistic DE, determine how long it will take the population to reach 2500.

4. A projectile fired from the surface of the earth has a velocity v at a height r (measured from the centre of the earth) that satisfies the DE

$$v\frac{dv}{dr} = -g\frac{R^2}{r^2}$$

where R is the radius of the earth and g is the acceleration due to gravity at the earth's surface.

a. If v_0 is the initial velocity (when $r = R$), and

$$v_0 < \sqrt{2gR}$$

show that the projectile will reach a maximum height of

$$H = \frac{2gR^2}{2gR - v_0^2}$$

b. Find the "escape velocity" for a projectile fired from earth, i.e., the smallest initial velocity v_0 that will ensure that the projectile travels away from earth indefinitely.

5. For populations that satisfy the logistic DE

$$\frac{dN}{dt} = kN\left[1 - \frac{N}{M}\right]$$

where k and M are constants, show that the graph of N versus t has a point of inflection when $N = \frac{M}{2}$.

6. The logistic equation

$$\frac{dN}{dt} = kN\left[1 - \frac{N}{M}\right]$$

where k and M are constants, can be solved differently than in the text by making a change of variable, as follows.

a. Let $y = \frac{M}{N} - 1$, and show that y satisfies the *DE*

$$\frac{dy}{dt} = -ky$$

b. If $N(0) = N_0$, use part (a) to show that

$$N(t) = \frac{M}{1 + \left(\dfrac{M}{N_0} - 1\right)e^{-kt}}$$

7. The number of bacteria $N(t)$ in a population increases according to the logistic equation

$$\frac{dN}{dt} = kN\left[1 - \frac{N}{M}\right]$$

where the carrying capacity is $M = 100\ 000$.

a. If the population increases from 50 000 to 60 000 in 5 h, find the natural growth rate k.

b. When will the population reach 90% of the carrying capacity?

Review Exercises

1. Find the general antiderivative of each function and verify your result by differentiation.

a. $5x^2 - 7x + 3$

b. $x^{\frac{5}{2}} - 6$

c. $\sin \pi x + \cos \pi x$

d. $e^{-\pi x} + 10 \sin x$

e. $e^{6x} - 2e^{3x}$

f. $\dfrac{1}{x} + \dfrac{1}{x^2} + \dfrac{1}{x^3}$

g. $3 \sin\left(2x + \dfrac{\pi}{4}\right)$

h. $(x + 5)^4$

i. $\sqrt{2x - 1}$

j. $(6x - 1)^9$

k. $\sin 6x + e^{-2x} + \pi$

l. $e^x + x^e$

m. $\dfrac{1}{5x + 1}$

n. $3 \sec^2 2x$

2. Find and sketch the family of curves whose slope is given. Find the curve that passes through the given point and illustrate it in your sketch.

a. $\dfrac{dy}{dx} = -3,\quad \left(\dfrac{1}{3}, 1\right)$

b. $\dfrac{dy}{dx} = 1 - 3x^2,\quad (1, 1)$

c. $\dfrac{dy}{dx} = 3\cos \pi x,\quad \left(\dfrac{1}{2}, 0\right)$

d. $\dfrac{dy}{dx} = 3e^{-\frac{1}{2}x},\quad (\ln 4, 2)$

3. a. Determine the equation of the curve $y = f(x)$ that passes through the point $(0, 3)$ and satisfies the differential equation

$$\frac{dy}{dx} = 2x + 1$$

b. Find the equation of the tangent line to the curve in part (a) at the point $(-2, 5)$.

c. Sketch the curve $y = f(x)$, showing all the features found in parts (a) and (b).

4. Find equations for the members of the family of curves determined by
$\dfrac{dy}{dx} = 2x + \dfrac{3}{2}\sqrt{x},\quad x \ge 0$, that pass through the following points:

a. $(0, 0)$

b. $(2, 0)$

5. If the driver of an automobile wishes to increase his speed from 40 km/h to 100 km/h while travelling a distance of 200 m, what constant acceleration should be maintained?

6. Find the equation of the curve $y = f(x)$ whose tangent line has a slope of

$$\frac{dy}{dx} = x - \sin \pi x$$

if the curve passes through the point $\left(1, \dfrac{1}{2}\right)$.

7. If $\dfrac{dy}{dt} = 3e^{-t} - e^{-3t}$ and $y(\ln 2) = 0$, find $\lim\limits_{t \to +\infty} y$.

8. If $\dfrac{dy}{dx} = \pi\sqrt{2 + \pi x}$ and $y\left(\dfrac{1}{\pi}\right) = \dfrac{2}{3} - 2\sqrt{3}$, find $y\left(\dfrac{2}{\pi}\right)$.

9. If $\dfrac{dy}{dt} = e^{2t} - 2e^t$, and $y(0) = 1$, find the maximum value and minimum value of y on the interval $0 \le t \le 3$.

10. A rocket takes off vertically at time $t = 0$, and during the first 10 s of flight its acceleration in m/s² is given by $a(t) = 10t - t^2$. Find the height reached by the rocket after 10 s.

11. How old is a Chinese artifact that has lost 60% of its carbon 14? The decay constant for carbon 14 is $\dfrac{1}{8000}$ per year.

12. The decay rate of krypton 85 is 6.3% per year. Find its half-life.

13. Certain office machinery constantly depreciates (decays in value) at a rate of 12% per year. How much will a $500 typewriter be worth in 10 years?

14. A certain small rodent reproduces very rapidly, so that its population increases at the rate of 40% per month. How large a population will two rodents generate in one year?

15. The acceleration of a car travelling in slow-moving traffic is $a(t) = \frac{1}{8} \sin\left(\frac{1}{16}t\right)$ m/s^2.

    a. If its initial velocity is $\frac{5}{2}$ m/s, how far will it travel in 10 min?

    b. Find the maximum and minimum velocity of the car during this time interval.

16. A kettle of boiling water (at 100°C) cools to 70°C in 10 min. Ten minutes later its temperature is 50°C. Find the room temperature. (Assume Newton's law of temperature change.)

17. The velocity of a skydiver, t seconds after jumping, is given by

$$v = 40(1 - e^{-\frac{1}{4}t}) \text{ m/s}$$

    a. How far will the skydiver fall in the first 10 s?
    b. How long will the skydiver take to fall 80 m?
    (Hint: Use Newton's method.)

18. The disease arteriosclerosis causes the walls of arteries to gradually thicken. Suppose that the inner radius of an artery decreases at a rate of $0.1e^{-0.01t}$ cm per year due to this process.

    a. Find the inner radius, at time t, of an artery whose inner radius is initially 1 cm ($t = 0$).

    b. After how many years will the cross-sectional area of the artery be reduced by 50%?

19. a. Find constants A and B such that

$$\frac{1}{x^2 - 1} = \frac{A}{x - 1} + \frac{B}{x + 1}$$

    b. If $\frac{dy}{dx} = \frac{1}{x^2 - 1}$ and $y(2) = -\ln 3$, find $y(4)$.

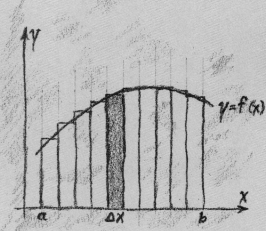

Bernhard Riemann *(1826–1866) was educated at Göttingen University in Germany. The presence of the legendary Gauss made this university the centre of the mathematical world. Riemann was one of the few great mathematicians who was also a pleasant person. He was shy and, when speaking in public, nervous. At the age of thirty-three, after many years of poverty, Riemann became a full professor at Göttingen. In poor health, he died at age thirty-nine. Riemann had a deep influence on the mathematics of the twentieth century. He made significant contributions to the theory of functions of a complex variable, and developed the concept of Riemann sums as the basis for the integral. Before being appointed an unpaid lecturer, candidates at Göttingen were required to name three topics in which they had some competence and lecture on the first such topic. Riemann listed his third topic as the foundations of geometry. Unfortunately, this was a topic of great interest to Gauss who insisted that Riemann give his lecture on this topic. Unprepared, Riemann devoted himself to geometry for two months and gave what is often regarded as the most important scientific lecture ever given. The field of Riemannian Geometry was born. Even Gauss (who rarely praised his contemporaries) was pleased. Later, Riemann's analysis was used as the framework for Einstein's theory of general relativity. In later years Riemann made significant contributions to number theory. In particular, this research led to the Riemann zeta function:*

$$\zeta(z) = 1 + \frac{1}{2^z} + \frac{1}{3^z} + \frac{1}{4^z} + \ldots$$

where z is a complex number, x + iy, and one of the most important unsolved problems in modern mathematics, the Riemann hypothesis: "In the interval 0 < x < 1, the only zeros of $\zeta(z)$ occur when $x = \frac{1}{2}$."

Areas and Integrals

In this chapter we shall consider the second geometric problem that gave rise to Calculus—the **problem of areas**: calculate the area A of the region under the curve $y = f(x)$ between $x = a$ and $x = b$.

We shall show how to solve this problem in two ways. The first method, in which we use rectangles to approximate the area of the region, leads to the concept of the **definite integral**. The second method makes use of **antiderivatives** to find the area. When combined, the two methods lead to the Fundamental Theorem of Calculus.

8.1 Areas and Riemann Sums

Consider the problem of finding the area A of the region bounded by the parabola $y = x^2$ and the x-axis, between $x = 0$ and $x = 1$.

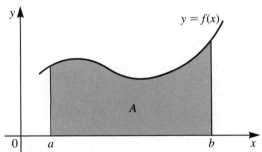

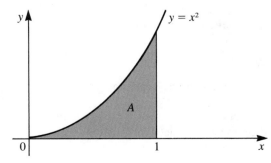

Subdivide the interval $0 \leq x \leq 1$ into four equal subintervals and construct rectangles above the subintervals, as shown in the diagram. The sum of the areas of the four rectangles is

$$\left(\tfrac{1}{4}\right)^2\left(\tfrac{1}{4}\right) + \left(\tfrac{1}{2}\right)^2\left(\tfrac{1}{4}\right) + \left(\tfrac{3}{4}\right)^2\left(\tfrac{1}{4}\right) + (1)^2\left(\tfrac{1}{4}\right)$$

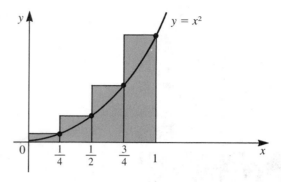

To see the pattern in this sum, write $\left(\tfrac{1}{2}\right)^2$ as $\left(\tfrac{2}{4}\right)^2$ and $(1)^2$ as $\left(\tfrac{4}{4}\right)^2$. Since the sum is greater than the area A,

$$A < \left(\tfrac{1}{4}\right)^3 (1^2 + 2^2 + 3^2 + 4^2)$$

Now consider the four rectangles whose heights are the y-values at the left endpoints of the subintervals (the rectangle on the first subinterval has a height of zero). From the diagram, the sum of the areas of these rectangles is

$$(0)^2\left(\tfrac{1}{4}\right) + \left(\tfrac{1}{4}\right)^2\left(\tfrac{1}{4}\right) + \left(\tfrac{1}{2}\right)^2\left(\tfrac{1}{4}\right) + \left(\tfrac{3}{4}\right)^2\left(\tfrac{1}{4}\right)$$

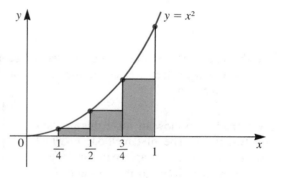

This is less than the area A. Thus,

$$\left(\tfrac{1}{4}\right)^3 (0^2 + 1^2 + 2^2 + 3^2) < A$$

Evaluating the sums leads to the inequality

$$\tfrac{7}{32} < A < \tfrac{15}{32}$$

These are rough bounds for the area A. However, if we increase the number of subintervals (that is, reduce the width of the rectangles), we expect to obtain more accurate approximations to the area A. For example, eight equal subintervals leads to the result

$$\tfrac{35}{128} < A < \tfrac{51}{128}$$

which is a more accurate approximation.

In Example 1, the area A is approximated as the sum of the areas of n rectangles. We can then obtain an exact expression for A by letting n increase without bound ($n \to +\infty$). Geometrically this means that the width of each rectangle tends to zero.

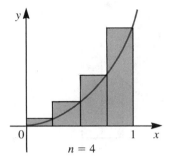
$n = 4$

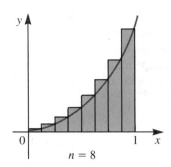
$n = 8$

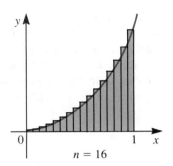
$n = 16$

In order to do this calculation, we need the summation formula

$$1^2 + 2^2 + \ldots + n^2 = \frac{1}{6}n(n + 1)(2n + 1)$$

Example 1. Find the area of the region bounded by the parabola $y = x^2$ and the x-axis, between $x = 0$ and $x = 1$.

Solution. Subdivide the interval $0 \le x \le 1$ into n equal subintervals of length

$$\Delta x = \frac{1}{n}$$

Over each subinterval draw the rectangle whose height equals the function value at the **right** endpoint. The x-coordinates of the right endpoints are

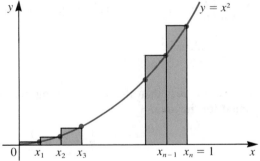

$$x_1 = \frac{1}{n}, \quad x_2 = \frac{2}{n}, \quad \ldots, \quad x_{n-1} = \frac{n-1}{n}, \quad x_n = \frac{n}{n} = 1$$

The sum S_n of the areas of the n rectangles is

$$S_n = \left(\frac{1}{n}\right)^2 \left(\frac{1}{n}\right) + \left(\frac{2}{n}\right)^2 \left(\frac{1}{n}\right) + \ldots + \left(\frac{n-1}{n}\right)^2 \left(\frac{1}{n}\right) + \left(\frac{n}{n}\right)^2 \left(\frac{1}{n}\right)$$

$$= \frac{1}{n^3}\left(1^2 + 2^2 + \ldots + n^2\right)$$

$$= \frac{1}{n^3}\left[\frac{1}{6}n(n + 1)(2n + 1)\right]$$

$$= \frac{1}{3} + \frac{1}{2n} + \frac{1}{6n^2}$$

where we have used the formula for the sum of the squares of the first n positive integers. It follows from the diagram that this sum is greater than the area A.

Now form a sum of areas of rectangles that is less than the area A. Over each subinterval draw the rectangle whose height is the function value at the **left** endpoint. It follows from the diagram that the sum of the areas of the n rectangles is

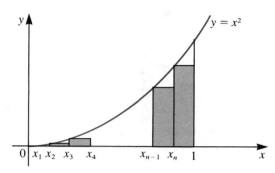

$$S_n = \left(\frac{0}{n}\right)^2\left(\frac{1}{n}\right) + \left(\frac{1}{n}\right)^2\left(\frac{1}{n}\right) + \left(\frac{2}{n}\right)^2\left(\frac{1}{n}\right) + \ldots + \left(\frac{n-1}{n}\right)^2\left(\frac{1}{n}\right)$$

$$= \frac{1}{n^3}[1^2 + 2^2 + \ldots + (n-1)^2]$$

$$= \frac{1}{n^3}\left[\frac{1}{6}(n-1)(n)(2n-1)\right] \quad \text{(replace } n \text{ by } n-1 \text{ in the summation formula)}$$

$$= \frac{1}{3} - \frac{1}{2n} + \frac{1}{6n^2}$$

This sum is less than the area A. Using both results, we have an upper bound and a lower bound for the area:

$$\frac{1}{3} - \frac{1}{2n} + \frac{1}{6n^2} < A < \frac{1}{3} + \frac{1}{2n} + \frac{1}{6n^2}$$

Since

$$\lim_{n \to +\infty} \frac{1}{n} = 0 \quad \text{and} \quad \lim_{n \to +\infty} \frac{1}{n^2} = 0$$

it follows that as n increases without bound, both sums approach the value $\frac{1}{3}$. Hence,

$$A = \frac{1}{3}$$

The required area is $\frac{1}{3}$ square units.

☐

Example 1 shows how the area under a curve can be calculated by taking the limit of a sum of areas of rectangles. If the y-values at the right endpoints of the subintervals are used as the heights of the rectangles, then one obtains the area as

$$A = \lim_{n \to +\infty} S_n$$

$$= \lim_{n \to +\infty} \left[\frac{1}{3} + \frac{1}{2n} + \frac{1}{6n^2} \right]$$

$$= \frac{1}{3}$$

The same value for A is obtained if the y-values at the left endpoints are chosen as the heights of the rectangles. In fact, we could equally well have used the y-values at the midpoints of the rectangles.

This method can be applied more generally.

Let f be a positive-valued function on the interval $a \leq x \leq b$. Subdivide the interval into n equal subintervals of width $\Delta x = \dfrac{b - a}{n}$. Choose a point x_k in the kth subinterval, where $k = 1, 2, \ldots, n$, and construct the rectangle of height $f(x_k)$ on the kth subinterval.

The area of this rectangle is

$$f(x_k)\Delta x$$

The sum S_n of the areas of the n rectangles is

$$S_n = f(x_1)\Delta x + f(x_2)\Delta x + \ldots + f(x_n)\Delta x$$

or, in sigma notation,

$$S_n = \sum_{k=1}^{n} f(x_k)\Delta x$$

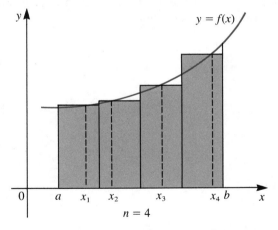

$n = 4$

This sum approximates the area A of the region bounded by the graph of $y = f(x)$ and the x-axis, for x between a and b, and is called **a Riemann sum for the function f over the interval $a \leq x \leq b$.** We expect that as the number of subintervals n (which equals the number of rectangles) increases without bound, the Riemann sums S_n will be an increasingly accurate approximation to the area A, as in Example 1. Indeed, it can be proved that if f is a continuous function, then $\lim\limits_{n \to +\infty} S_n$ does exist and is independent of how the points x_k are chosen in the subintervals. We can thus calculate the area A bounded by a continuous curve and the x-axis, as the limit of a Riemann sum:

$$A = \lim_{n \to +\infty} S_n$$

for any choice of the points x_k.

Area Bounded by a Curve

The area A of the region bounded by the graph of the continuous function $y = f(x)$ and the x-axis, for $a \leq x \leq b$, is given by

$$A = \lim_{n \to +\infty} S_n$$

where S_n is a Riemann sum for $f(x)$ on the interval $a \leq x \leq b$,

$$S_n = \sum_{k=1}^{n} f(x_k) \Delta x$$

and

$$\Delta x = \frac{b - a}{n}.$$

It is convenient to use sigma notation when working with Riemann sums. Recall some of the basic properties of sums:

Properties of Sums

$$\sum_{k=1}^{n} (a_k + b_k) = \sum_{k=1}^{n} a_k + \sum_{k=1}^{n} b_k$$

$$\sum_{k=1}^{n} (Ca_k) = C \sum_{k=1}^{n} a_k, \quad \text{where } C \text{ is a constant}$$

Summation Formulas

$$\sum_{k=1}^{n} (1) = n$$

$$\sum_{k=1}^{n} k = \frac{1}{2}n(n + 1)$$

$$\sum_{k=1}^{n} k^2 = \frac{1}{6}n(n + 1)(2n + 1)$$

In Example 2, the sigma notation is used in an area calculation.

Example 2. Find the area of the region bounded by $y = 16 - x^2$ and the x-axis, for $1 \le x \le 3$.

Solution. Subdivide the interval $1 \le x \le 3$ into n equal subintervals of length

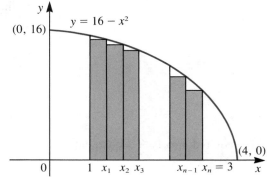

$$\Delta x = \frac{3 - 1}{n}$$

$$= \frac{2}{n}$$

For each subinterval consider the rectangle whose height is the y-value at the right end-point. The right endpoints are given by

$$x_1 = 1 + \frac{2}{n}, \quad x_2 = 1 + 2\left(\frac{2}{n}\right), \quad \ldots, \quad x_n = 1 + n\left(\frac{2}{n}\right)$$

or, more concisely,

$$x_k = 1 + k\left(\frac{2}{n}\right), \text{ where } k = 1, 2, \ldots, n$$

The height of the kth rectangle is

$$f(x_k) = 16 - x_k^2$$

$$= 16 - \left(1 + \frac{2k}{n}\right)^2$$

$$= 15 - \frac{4k}{n} - \frac{4k^2}{n^2}$$

The sum S_n of the areas of the n rectangles is

$$S_n = \sum_{k=1}^{n} f(x_k)\Delta x$$

$$= \sum_{k=1}^{n} \left[\left(15 - \frac{4k}{n} - \frac{4k^2}{n^2}\right)\frac{2}{n}\right]$$

$$= \frac{30}{n}\sum_{k=1}^{n}(1) - \frac{8}{n^2}\sum_{k=1}^{n}k - \frac{8}{n^3}\sum_{k=1}^{n}k^2$$

$$= \left(\frac{30}{n}\right)(n) - \left[\frac{8}{n^2}\right]\left[\frac{1}{2}n(n+1)\right] - \left[\frac{8}{n^3}\right]\left[\frac{1}{6}n(n+1)(2n+1)\right]$$

$$= \frac{70}{3} - \frac{8}{n} - \frac{4}{3n^2}$$

It follows that

$$A = \lim_{n \to +\infty} S_n$$

$$= \lim_{n \to +\infty} \left[\frac{70}{3} - \frac{8}{n} - \frac{4}{3n^2} \right]$$

$$= \frac{70}{3}$$

The required area is $\frac{70}{3}$ square units   □

Exercises 8.1

1. Let A be the area of the region bounded by the graph of $y = f(x)$ and the x-axis, between $x = 1$ and $x = 3$. Find an approximate value for A as a sum of the areas of four rectangles of equal width. Choose the height of the rectangles to be the y-values at the right endpoints of the four subintervals. Make a sketch showing the region and the rectangles.

   a. $f(x) = x^2$ **b.** $f(x) = 2 - \frac{1}{2}x$

   c. $f(x) = 9 - x^2$ **d.** $f(x) = 2(x - 1)^2$

2. Repeat Exercise 1, but choose the height of the rectangles to be the y-values at the left endpoints of the subintervals.

3. Repeat Exercise 1, but choose the height of the rectangles to be the y-values at the midpoints of the subintervals.

4. Referring to Exercise 1, find A by evaluating $\lim_{n \to +\infty} S_n$ where S_n is a Riemann sum that represents the sum of the areas of n rectangles.

5. **a.** Show that $\sum_{k=1}^{n} \left(k - \frac{1}{2}\right)^2 = \frac{1}{12}n(4n^2 - 1)$.

   b. Consider the region bounded by the parabola $y = x^2$ and the x-axis, for $0 \le x \le 1$. Subdivide the interval into n equal subintervals and consider the approximating rectangles whose heights are the y-values at the midpoints of the subintervals. Use the result of part (a) to find the sum S_n of the areas of the n rectangles.

   c. Find the difference between S_n and the area A of the region if $n = 10$ and if $n = 100$.

6. a. Let A be the area of the region bounded by the curve $y = \dfrac{1}{x}$ and the x-axis for x between 1 and 2. By approximating the area A with five rectangles of equal width, show that

$$\frac{1}{6} + \frac{1}{7} + \frac{1}{8} + \frac{1}{9} + \frac{1}{10} < A < \frac{1}{5} + \frac{1}{6} + \frac{1}{7} + \frac{1}{8} + \frac{1}{9}$$

b. By approximating the area A with n rectangles of equal width, show that

$$\frac{1}{n+1} + \frac{1}{n+2} + \dots + \frac{1}{n+n} < A < \frac{1}{n} + \frac{1}{n+1} + \dots + \frac{1}{n+(n-1)}$$

c. Use part (b) to find an approximate value of A with an error less than 0.01.

7. Find the area enclosed by the parabola $y = -3x^2 + 6x$ and the x-axis.

Problems 8.1

1. Use the summation formula

$$\sum_{k=1}^{n} k^3 = \frac{1}{4}n^2(n+1)^2$$

to find the area of the region bounded by $y = x^3$ and the x-axis, for $0 \le x \le 1$.

2. a. Evaluate $\displaystyle\lim_{n \to +\infty} \dfrac{\sin\left(\dfrac{\pi}{2n}\right)}{\dfrac{\pi}{2n}}$ by using the fundamental trigonometric limit.

b. Given the identity

$$\sin h + \sin 2h + \dots + \sin nh = \frac{\cos\left(\dfrac{h}{2}\right) - \cos\left[\dfrac{(2n+1)h}{2}\right]}{2\sin\left(\dfrac{h}{2}\right)}$$

use a Riemann sum to find the area enclosed by $y = \sin x$ and the x-axis, from $x = 0$ to $x = \pi$.

3. a. Evaluate $\displaystyle\lim_{h \to 0} \dfrac{e^h - 1}{h}$ by using the definition of the derivative.

b. Let A be the area of the region bounded by $y = e^x$ and the x-axis, between $x = 0$ and $x = 1$. Using the sum of a geometric series, show that

$$A = \lim_{n \to +\infty} \frac{(e-1)e^{\frac{1}{n}}}{n(e^{\frac{1}{n}} - 1)}$$

c. Use parts (a) and (b) to find A.

8.2 Other Applications of Riemann Sums

Suppose that you are travelling in a car whose odometer is broken, but which has a working speedometer and clock. Can you determine the distance travelled between two given times? The answer is NO, if the velocity of the car is not constant. But you can calculate an approximate value for the distance travelled by noting the velocity of the car at frequent intervals and treating the velocity as constant between each reading. This procedure leads to a Riemann sum approximation for the distance travelled, as is illustrated in Example 1.

Example 1. The velocity of a moving object in m/s is $v(t) = t^2$, where the time t is measured in s. Use a Riemann sum with four subintervals to approximate the distance travelled between times $t = 0$ and $t = 4$.

Solution. Subdivide the time interval $0 \leq t \leq 4$ into four subintervals, each of length

$$\Delta t = \frac{4 - 0}{4}$$
$$= 1$$

Choose a point in each subinterval and denote them by t_1, t_2, t_3, and t_4. At time t_k, where $k = 1, 2, 3, 4$, the velocity is

$$v(t_k) = (t_k)^2$$

During the kth subinterval, the distance travelled is approximated by

$$v(t_k)\Delta t$$

The total distance travelled between times $t = 0$ and $t = 4$ is approximated by the sum S_4 of the distances travelled during the four subintervals:

$$S_4 = \sum_{k=1}^{4} v(t_k)\,\Delta t$$

$$= \sum_{k=1}^{4} (t_k)^2(1)$$

If we choose the points t_k as the **midpoints** of the subintervals, then

$$t_1 = \frac{1}{2}, \quad t_2 = \frac{3}{2}, \quad t_3 = \frac{5}{2}, \quad t_4 = \frac{7}{2}$$

and

$$S_4 = \left(\frac{1}{2}\right)^2(1) + \left(\frac{3}{2}\right)^2(1) + \left(\frac{5}{2}\right)^2(1) + \left(\frac{7}{2}\right)^2(1)$$
$$= 21$$

Thus the distance travelled is approximately 21 m.   □

In general, consider an object that moves with (positive) velocity $v(t)$. As in Example 1, the distance travelled between times $t = a$ and $t = b$ can be approximated by the Riemann sum

$$S_n = \sum_{k=1}^{n} v(t_k)\Delta t$$

Here $\Delta t = \dfrac{b - a}{n}$ is the length of one subinterval, and the points t_k, where $k = 1, 2, \dots , n$, are chosen in the n subintervals. The exact distance s is the limit of this sum as $n \to +\infty$, or equivalently as $\Delta t \to 0$:

$$s = \lim_{n \to +\infty} \sum_{k=1}^{n} v(t_k)\Delta t$$

Riemann sums can also be used to approximate volumes. The idea is to approximate the given solid by (thin) cylinders, and use the result that the volume V of a cylinder equals cross-sectional area A times height h:

$$V = Ah$$

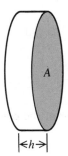

The height h will be denoted by Δx, and the thin cylinder will be called a **disk of thickness** Δx.

Example 2. Approximate the volume of a cone of height 2 units and radius 1 unit, by using four disks of equal thickness.

Solution. Subdivide the cone into four pieces by means of planes perpendicular to its axis. Approximate each piece by a disk of thickness $\Delta x = \dfrac{1}{2}$, as shown in the diagram. The cross-sectional areas of the disks have been chosen to equal the cross-sectional areas of the cone when $x = \dfrac{1}{4}, \dfrac{3}{4}, \dfrac{5}{4}$, and $\dfrac{7}{4}$ respectively.

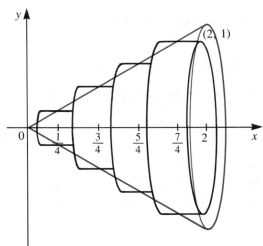

The cross-sectional area of the cone at position x is

$$A(x) = \pi y^2$$
$$= \pi\left(\frac{x}{2}\right)^2$$

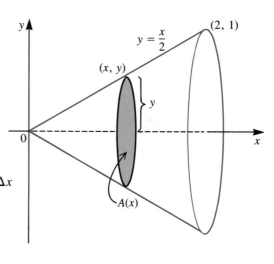

The sum of the volumes of the four disks of thickness $\Delta x = \frac{1}{2}$ is

$$A\left(\frac{1}{4}\right)\Delta x + A\left(\frac{3}{4}\right)\Delta x + A\left(\frac{5}{4}\right)\Delta x + A\left(\frac{7}{4}\right)\Delta x$$

$$= \frac{1}{2}\left[\pi\left(\frac{1}{8}\right)^2 + \pi\left(\frac{3}{8}\right)^2 + \pi\left(\frac{5}{8}\right)^2 + \pi\left(\frac{7}{8}\right)^2\right]$$

$$= \frac{\pi}{128}(1^2 + 3^2 + 5^2 + 7^2)$$

$$= \frac{21\pi}{32}$$

Thus, the volume of the cone is approximately $\dfrac{21\pi}{32}$ cubic units.   □

The approximation obtained in Example 2 is quite accurate, since the volume of this cone is

$$V = \frac{1}{3}(\text{area of base})(\text{height})$$
$$= \frac{2\pi}{3}$$

as we shall verify in section 8.7.

In general, we could subdivide the cone into n thin disks of equal thickness $\Delta x = \dfrac{2}{n}$. The volume of the cone is approximated by the sum of the volumes of the disks:

$$\sum_{k=1}^{n} A(x_k)\Delta x$$

where the x_k, for $k = 1, 2, \ldots, n$, are suitably chosen x-values. The essential point is that this sum is a Riemann sum for the function $A(x)$, where $A(x)$ is the cross-sectional area of the cone. The exact volume is obtained in the limit as $n \to +\infty$:

$$V = \lim_{n \to +\infty} \sum_{k=1}^{n} A(x_k)\Delta x$$

In this section, we have used Riemann sums of the form

$$\sum_{k=1}^{n} f(x_k)\Delta x$$

to approximate two quite different quantities—the distance travelled in a given time interval, and the volume of a solid. There are many other applications. For example, a Riemann sum can be used to approximate the fluid force exerted on the wall of a dam, the energy required to pump the water out of a swimming pool, or the mass of an object with variable density (see Exercise 3). Thus, Riemann sums are not restricted to the calculation of areas.

Exercises 8.2

1. The velocity of a moving object in m/s is $v(t) = 9 - t^2$. Use a Riemann sum to approximate the distance travelled between times $t = 0$ and $t = 3$. Use six subintervals, and evaluate $v(t)$ at the midpoint of each subinterval.

2. a. Approximate the volume V of a hemisphere of radius 1 by using four disks of equal thickness, with the cross-sectional area evaluated at $x = \frac{1}{8}, \frac{3}{8}, \frac{5}{8},$ and $\frac{7}{8}$.

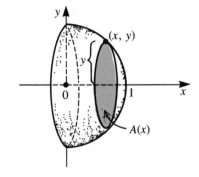

   b. By using n disks and evaluating y at the right endpoints, show that the volume V of the hemisphere is

$$V = \lim_{n \to +\infty} \sum_{k=1}^{n} \pi\left[1 - \left(\frac{k}{n}\right)^2\right]\left(\frac{1}{n}\right)$$

   c. Use the result of part (b) to verify that $V = \frac{2}{3}\pi$ cubic units.

3. a. The mass per unit length (in g/cm) of a metal rod depends on position according to $f(x) = 5 + \frac{1}{4}x$, where $0 \le x \le 20$. Use a Riemann sum to approximate the total mass M of the rod. Use five subintervals and evaluate $f(x)$ at the midpoint of each subinterval.

   b. By evaluating $f(x)$ at the right endpoint of each subinterval, show that the total mass M of the rod is

$$M = \lim_{n \to +\infty} \sum_{k=1}^{n} \left[5 + \frac{1}{4}\left(\frac{20k}{n}\right)\right]\left(\frac{20}{n}\right)$$

   c. Use the result of part (b) to verify that $M = 150$ g.

8.3 The Area Function

We now develop a second method for finding the area of a region bounded by a curve $y = f(x)$ and the x-axis. In this method we find an antiderivative instead of evaluating the limit of a Riemann sum. It can be applied efficiently to a wide variety of curves.

We wish to find the area of the region bounded by a curve $y = f(x)$ and the x-axis between $x = a$ and $x = b$. Let $A(x)$ denote the area of the region bounded by $y = f(x)$ and the x-axis between a and x. The function $A(x)$ is called **the area function of** $f(x)$ **on the interval** $a \leq x \leq b$. As x increases, $A(x)$ increases, and it is natural to ask: "What is the rate of change $A'(x)$ of the area function?"

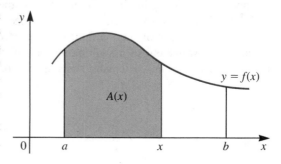

In Example 1, the area function $A(x)$ can be found by using simple geometry, and the result provides an answer to this question.

Example 1. Find the area function $A(x)$ for

$$f(x) = 2x - 1$$

on the interval $1 \leq x \leq 2$. Evaluate $A(1)$ and $A(2)$ and interpret the results.

Solution. Note that $A(x)$ is the area of a trapezium. This area can be calculated in a simple way as the difference of the areas of the triangles formed by the lines $y = 2x - 1$, $y = 0$ and the vertical lines through $(1, 0)$ and $(x, 0)$. Thus,

$$A(x) = \tfrac{1}{2}\left(x - \tfrac{1}{2}\right)(2x - 1) - \tfrac{1}{2}\left(\tfrac{1}{2}\right)(1)$$

which, after simplifying, becomes

$$A(x) = x^2 - x$$

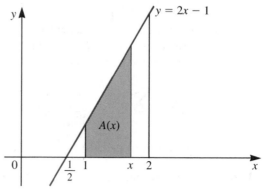

This is the desired area function. It follows that $A(1) = 0$, in agreement with the diagram. Secondly, $A(2) = 2$, and this value of the area function gives the area bounded by $y = 2x - 1$ and the x-axis for $1 \leq x \leq 2$.   □

It is usually impossible to determine the area function $A(x)$ for a nonlinear function $f(x)$ by geometric means. However, there is a relationship between a function $f(x)$ and the derivative $A'(x)$ of its area function. In Example 1, it follows from the expression for $A(x)$ that

$$A'(x) = 2x - 1$$

On noting the form of $f(x)$ in Example 1, we make the important observation that

$$A'(x) = f(x)$$

This remarkable relationship holds for any positive continuous function f. It states that, as x increases, the area of the region bounded by $y = f(x)$ and the x-axis from a to x increases at a rate that is precisely equal to the value of the function at position x.

If $A(x)$ is the area function of the function $f(x)$, then

$$A'(x) = f(x)$$

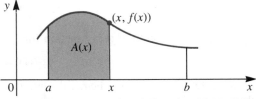

Proof. Let $f(x)$ be a function that is positive and continuous on an interval $a \leq x \leq b$, and let $A(x)$ be the area function of $f(x)$.

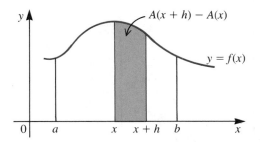 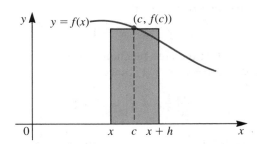

Consider the change in $A(x)$ from x to $x + h$. Since $A(x + h)$ is the area from a to $x + h$, and $A(x)$ is the area from a to x, the difference

$$A(x + h) - A(x)$$

is the area of the shaded region. We now choose a number c between x and $x + h$ so that the area of the shaded region equals the area of the rectangle of height $f(c)$ and width h:

$$A(x + h) - A(x) = hf(c)$$

where $x < c < x + h$. It follows that

$$\frac{A(x + h) - A(x)}{h} = f(c)$$

By definition of the derivative,

$$A'(x) = \lim_{h \to 0} \frac{A(x + h) - A(x)}{h}$$
$$= \lim_{h \to 0} f(c)$$
$$= \lim_{c \to x} f(c) \quad \text{(since } x < c < x + h\text{)}$$
$$= f(x) \quad \text{(since } f \text{ is continuous)} \qquad \square$$

The fundamental relation $A'(x) = f(x)$ can be used to calculate area functions, and hence areas, in examples where simple geometry is inadequate. A rewording of this fundamental result provides the basis for the method.

> The area function $A(x)$ of a function $f(x)$ is an antiderivative of $f(x)$.

Example 2. Find the area function for

$$f(x) = x^2 + 1$$

on the interval $1 \le x \le 3$. Then, calculate the area of the region bounded by $y = x^2 + 1$ and the x-axis for $1 \le x \le 3$.

Solution. The fundamental relation between $A(x)$ and $f(x)$ states that

$$A'(x) = x^2 + 1$$

i.e., that the area function $A(x)$ is an antiderivative of $x^2 + 1$. Since

$$\frac{d}{dx}\left[\frac{1}{3}x^3 + x\right] = x^2 + 1$$

the function $\frac{1}{3}x^3 + x$ is an antiderivative of $x^2 + 1$. Since two antiderivatives of a function differ by a constant C, the area function $A(x)$ is of the form

$$A(x) = \frac{1}{3}x^3 + x + C$$

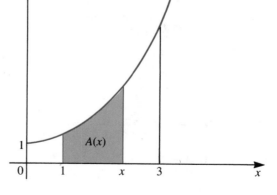

In order to evaluate C, use the fact that $A(1) = 0$, as follows from the diagram. On setting $x = 1$ in the equation for $A(x)$, we obtain

$$0 = \frac{1}{3} + 1 + C$$

and

$$C = -\frac{4}{3}$$

so that

$$A(x) = \frac{1}{3}x^3 + x - \frac{4}{3}$$

It follows from the diagram that the area of the region bounded by $y = x^2 + 1$ and the x-axis for $1 \le x \le 3$ is

$$A(3) = \tfrac{1}{3}(3)^3 + 3 - \tfrac{4}{3}$$
$$= \tfrac{32}{3}$$

The required area is $\tfrac{32}{3}$ square units. □

Example 3. Find the area A of the region bounded by one loop of the sine curve and the x-axis.

Solution. First find the area function $A(x)$ for $f(x) = \sin x$ on the interval $0 \le x \le \pi$. The required area A is then given by $A(\pi)$.

The fundamental relation between $A(x)$ and $f(x)$ states that

$$A'(x) = \sin x$$

Since

$$\frac{d}{dx}(-\cos x) = \sin x$$

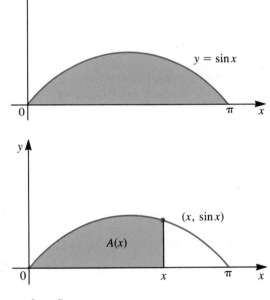

the function $-\cos x$ is an antiderivative of $\sin x$. It follows that

$$A(x) = -\cos x + C$$

where C is a constant. In order to evaluate C, use the fact that $A(0) = 0$. On setting $x = 0$ in the equation for $A(x)$, we obtain

$$0 = -\cos 0 + C$$

and

$$C = 1$$

so that

$$A(x) = 1 - \cos x$$

The required area A is

$$A(\pi) = 1 - \cos \pi$$
$$= 2$$

Thus the area of the region bounded by one loop of the sine curve and the x-axis is 2 square units. □

Exercises 8.3

1. Using simple geometry, find the area function $A(x)$ for each straight-line function on the given interval.

a. $f(x) = 2x + 6, \quad -2 \le x \le 2$
b. $f(x) = -4x + 8, \quad -1 \le x \le 2$

2. Referring to Exercise 1, calculate $A(2)$ in each case and sketch the region whose area equals this value.

3. Referring to Exercise 1, calculate $A'(x)$ and verify that $A'(x) = f(x)$.

4. For each function $f(x)$, find an antiderivative $F(x)$ such that $F(0) = 0$.

a. $f(x) = 1 + e^{2x}$
c. $f(x) = (3x + 1)^2$
e. $f(x) = \sqrt{x + 4}$

b. $f(x) = 2x + \sin x$
d. $f(x) = 2\cos x + \cos 2x$
f. $f(x) = \dfrac{1}{x + 2}$

5. For each function, find the area function $A(x)$ on the given interval. Sketch the graph of the given function and indicate the region whose area is given by $A(x)$.

a. $f(x) = x^2 + 1, \quad -1 \le x \le 2$
c. $f(x) = e^{-\frac{x}{2}}, \quad 0 \le x \le \ln 4$
e. $f(x) = x + \dfrac{1}{x}, \quad 1 \le x \le 4$
g. $f(x) = 2 + \sin 2x, \quad -\dfrac{\pi}{2} \le x \le \dfrac{\pi}{2}$

b. $f(x) = 2x^3 + 3x^2, \quad -1 \le x \le 1$
d. $f(x) = \dfrac{1}{\sqrt{x}}, \quad 1 \le x \le 4$
f. $f(x) = \dfrac{1}{x + 2}, \quad 0 \le x \le 4$
h. $f(x) = \sqrt{x + 4}, \quad -3 \le x \le 3$

6. Find the area above the x-axis and below the curve $y = 4 - x^2$.

7. Referring to Exercise 5, in each case calculate the area between the curve $y = f(x)$ and the x-axis, over the given interval. Use the area functions that you found in Exercise 5.

Problems 8.3

1. a. Let A_1 and A_2 be the areas of the shaded regions in the diagram, where n is a positive integer. Show that

$$\frac{A_1}{A_2} = \frac{1}{n}$$

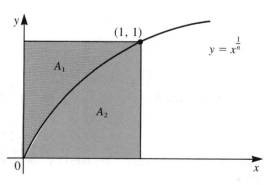

b. What does this result tell you about the shape of the curve $y = x^{\frac{1}{n}}$, for $0 \le x \le 1$, when n is large?

2. Calculate the area of the region bounded by one loop of the curve $y = \sin^2 x$ and the x-axis. You will have to use a trigonometric identity in order to find the appropriate antiderivative. Before starting, determine whether this area will be greater or less than the area bounded by one loop of the curve $y = \sin x$ and the x-axis. Use a geometric argument.

8.4 Areas and Antiderivatives

In this section we streamline the method for calculating areas described in section 8.3, thereby paving the way for the Fundamental Theorem of Calculus in section 8.5

Consider again the problem of calculating the area A of the region bounded by the graph of the positive function $y = f(x)$ and the x-axis, between $x = a$ and $x = b$. Let $A(x)$ be the area function of $f(x)$ on the interval $a \le x \le b$. The required area A is the value of $A(x)$ when $x = b$; that is,

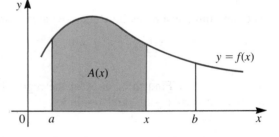

$$A = A(b)$$

In section 8.3 we showed that $A(x)$ is an antiderivative of $f(x)$,

$$A'(x) = f(x)$$

Suppose that $F(x)$ is a **known** antiderivative of $f(x)$,

$$F'(x) = f(x)$$

Since two antiderivatives of the same function $f(x)$ differ by a constant (see section 7.1), it follows that

$$A(x) = F(x) + C$$

In order to find C, use the fact that $A(a) = 0$. On setting $x = a$ in the equation for $A(x)$ we obtain

$$0 = F(a) + C$$

and

$$C = -F(a)$$

so that

$$A(x) = F(x) - F(a)$$

Since the required area is $A = A(b)$, we set $x = b$ in the equation for $A(x)$ to obtain

$$A = F(b) - F(a)$$

This result is summarized below.

Let $f(x)$ be a positive continuous function, and let $F(x)$ be any antiderivative of $f(x)$; i.e.,

$$F'(x) = f(x)$$

Then the area A of the region bounded by the graph of $y = f(x)$ and the x-axis between $x = a$ and $x = b$ is

$$A = F(b) - F(a)$$

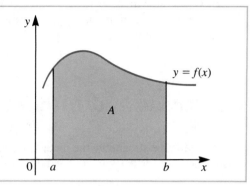

The next three examples illustrate how areas can be found by the above method.

Example 1. Find the area A of the region bounded by the graph of $f(x) = e^{-2x}$ and the x-axis, between $x = \ln 2$ and $x = \ln 3$.

Solution. To calculate the area A, we have to find an antiderivative of the function $f(x) = e^{-2x}$. Since

$$\frac{d}{dx}\left(-\frac{1}{2}e^{-2x}\right) = e^{-2x}$$

an antiderivative of e^{-2x} is

$$F(x) = -\frac{1}{2}e^{-2x}$$

The area A is thus given by

$$A = F(\ln 3) - F(\ln 2)$$
$$= \left(-\frac{1}{2}e^{-2\ln 3}\right) - \left(-\frac{1}{2}e^{-2\ln 2}\right)$$

On using properties of logarithms and exponentials, we obtain

$$e^{-2\ln 3} = e^{\ln(3^{-2})}$$
$$= \frac{1}{9}$$

and similarly

$$e^{-2\ln 2} = \frac{1}{4}$$

It follows that

$$A = -\frac{1}{18} + \frac{1}{8}$$

$$= \frac{5}{72} \text{ square units}$$ □

Example 2. Find the area A of the region bounded by the curve $y = -x^2 + x + 2$ and the x-axis.

Solution. Since $-x^2 + x + 2 = -(x + 1)(x - 2)$, the x-intercepts of the parabola are $x = -1$ and $x = 2$, and so we obtain the given diagram. To calculate the area A, we have to find an antiderivative $F(x)$ of the function

$$f(x) = -x^2 + x + 2$$

Since

$$\frac{d}{dx}\left(-\frac{1}{3}x^3 + \frac{1}{2}x^2 + 2x\right) = -x^2 + x + 2$$

an antiderivative of $f(x)$ is

$$F(x) = -\frac{1}{3}x^3 + \frac{1}{2}x^2 + 2x$$

The area A is thus given by

$$A = F(2) - F(-1)$$
$$= \left(-\frac{8}{3} + 2 + 4\right) - \left(\frac{1}{3} + \frac{1}{2} - 2\right)$$
$$= \frac{9}{2} \text{ square units}$$ □

Example 3 illustrates a geometric interpretation of the (natural) logarithm function.

Example 3. Find the area of the region bounded by the curve $y = \frac{1}{x}$ and the x-axis, between $x = 1$ and $x = b$, where b is constant, and $b > 1$.

Solution. Since

$$\frac{d}{dx}(\ln x) = \frac{1}{x}$$

it follows that $F(x) = \ln x$ is an antiderivative of $f(x) = \frac{1}{x}$. The required area is thus

$$A = F(b) - F(1)$$
$$= \ln b - \ln 1$$

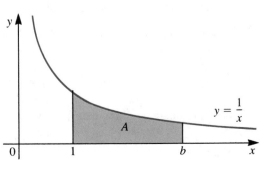

Since $\ln 1 = 0$, we have

$$A = \ln b$$

In other words, $\ln b$ equals the area bounded by $y = \dfrac{1}{x}$ and the x-axis, between $x = 1$ and $x = b$. In particular, since $\ln e = 1$, the number e is the value of b that gives a unit area. $\square$

Exercises 8.4

1. Find the area of the region bounded by the graph of each function and the x-axis over the given interval. In each case sketch the graph and indicate the required region.

   a. $f(x) = 3x^5, \quad 0 \le x \le 1$

   b. $f(x) = \dfrac{2}{x}, \quad 1 \le x \le 3$

   c. $f(x) = \sqrt{x}, \quad 4 \le x \le 9$

   d. $f(x) = 3 \sin 2x, \quad 0 \le x \le \dfrac{\pi}{2}$

   e. $f(x) = (x + 1)^2, \quad -2 \le x \le 2$

   f. $f(x) = x + \dfrac{1}{x}, \quad 1 \le x \le 4$

   g. $f(x) = \cos \pi x, \quad -\dfrac{1}{2} \le x \le 0$

   h. $f(x) = e^x + e^{-x}, \quad -\ln 2 \le x \le \ln 2$

2. Find the area of the region above the x-axis that is bounded by the graph of the function f defined by
   $$f(x) = 2 \cos x - 1, \quad -\dfrac{\pi}{2} \le x \le \dfrac{\pi}{2}$$

3. Find the area of the region under one arch of the curve $y = 2 \cos 3x$.

4. Find the area of the region in the first quadrant bounded by $y = \sqrt{4 - x}$, the x-axis, and the y-axis.

5. Find the area of the region bounded by the curve $y = -e^{-2x} + 3e^{-x} - 2$ and the x-axis.

6. Find the area of the region bounded by $y = 2e^{-x}, y = 0, x = 0$, and $x = \ln 8$.

7. Find the area of the region bounded by $y = x^3 - 1, y = 0$, and $x = 2$.

Problems 8.4

1. Show that the area of the region bounded by $y = \dfrac{1}{x}$ and the x-axis between $x = b$ and $x = 2b$ is independent of the value of b.

2. Find the area of the region bounded by the curve $y = \tan^2 x$, the x-axis, and the line $x = \dfrac{\pi}{4}$.

3. Let $A_1(b)$ be the area of the region bounded by $y = e^{-x}$ and the x-axis, between $x = 0$ and $x = b$. Let $A_2(b)$ be the area of the region bounded by $y = e^{-2x}$ and the x-axis over the same interval. Show that if $b > 0$ then
   $$A_2(b) > \dfrac{1}{2}A_1(b)$$
   What happens as $b \to +\infty$?

8.5 The Definite Integral and the Fundamental Theorem of Calculus

In section 8.1 we showed that the area A under the graph of a function $f(x)$ on the interval $a \le x \le b$ can be calculated as the limit of a Riemann sum:

$$A = \lim_{n \to +\infty} \sum_{k=1}^{n} f(x_k)\, \Delta x$$

where $\Delta x = \dfrac{b-a}{n}$ is the length of each of the n equal subintervals.

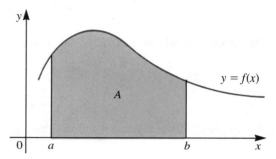

In section 8.2, we showed that a variety of other quantities can be calculated as the limit of a Riemann sum; for example,

- distance travelled is the limit of a Riemann sum of the velocity,

- volume is the limit of a Riemann sum of the cross-sectional area, and

- mass is the limit of a Riemann sum of the density.

Indeed, limits of Riemann sums can be used to solve a variety of problems in science and engineering.

For convenience, the limit of the Riemann sum of the function $f(x)$ over the interval $a \le x \le b$ is given a shorthand notation,

$$\int_a^b f(x)\, dx$$

and is called **the definite integral of f from a to b**. The integral symbol $\int$ is an elongated S for "limit of a sum", and the dx reminds one of the Δx in the Riemann sum and specifies **the variable of integration** x. The function $f(x)$ is called the **integrand**. The end points of the interval are called **the limits of integration**.

We now define the definite integral formally.

Let f be a continuous function on an interval $a \le x \le b$. Subdivide the interval into n equal subintervals of length Δx. Choose a point x_k, where $k = 1, 2, \ldots, n$, in each subinterval. The **definite integral of f from a to b** is defined by

$$\int_a^b f(x)\, dx = \lim_{n \to +\infty} \sum_{k=1}^{n} f(x_k)\, \Delta x$$

Note that if $f(x)$ is positive in the interval $a \leq x \leq b$, then the definite integral $\int_a^b f(x)\,dx$ can be interpreted as the area of a certain region.

We are now in a position to discuss the Fundamental Theorem of Calculus. Let A denote the area of the region bounded by the curve $y = f(x)$ and the x-axis for $a \leq x \leq b$. According to the method of Riemann sums,

$$A = \lim_{n \to +\infty} \sum_{k=1}^{n} f(x_k)\,\Delta x$$

On the other hand, the method of antiderivatives shows that

$$A = F(b) - F(a)$$

where

$$F'(x) = f(x)$$

By combining these results, it follows that

$$\lim_{n \to +\infty} \sum_{k=1}^{n} f(x_k)\,\Delta x = F(b) - F(a)$$

In words, the limit of a Riemann sum of the function $f(x)$ can be evaluated by finding an antiderivative $F(x)$ of $f(x)$. In terms of the integral notation this reads

$$\int_a^b f(x)\,dx = F(b) - F(a)$$

This result is called the Fundamental Theorem of Calculus. Besides the computational power that it provides, the Fundamental Theorem provides a link between definite integrals and antiderivatives.

Fundamental Theorem of Calculus

If $f(x)$ is continuous and

$$F'(x) = f(x), \text{ for } a \leq x \leq b,$$

then

$$\int_a^b f(x)\,dx = F(b) - F(a)$$

Example 1. Use the Fundamental Theorem to evaluate $\int_0^2 \dfrac{5}{(2x + 1)^2}\,dx$.

Solution. The integrand is $f(x) = \dfrac{5}{(2x + 1)^2}$

Since

$$\frac{d}{dx}\left(\frac{1}{2x+1}\right) = -\frac{2}{(2x+1)^2}$$

it follows that

$$F(x) = -\frac{5}{2(2x+1)}$$

is an antiderivative of $f(x)$. Thus, by the Fundamental Theorem,

$$\int_0^2 \frac{5}{(2x+1)^2}\,dx = F(2) - F(0)$$

$$= \left(-\frac{1}{2}\right) - \left(-\frac{5}{2}\right)$$

$$= 2 \qquad \square$$

There is a standard notation for the expression $F(b) - F(a)$ that appears in the Fundamental Theorem:

$$F(x)\Big|_a^b = F(b) - F(a)$$

This notation permits integrals to be evaluated more concisely. The solution for Example 1 can now be written as follows:

$$\int_0^2 \frac{5}{(2x+1)^2}\,dx = -\frac{5}{2(2x+1)}\Big|_0^2$$

$$= \left(-\frac{1}{2}\right) - \left(-\frac{5}{2}\right)$$

$$= 2$$

Example 2. Use the Fundamental Theorem to evaluate

$$\int_{\frac{\pi}{8}}^{\frac{\pi}{4}} (\sin 2x + \cos 2x)\,dx$$

Solution. **By the Fundamental Theorem,**

$$\int_{\frac{\pi}{8}}^{\frac{\pi}{4}} (\sin 2x + \cos 2x)\,dx = \left[-\frac{1}{2}\cos 2x + \frac{1}{2}\sin 2x\right]\Big|_{\frac{\pi}{8}}^{\frac{\pi}{4}}$$

$$= \left(-\frac{1}{2}\cos\frac{\pi}{2} + \frac{1}{2}\sin\frac{\pi}{2}\right) - \left(-\frac{1}{2}\cos\frac{\pi}{4} + \frac{1}{2}\sin\frac{\pi}{4}\right)$$

$$= \frac{1}{2}$$

To check the antiderivative, note that

$$\frac{d}{dx}\left(-\frac{1}{2}\cos 2x + \frac{1}{2}\sin 2x\right) = \sin 2x + \cos 2x \qquad \square$$

Example 3. Use the Fundamental Theorem of Calculus to find the area of the region bounded by $y = 2e^{-x}$ and the x-axis, between $x = 0$ and $x = \ln 2$.

Solution. The area A is given by

$$A = \lim_{n \to +\infty} \sum_{k=1}^{n} f(x_k)\, \Delta x$$

where $\Delta x = \dfrac{\ln 2}{n}$ and

$$f(x) = 2e^{-x}$$

or, in terms of the integral notation,

$$A = \int_{0}^{\ln 2} (2e^{-x})\, dx$$

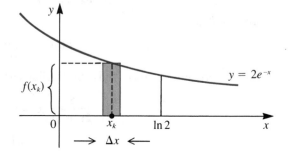

By the Fundamental Theorem of Calculus,

$$A = (-2e^{-x}) \Big|_{0}^{\ln 2}$$
$$= (-2e^{-\ln 2}) - (-2e^{-0})$$
$$= (-2)\left(\tfrac{1}{2}\right) + 2$$
$$= 1$$

To check the antiderivative, note that

$$\frac{d}{dx}(-2e^{-x}) = 2e^{-x} \qquad\qquad \square$$

We have seen in Examples 1 to 3 that the Fundamental Theorem makes it easy to evaluate the definite integral

$$\int_{a}^{b} f(x)\,dx = \lim_{n \to +\infty} \sum_{k=1}^{n} f(x_k)\, \Delta x$$

provided that one knows an antiderivative of the integrand $f(x)$. The catch is that it is not always easy (or possible!) to find an antiderivative of a given function f. This problem forms a contrast to the problem of differentiating a given function, which is straightforward in that we have theorems (e.g., the Product Rule and Chain Rule) that provide an algorithm to cover all possible situations. Over the centuries, various techniques, collectively referred to as "techniques of integration," have been developed for finding antiderivatives of special classes of functions. In this book, however, we shall limit ourselves to simple functions for which an antiderivative can be found **by inspection**, as has been the case so far.

Exercises 8.5

1. Use the Fundamental Theorem to evaluate each definite integral. In each case, check your antiderivative by differentiation.

   a. $\int_{-1}^{2} (3x^2 + x) \, dx$

   b. $\int_{0}^{1} (2x + 1)^3 \, dx$

   c. $\int_{1}^{4} \left(\sqrt{x} + \frac{1}{\sqrt{x}} \right) dx$

   d. $\int_{2}^{4} \frac{1}{x} \, dx$

   e. $\int_{0}^{\ln 2} (e^{2x} + 2e^{-x}) \, dx$

   f. $\int_{\frac{\pi}{4}}^{\frac{\pi}{2}} \cos x \, dx$

   g. $\int_{1}^{8} \left(x^{-\frac{1}{3}} + x^{\frac{1}{3}} \right) dx$

   h. $\int_{1}^{3} \left(x - \frac{1}{x} \right)^2 dx$

   i. $\int_{0}^{8} \frac{1}{\sqrt{1 + x}} \, dx$

   j. $\int_{0}^{\frac{\pi}{3}} \sin 3x \, dx$

   k. $\int_{e}^{e^2} \frac{4}{x} \, dx$

   l. $\int_{-1}^{1} (e^{3x} + 2) \, dx$

   m. $\int_{\frac{1}{6}}^{1} \cos \pi x \, dx$

   n. $\int_{-1}^{e^{-2}} \frac{1}{2 + x} \, dx$

   o. $\int_{\frac{\pi}{4}}^{\frac{\pi}{2}} \csc^2 x \, dx$

   p. $\int_{0}^{2} (3x + 2)^{\frac{1}{3}} \, dx$

   q. $\int_{0}^{\frac{1}{4}} \sec^2 \pi x \, dx$

   r. $\int_{0}^{\frac{\pi}{12}} \sec 3x \tan 3x \, dx$

2. Let A be the area of the region bounded by the curve $y = f(x)$ and the x-axis, over the given interval. Express A as a definite integral and find its value using the Fundamental Theorem of Calculus. Sketch area A and a typical rectangle in the Riemann sum.

   a. $f(x) = 2x^2, \quad 0 \le x \le 3$

   b. $f(x) = 3x - x^2, \quad 0 \le x \le 3$

   c. $f(x) = 4x - x^3, \quad 0 \le x \le 2$

   d. $f(x) = 3 \sin \left(\frac{x}{2} \right), \quad \pi \le x \le 2\pi$

   e. $f(x) = 4 - e^{2x}, \quad 0 \le x \le \ln 2$

   f. $f(x) = \frac{2}{x + 1}, \quad 1 \le x \le 3$

   g. $f(x) = \frac{2}{(x + 1)^2}, \quad 1 \le x \le 3$

   h. $f(x) = x + \frac{1}{x}, \quad 1 \le x \le e^2$

   i. $f(x) = 9 - e^{-2x}, \quad -\ln 3 \le x \le \ln 3$

   j. $f(x) = 4 - \frac{1}{x^2}, \quad \frac{1}{2} \le x \le 2$

3. For what positive value of b does $\int_{b}^{b^2} \frac{1}{x} \, dx = 1$? Interpret the result in terms of an area.

4. In each case, sketch the region whose area is represented by the limit of the Riemann sum. Express $\lim\limits_{n \to +\infty} S_n$ as a definite integral and find its value by using the Fundamental Theorem of Calculus.

a. $S_n = \sum\limits_{k=1}^{n} \left(\dfrac{k}{n}\right)^3 \Delta x, \quad 0 \le x \le 1$

b. $S_n = \sum\limits_{k=1}^{n} \left(-1 + \dfrac{3k}{n}\right)^2 \Delta x, \quad -1 \le x \le 2$

c. $S_n = \sum\limits_{k=1}^{n} \left[1 + \dfrac{2(k-1)}{n}\right]^4 \Delta x, \quad 1 \le x \le 3$

d. $S_n = \sum\limits_{k=1}^{n} \left[\dfrac{1}{1 + \frac{k}{n}}\right] \Delta x, \quad 1 \le x \le 2$

e. $S_n = \sum\limits_{k=1}^{n} \cos\left(-\dfrac{\pi}{2} + \dfrac{3k\pi}{4n}\right) \Delta x, \quad -\dfrac{\pi}{2} \le x \le \dfrac{\pi}{4}$

f. $S_n = \sum\limits_{k=1}^{n} e^{\left(\frac{k}{n}\right)\ln 2} \Delta x, \quad 0 \le x \le \ln 2$

5. Use the Fundamental Theorem to evaluate each integral. You may find it helpful to rewrite the integrand by using identities.

a. $\displaystyle\int_0^{\frac{\pi}{4}} \tan^2 x \, dx$

b. $\displaystyle\int_{\frac{\pi}{4}}^{\frac{\pi}{2}} \sin x \cos x \, dx$

c. $\displaystyle\int_0^1 \sin^2(\pi x) \, dx$

Problems 8.5

1. Show that $\displaystyle\int_0^1 \dfrac{1}{\sqrt{x+1} - \sqrt{x}} \, dx = \dfrac{4\sqrt{2}}{3}$.

2. Prove that $\int_0^\pi \sin^2(nx)\,dx = \dfrac{\pi}{2}$, for any positive integer n.

3. Evaluate $\lim\limits_{n \to +\infty} \left(\dfrac{1}{n+1} + \dfrac{1}{n+2} + \ldots + \dfrac{1}{2n} \right)$ by interpreting it as the limit of a Riemann sum for the function $f(x) = \dfrac{1}{x+1}$, over the interval $0 \le x \le 1$.

4. When defining area it is unnecessary to choose subintervals of equal length, as long as the lengths of the subintervals tend to zero as $n \to +\infty$. Here is an application of this fact.

Obtain a Riemann sum for the area A under the graph of $f(x) = \dfrac{1}{x}$, where $1 \le x \le 2$, as follows. Subdivide the interval $1 \le x \le 2$ into n subintervals by means of the numbers $1, p, p^2, \ldots, p^{n-1}, p^n = 2$, where $p = 2^{\frac{1}{n}}$. Choose the left endpoints to evaluate the heights of the rectangles and verify that all n rectangles have equal area. Show that

$$A = \lim_{n \to +\infty} n \left(2^{\frac{1}{n}} - 1 \right)$$

Now evaluate this limit by finding A, using the Fundamental Theorem of Calculus.

5. a. By considering a Riemann sum with n equal subintervals for the function $f(x) = \dfrac{1}{x}$ on the interval $1 \le x \le n+1$, show that

$$1 + \frac{1}{2} + \ldots + \frac{1}{n} > \ln(n+1)$$

for any integer $n \ge 1$.

b. Use the result of part (a) to show that the infinite series $\sum\limits_{k=1}^{\infty} \dfrac{1}{k}$ does not have a finite sum. Estimate how many terms of this series must be added in order that the sum exceed 20.

6. Evaluate each limit by using the definition of the definite integral and the Fundamental Theorem of Calculus.

a. $\lim\limits_{n \to +\infty} \dfrac{1}{n}\left[\sqrt{\dfrac{1}{n}} + \sqrt{\dfrac{2}{n}} + \ldots + \sqrt{\dfrac{n-1}{n}} + 1 \right]$

b. $\lim\limits_{n \to +\infty} \dfrac{1}{n^{\frac{3}{2}}}(\sqrt{1} + \sqrt{2} + \sqrt{3} + \ldots + \sqrt{n})$

c. $\lim\limits_{n \to +\infty} \dfrac{\pi}{2n}\left[\sin\dfrac{\pi}{2n} + \sin\dfrac{2\pi}{2n} + \sin\dfrac{3\pi}{2n} + \ldots + \sin\dfrac{\pi}{2} \right]$

8.6 Areas and Definite Integrals

In this section we introduce the concept of "element of area," which provides a simple yet general method for expressing areas as integrals. In particular, we show how to calculate areas bounded by two curves.

Example 1. Find the area A enclosed by the parabola $y = 2 - x^2$ and the line $y = -x$.

Solution. The x-values of the points of intersection of the parabola and the line are obtained by solving the equation

$$2 - x^2 = -x$$

giving

$$x = 2 \quad \text{and} \quad x = -1$$

Subdivide the interval $-1 \leq x \leq 2$ into n equal subintervals of length

$$\Delta x = \frac{3}{n}$$

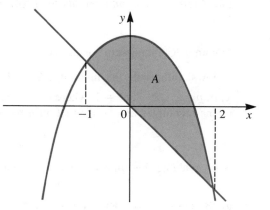

Construct a rectangle above a typical subinterval, as shown. The length $L(x)$ of the rectangle at position x is

$$\begin{aligned} L(x) &= y_2 - y_1 \\ &= (2 - x^2) - (-x) \\ &= 2 + x - x^2 \end{aligned}$$

The area ΔA of this rectangle is

$$\Delta A = L(x)\,\Delta x$$

The total area A is the limit as $n \to +\infty$ of the sum of the areas of the n rectangles:

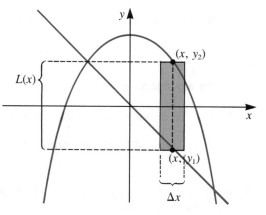

$$A = \lim_{n \to +\infty} \sum_{k=1}^{n} L(x_k)\,\Delta x$$

where x_k is a point in the kth subinterval. By definition of the definite integral,

$$A = \int_{-1}^{2} L(x)\,dx$$

Using the formula for $L(x)$, and the Fundamental Theorem of Calculus,

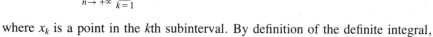

$$A = \int_{-1}^{2} (2 + x - x^2) \, dx$$

$$= \left(2x + \tfrac{1}{2}x^2 - \tfrac{1}{3}x^3\right) \Big|_{-1}^{2}$$

$$= \left(4 + 2 - \tfrac{8}{3}\right) - \left(-2 + \tfrac{1}{2} + \tfrac{1}{3}\right)$$

$$= \tfrac{9}{2}$$

The required area is $\tfrac{9}{2}$ square units. □

The area ΔA of the rectangle at position x will be referred to as the **element of area**. This is a useful concept, because it leads directly to the definite integral that gives the total area. In Example 1 the element of area is

$$\Delta A = (2 + x - x^2) \, \Delta x, \text{ for } -1 \le x \le 2$$

and the total area is

$$A = \int_{-1}^{2} (2 + x - x^2) \, dx$$

One thinks of the integral as the limit of the sum of the areas of n rectangles (limit of a Riemann sum), but it is not necessary to write down this Riemann sum in each example. The length of the rectangle, which in Example 1 is $2 + x - x^2$, becomes the function in the integral (the integrand), and the end points of the interval over which the area is defined give the limits of integration.

We summarize the procedure below.

If the element of area for a region is

$$\Delta A = L(x) \, \Delta x$$

then the area of that region over the interval $a \le x \le b$ is

$$A = \int_{a}^{b} L(x) \, dx$$

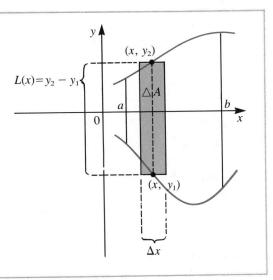

Example 2. Find the area A of the region bounded by the curves $y = 2 \cos x + 1$ and $y = 1 - 2 \sin x$, between $x = 0$ and $x = \dfrac{3\pi}{4}$.

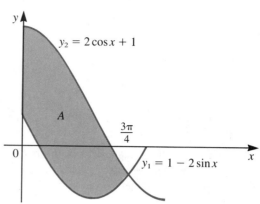

Solution. The region of interest is shown in the first diagram. The upper curve is

$$y_2 = 2 \cos x + 1$$

and the lower curve is

$$y_1 = 1 - 2 \sin x$$

The second diagram shows the element of area. We have

$$\Delta A = (y_2 - y_1) \, \Delta x$$
$$= [(2 \cos x + 1) - (1 - 2 \sin x)] \, \Delta x$$
$$= (2 \cos x + 2 \sin x) \, \Delta x$$

It follows that the area A is

$$A = \int_0^{\frac{3\pi}{4}} (2 \cos x + 2 \sin x) \, dx$$

$$= [2 \sin x - 2 \cos x] \Big|_0^{\frac{3\pi}{4}}$$

$$= \left(2 \sin \frac{3\pi}{4} - 2 \cos \frac{3\pi}{4} \right) - (2 \sin 0 - 2 \cos 0)$$

$$= 2 \left(\frac{1}{\sqrt{2}} \right) - 2 \left(-\frac{1}{\sqrt{2}} \right) + 2$$

$$= 2\sqrt{2} + 2$$

The required area is $2\sqrt{2} + 2$ square units.   □

We emphasize that it is not important whether the bounding curves $y = y_1(x)$ and $y = y_2(x)$ lie above or below the x-axis. The essential point is to identify the upper curve $[y = y_2(x)]$ and the lower curve $[y = y_1(x)]$. Then the length of the rectangle at position x, given by

$$L(x) = y_2(x) - y_1(x),$$

is automatically positive, since $y_2(x) > y_1(x)$. This implies that the element of area, and hence the integral (the total area), is positive.

Two special cases should be noted. If the lower curve is the x-axis ($y_1(x) = 0$), then

$$\Delta A = (y_2 - y_1)\, \Delta x$$
$$= [f(x) - 0]\, \Delta x$$

and

$$A = \int_a^b f(x)\, dx$$

as in section 8.5.

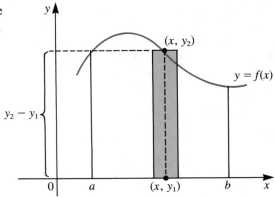

If the upper curve is the x-axis ($y_2(x) = 0$), then

$$\Delta A = (y_2 - y_1)\, \Delta x$$
$$= [0 - f(x)]\, \Delta x$$

and

$$A = \int_a^b [-f(x)]\, dx$$

In Example 3, we illustrate a situation where the two curves intersect and cross over.

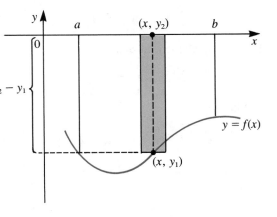

Example 3. Find the total area enclosed by the curve $y = x^3 + x^2$ and the straight line $y = 2x$.

Solution. The points of intersection are obtained by solving the equation

$$x^3 + x^2 = 2x$$

This leads to

$$x(x + 2)(x - 1) = 0$$

and hence

$$x = -2, \quad x = 0, \quad \text{or} \quad x = 1$$

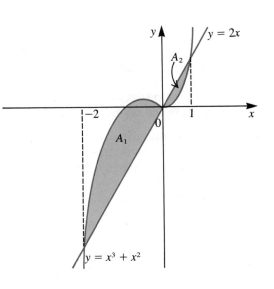

Since the cubic curve is the upper curve for $-2 \leq x \leq 0$, and the straight line is the upper curve for $0 \leq x \leq 1$, we have to calculate the total area enclosed as the sum of two areas,

$$A = A_1 + A_2$$

as in the diagram.

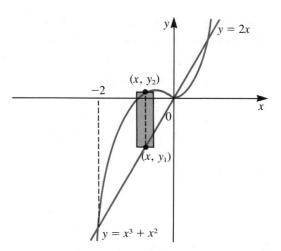

For A_1, the element of area is

$$\Delta A = (y_2 - y_1)\, \Delta x$$
$$= (x^3 + x^2 - 2x)\, \Delta x$$

and hence

$$A_1 = \int_{-2}^{0} (x^3 + x^2 - 2x)\, dx$$

For A_2, the element of area is

$$\Delta A = (y_2 - y_1)\, \Delta x$$
$$= (2x - x^3 - x^2)\, \Delta x$$

and hence

$$A_2 = \int_{0}^{1} (2x - x^3 - x^2)\, dx$$

In Exercise 5, we ask you to complete the calculation for this example. The result is

$$A = \tfrac{8}{3} + \tfrac{5}{12}$$

$$= \tfrac{37}{12} \text{ square units}$$

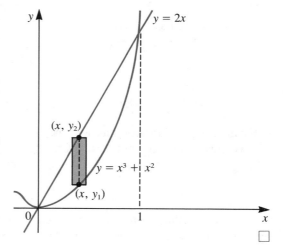

In Example 4, we illustrate the use of a different element of area.

Example 4. Find the area A between the parabola $y^2 = 4x$ and the line $y = 2x - 4$.

Solution. The points of intersection $(1, -2)$ and $(4, 4)$ are found in the usual way. The enclosed region is shown in the diagram.

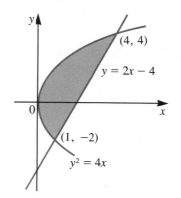

Observe that the lower bounding curve of the region changes from being the parabola to the line at $x = 1$. This means that we could calculate the enclosed area as the sum of two parts

$$A = A_1 + A_2$$

as shown.

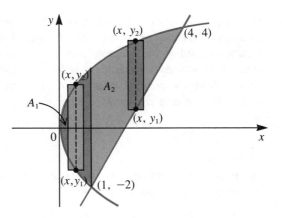

In order to solve the problem more simply, choose as the element of area a horizontal rectangle of width Δy, located at position y.

The length $L(y)$ of the rectangle (in the x-direction) is

$$L(y) = x_2 - x_1$$

where the upper curve (in the x-direction) is

$$x_2 = \tfrac{1}{2}y + 2$$

and the lower curve is

$$x_1 = \tfrac{1}{4}y^2$$

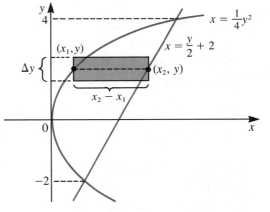

The element of area is

$$\Delta A = (x_2 - x_1)\,\Delta y$$

$$= \left[\left(\tfrac{1}{2}y + 2\right) - \left(\tfrac{1}{4}y^2\right)\right]\Delta y$$

The total area A over the interval $-2 \le y \le 4$ is

$$A = \int_{-2}^{4}\left[\tfrac{1}{2}y + 2 - \tfrac{1}{4}y^2\right]dy$$

$$= \left[\tfrac{1}{4}y^2 + 2y - \tfrac{1}{12}y^3\right]\Big|_{-2}^{4}$$

$$= \left[\tfrac{1}{4}(4)^2 + 2(4) - \tfrac{1}{12}(4)^3\right] - \left[\tfrac{1}{4}(-2)^2 + 2(-2) + \tfrac{1}{12}(-2)^3\right]$$

$$= \frac{31}{3}$$

The required area is $\frac{31}{3}$ square units.

It is important to note the similarities between using a vertical rectangle and a horizontal rectangle as the element of area. In Examples 1 to 3, x varies as one sums the area of (vertical) rectangles, and so we integrate with respect to x, but in Example 4, y varies as we sum the areas of (horizontal) rectangles, and so we integrate with respect to y. The procedure for passing from the element of area ΔA to the integral is the same in both cases—one thinks of the integral as the limit of a sum of the areas of n rectangles (i.e., limit of a Riemann sum).

Exercises 8.6

1. In each case, find the area between the two curves over the given interval. Draw a sketch showing the element of area.

   a. $y = x^2$, $y = 8\sqrt{x}$, $0 \le x \le 4$

   b. $y = \sin x$, $y = \dfrac{2}{\pi}x$, $0 \le x \le \dfrac{\pi}{2}$

   c. $y = e^x$, $y = 2$, $0 \le x \le \ln 2$

   d. $y = 1 - e^x$, $y = x$, $0 \le x \le 1$

   e. $y = \sin x$, $y = \cos x$, $0 \le x \le \dfrac{\pi}{4}$

   f. $y = -x^2 - x$, $y = x$, $-2 \le x \le 0$

   g. $y = \dfrac{4}{x + 2} - 1$, $y = x^2 - 4$, $-1 \le x \le 2$

2. Find the area enclosed by the curve $y = x^2 - 1$ and the straight line that passes through the points $(-1, 0)$ and $(2, 3)$.

3. Find the area enclosed by the parabola $x^2 - 6x - 4y + 1 = 0$ and the chord joining the points $(5, -1)$ and $(-1, 2)$.

4. Find the area enclosed by the curves $y = x^3$ and $y = x^2$.

5. Complete the calculation in Example 3; that is, find the total area enclosed by the curve $y = x^3 + x^2$ and the straight line $y = 2x$.

6. Find the total area enclosed by the curves $y = x^3 - x$ and $y = x^2 + x$.

7. Find the area enclosed by the curves $y = 4e^{-x}$ and $y = 3 - 2e^{-x}$, and the x-axis.

8. Show that the area enclosed by the curves $y = x^2 - k^2$ and $y = -(x - k)^2$, where k is a positive constant, is $\dfrac{1}{3}k^3$ square units.

   In Exercises 9 to 12, it may be helpful to use a horizontal rectangle as the element of area.

9. Find the area enclosed by the hyperbola $y = \dfrac{2}{x}$ and the straight lines $y = x + 1$ and $y = 1$.

10. Find the area enclosed by the curve $y = \ln (x + 1)$ and the lines $x = 3$ and $y = 0$.

11. Find the area enclosed by the parabola $x = y^2 - 2$ and the line $y = x$.

12. Find the area enclosed by the curves $y^2 = 5 - x$ and $y^2 = 4x$.

13. Evaluate each integral and interpret the result in terms of areas of regions.

    a. $\displaystyle\int_{-4}^{3} (x^2 - 4)\, dx$ **b.** $\displaystyle\int_{-\frac{\pi}{4}}^{\frac{\pi}{4}} \sin x\, dx$ **c.** $\displaystyle\int_{0}^{\ln 4} (1 - 2e^{-x})\, dx$

Problems 8.6

1. A manufacturer is designing square floor tiles with sides of unit length, with two curves separating the two colours as shown. Find the value of n that will give equal amounts of each colour.

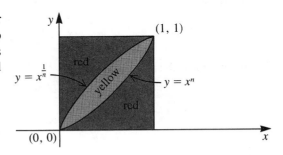

2. Consider the area of the region bounded by the parabola $y = x^2$, the y-axis, and the straight line of slope m through the point $(1, 1)$. For what value of m does the area equal one square unit?

3. Find the area enclosed by $y = \ln x$, the tangent line to this curve at $(e, 1)$, and the x-axis.

4. Show that the area of the region bounded by one arch of the curve $y = k \sin kx$, and the x-axis is independent of the value of the positive constant k. How is the shape of the region affected by the value of k?

5. Evaluate $\displaystyle\int_{-4}^{4} \sqrt{16 - x^2}\, dx$.

    (*Hint:* Interpret the integral geometrically.)

6. If the areas of the shaded regions in the diagram are equal, find b.

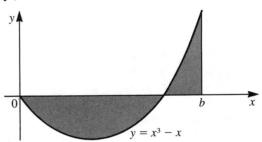

7. Evaluate each integral and interpret geometrically.

    a. $\displaystyle\int_{0}^{1} |2x^2 - x|\, dx$ **b.** $\displaystyle\int_{0}^{1} |2\cos \pi x - 1|\, dx$ **c.** $\displaystyle\int_{-1}^{\ln 2} |e^x - 1|\, dx$

8.7 Other Applications of Definite Integrals

In this section we shall show how definite integrals can be used to calculate quantities other than area.

Example 1. The velocity of a moving object in m/s is $v(t) = t^2$, where t is time. Use the Fundamental Theorem of Calculus to find the distance travelled between $t = 0$ and $t = 4$.

Solution. In section 8.2 we showed that the distance s travelled between $t = 0$ and $t = 4$ can be written as the limit of a Riemann sum of the velocity:

$$s = \lim_{n \to +\infty} \sum_{k=1}^{n} v(t_k) \, \Delta t$$

By definition of the integral,

$$s = \int_0^4 v(t) \, dt$$

$$= \int_0^4 t^2 \, dt$$

$$= \left. \frac{1}{3} t^3 \right|_0^4$$

$$= \frac{1}{3}(4)^3 - \frac{1}{3}(0)^3$$

$$= \frac{64}{3}$$

The distance travelled is $\frac{64}{3}$ m. (Compare this result with the approximation obtained in Example 1 of section 8.2.)   □

In writing the Riemann sum, we have subdivided the time interval $0 \le t \le 4$ into n subintervals of duration $\Delta t = \dfrac{4}{n}$ and treated the velocity as constant over each subinterval. The distance Δs travelled at this (assumed) constant velocity during the time interval at time t is given by

$$\Delta s = v(t) \, \Delta t$$

This quantity is referred to as **the element of distance**, because it plays the same role as the element of area in section 8.6—the element of distance leads directly to the definite integral that gives the total distance. In Example 1, the element of distance is

$$\Delta s = t^2 \, \Delta t, \quad 0 \le t \le 4$$

and the total distance is

$$s = \int_0^4 t^2 \, dt$$

In general, the element of distance is

$$\Delta s = v(t) \, \Delta t, \quad a \le t \le b$$

and the total distance is

$$s = \int_a^b v(t)\, dt$$

Example 2. A cone is formed by rotating the line segment $y = \frac{1}{2}x,\ 0 \le x \le 2$, about the x-axis. By using the Fundamental Theorem of Calculus find the volume of the cone.

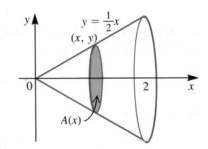

Solution. Let $A(x)$ denote the cross-sectional area of the cone at position x. In section 8.2 we showed that the volume V can be written as the limit of a Riemann sum of the cross-sectional area:

$$V = \lim_{n \to +\infty} \sum_{k=1}^n A(x_k)\Delta x$$

By definition of the integral,

$$V = \int_0^2 A(x)\, dx$$

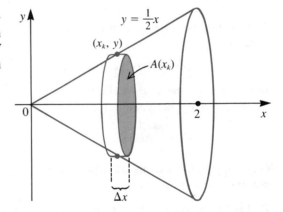

From the diagram, the cross section is a disk of radius y, and in this example $y = \frac{1}{2}x$. It follows that

$$A(x) = \pi\left(\frac{x}{2}\right)^2$$

Hence,

$$
\begin{aligned}
V &= \int_0^2 \frac{\pi}{4}x^2 dx \\
&= \left.\frac{\pi}{12}x^3\right|_0^2 \\
&= \frac{\pi}{12}(2)^3 - \frac{\pi}{12}(0)^3 \\
&= \frac{2}{3}\pi
\end{aligned}
$$

The volume of the cone is $\frac{2}{3}\pi$ cubic units. (Compare this result to the approximate value obtained in Example 2 of section 8.2.) $\square$

In writing the volume as the limit of a Riemann sum, we have subdivided the cone into thin disks, of thickness Δx and cross-sectional area $A(x)$.

The volume ΔV of the disk at position x,

$$\Delta V = A(x)\,\Delta x$$

is called **the element of volume**. The element of volume leads directly to the definite integral that gives the total volume. In Example 2, the element of volume is

$$\Delta V = \frac{\pi}{4}x^2\,\Delta x, \quad 0 \le x \le 2$$

and the total volume is

$$V = \int_0^2 \frac{\pi}{4}x^2\,dx$$

The method is not restricted to cones. In general

$$\Delta V = A(x)\,\Delta x$$

where $A(x)$ is the cross-sectional area at position x. The total volume V is

$$V = \int_a^b A(x)\,dx$$

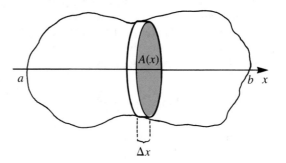

Other applications of the definite integral are illustrated in the exercises.

If Q is the quantity to be calculated, the idea is to write the "element of Q" as

$$\Delta Q = f(x)\,\Delta x, \text{ for } a \le x \le b$$

Then the integral (the limit of the sum over all elements) gives Q:

$$Q = \int_a^b f(x)\,dx$$

Exercises 8.7

1. The velocity of a moving object in m/s is $v(t) = 9 - t^2$. Calculate the distance travelled between $t = 0$ and $t = 3$ by expressing it as a definite integral.

2. Calculate the volume V of a hemi-sphere of radius 1 by using a definite integral.

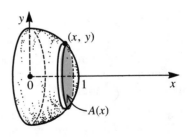

3. Derive the formula for the volume V of a right circular cone of height h and base radius r by expressing it as a definite integral.

4. The mass per unit length (in grams per centimetre) of a metal rod of length 20 cm depends on position x according to $f(x) = 5 + \frac{1}{4}x$ for $0 \le x \le 20$. Find the total mass M of the rod. (*Hint:* The element of mass is $\Delta M = f(x)\,\Delta x$).

5. The shape of a bullet is formed by rotating the curve $y = \sqrt{x}$, with $0 \le x \le b$, about the x-axis.

   a. If the bullet is 1 cm long ($b = 1$), find the volume of metal required to form it.

   b. What length of bullet can be formed by using an amount of metal of volume 3 cm³?

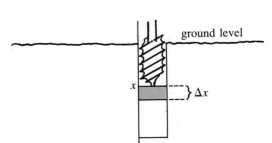

6. A farmer wishes to have a well of depth 20 m drilled on his property. The unit cost of drilling, expressed in dollars per metre, depends on the depth x of the drill bit according to the formula

$$h(x) = 50\left(1 + \frac{3}{100}x^2\right)$$

Find the total cost C of drilling the well.
(*Hint:* The element of cost is $\Delta C = h(x)\,\Delta x$.)

7. A column of soldier ants of length 10 m crawls in a straight line. The head of the column is labelled $x = 10$, and the rear is labelled $x = 0$. The number density of ants (i.e., number of ants per metre length of the column) is not constant but depends on position x in the column. If the number density of ants is

$$n(x) = 30(-x^2 + 10x + 1), \quad 0 \le x \le 10$$

find the total number N of ants in the column.
(*Hint:* The number of ants in a segment of the column of length Δx at position x is $\Delta N = n(x)\,\Delta x$.)

Problems 8.7

1. A barrel is formed by rotating the truncated half ellipse in the diagram about its horizontal edge. Calculate the volume V of the barrel.

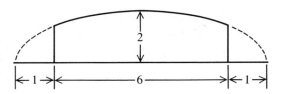

2. The number density of cars (number of cars per unit distance) on a 10 km section of Highway 401 varies with position x owing to a slowdown caused by construction work. If the number density at a particular instant of time is given by

$$n(x) = 200\left[1 - \frac{1}{10}x + \frac{\pi}{10}\sin\left(\pi\frac{x}{10}\right)\right], \quad 0 \le x \le 10$$

find the total number of cars N on the section of highway at that time.

3. A nuclear fuel rod has a length of 80 cm and a cross-sectional area of 10 cm². The density d of the material in the rod (in g/cm³) depends on position x in the rod according to

$$d(x) = 8\left[1 + \frac{3}{4}\left(\frac{x}{80}\right)^2 - \frac{1}{4}\left(\frac{x}{80}\right)^3\right], \quad 0 \le x \le 80$$

Find the total mass M of the rod.

4. Find the volume of a pyramid with a vertical height of h and a square base of side a.

5. The shape of a doughnut is formed by rotating a disk of radius r about a line a distance R from the centre of the circle. Show that if $R \ge r$, then the volume of the doughnut is

$$V = 2\pi^2Rr^2$$

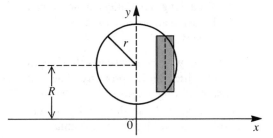

Review Exercises

1. Evaluate each definite integral.

a. $\displaystyle\int_1^2 x^4\, dx$

b. $\displaystyle\int_{-2}^3 7\, dx$

c. $\displaystyle\int_0^{2\pi} (x^3 + \pi^3)\, dx$

d. $\displaystyle\int_4^9 \frac{1}{\sqrt{t}}\, dt$

e. $\displaystyle\int_1^2 \left(2x^3 - \frac{3}{x^3} + 4\right) dx$

f. $\displaystyle\int_0^4 (2x + 1)^{\frac{3}{2}}\, dx$

g. $\displaystyle\int_0^{\ln 3} e^{3x}\, dx$

h. $\displaystyle\int_1^{e^3} \frac{1}{x}\, dx$

i. $\displaystyle\int_0^{\frac{\pi}{2}} (2\cos x + \cos 2x)\, dx$

j. $\displaystyle\int_{\frac{\pi}{8}}^{\frac{\pi}{4}} \csc^2 2x\, dx$

k. $\displaystyle\int_3^3 (x^5 - 7x^2 + 6)\, dx$

l. $\displaystyle\int_{-1}^1 \frac{1}{2 - x}\, dx$

2. Determine the area A of the region bounded by the curve $y = f(x)$ and the x-axis, over the given interval. Draw a sketch showing the region and a typical element of area.

a. $f(x) = x + 1, \quad 2 \leq x \leq 5$

b. $f(x) = \dfrac{1}{x^2}, \quad 1 \leq x \leq 3$

c. $f(x) = \sqrt{x}, \quad 4 \leq x \leq 9$

d. $f(x) = 1 - 2 \sin \dfrac{x}{2}, \quad 0 \leq x \leq \dfrac{\pi}{3}$

e. $f(x) = 2 - e^{-x}, \quad -\ln 2 \leq x \leq \ln 2$

f. $f(x) = \dfrac{3}{x}, \quad \dfrac{2}{e} \leq x \leq e$

g. $f(x) = \dfrac{1}{1 + x}, \quad 0 \leq x \leq 10$

h. $f(x) = \dfrac{1}{\sqrt{4 - x}}, \quad 0 \leq x \leq 3$

3. Find each of the following areas. In each case, draw a sketch showing the element of area.

a. The area enclosed by the curve $y = -x^2 - x + 6$ and the x-axis.

b. The area of the region bounded by the curve $y = x(x - \pi)^2$ and the x-axis.

c. The area of the region bounded by $y = -e^{-2x} + 6e^{-x} - 8$ and the x-axis.

d. The area of the region bounded by $y = \pi e^{-x} - 1$, $y = 0$, and $x = 0$.

e. The area of one loop of the curve $y = 3 \sin 2x$.

4. For what value of the constant b does the area of the region bounded by $y = x^2$ and the x-axis, for $0 \leq x \leq b$, equal 72 square units?

5. For what value of the constant k does the area of the region bounded by the parabola $y = x(k - x)$ and the x-axis equal 36 square units?

6. The wall of a dam is 3 m thick, and its cross section has the shape of a parabola, with dimensions as shown. Find the volume of concrete in the wall.

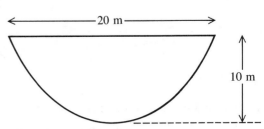

7. Find the area enclosed by $y = e$, $y = e^x$, and the y-axis.

8. a. Sketch the graph of $y = x^2(3 - x)$.

   b. Find the area enclosed by the graph of $y = x^2(3 - x)$ and the line $y = 4$.

9. Find the area enclosed by the parabola $y = -x^2 + x + 6$ and the line $y = 4$.

10. For what value of the positive constant m does the area enclosed by $y = x^2$ and $y = mx$ equal 4?

11. Find the area enclosed by the curves $y = \sin 2x$ and $y = \sin x$, between $x = 0$ and their next point of intersection.

12. Find the area enclosed by the parabola $y^2 + y = -x$ and $y = x$.

13. Find the area above the x-axis and below the curve $y = x^2 - x^4$.

14. Each limit represents the area A of a certain region. Find A by evaluating the corresponding integral, and sketch the region.

    a. $\displaystyle\lim_{n \to +\infty} \left[\left(\frac{2}{n}\right)^2 + \left(\frac{4}{n}\right)^2 + \cdots + \left(\frac{2n}{n}\right)^2 \right]\left(\frac{1}{n}\right)$

    b. $\displaystyle\lim_{n \to +\infty} \left[\cos\left(-\frac{\pi}{2} + \frac{\pi}{n}\right) + \cos\left(-\frac{\pi}{2} + 2\frac{\pi}{n}\right) + \cdots + \cos\left(-\frac{\pi}{2} + n\frac{\pi}{n}\right) \right]\left(\frac{\pi}{n}\right)$

    c. $\displaystyle\lim_{n \to +\infty} \left[\frac{1}{\left(1 + \frac{1}{n}\right)^2} + \frac{1}{\left(1 + \frac{2}{n}\right)^2} + \cdots + \frac{1}{\left(1 + \frac{n}{n}\right)^2} \right]\left(\frac{1}{n}\right)$

15. Let A_n be the area in the first quadrant that is enclosed by the curves $y = x^n$ and $y = x^{\frac{1}{n}}$, where n is a positive integer.

    a. Show that $A_n = \dfrac{n - 1}{n + 1}$.

    b. Evaluate $\displaystyle\lim_{n \to +\infty} A_n$ and interpret the result geometrically.

16. Find the area enclosed by the curves $y = e^x$ and $y = 4e^{-x}$, and the y-axis.

17. Find the area of the indicated region.

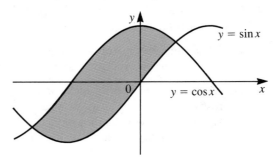

18. a. Find the area in the first quadrant enclosed by $y = x^{\frac{1}{3}}$ and $y = \frac{1}{2}x$.

    b. Verify your answer in part (a) by solving the problem using a horizontal rectangle as the element of area.

19. Let $A(b)$ be the area between the curve $y = \dfrac{1}{x^2}$ and the x-axis, for $1 \le x \le b$. Evaluate $\displaystyle\lim_{b \to +\infty} A(b)$.

20. Let $A(c)$ be the area between the curve $y = \dfrac{1}{x}$ and the x-axis, for $1 \le x \le c$. For what value of c does $A(c)$ equal 100 square units?

21. Show that the area of the region bounded by the curve $y = \ln x$ and the lines $y = 0$ and $x = e^2$ equals $e^2 + 1$ square units.

Epilogue

We began our study of Calculus by posing two problems: the problem of tangents and the problems of areas. In order to solve the first of these we introduced the derivative, based upon the notion of a limit. For the second problem we considered an approximating area, called a Riemann sum. This led to the definite integral $\int_a^b f(x)dx$ (also based upon the notion of limit). The relationship between these seemingly distinct concepts (which constitute the Differential and Integral Calculus) was discovered through the simple yet ingenious device of using the Area function $A(x)$ of a given function $f(x)$. The function $A(x)$ was shown to be an antiderivative of the function $f(x)$. This led to an elegant method for evaluating definite integrals (enunciated as the Fundamental Theorem), avoiding the difficult task of dealing directly with Riemann sums and their limiting values. (Indeed, this intimate relation between the definite integral and antiderivatives is the basis for a commonly used notation for the general antiderivative of a function f, namely $\int f(x)dx$, where the limits of integration are omitted).

Having come this far there are many questions that you might ask:

- What function has $\dfrac{1}{\sqrt{1-x^2}}$ as its derivative? What about $\sqrt{1-x^2}$ or e^{-x^2}?

- How can we calculate and interpret $\int_1^\infty \dfrac{1}{x^2}dx$, when the Riemann sum definition is not applicable?

- How does a calculator compute $\sin x$ or $\ln x$?

- Can one improve upon the tangent approximation to a function $f(x)$ by using a quadratic or cubic polynomial? (You might try plotting $\sin x$ and $x - \dfrac{x^3}{6}$ on the same axes.)

- What if a differential equation contains second derivatives? For example, how can one solve $\dfrac{d^2y}{dx^2} = ky$?

- What if a function f depends on more than one variable? The temperature T at a point in the atmosphere clearly depends upon the coordinates of the point, say (x, y, z) representing latitude, longitude and elevation, as well as the time t. In this situation we write $T = f(x, y, z, t)$. How should the limit, the derivative or the definite integral be defined for such functions?

Each of these questions leads to a chapter in the development and application of Calculus. Clearly much lies ahead.

Answers

Chapter 1

Exercises 1.2

1. a. $\frac{5}{2}$ **b.** $-\frac{4}{5}$ **c.** $-\frac{b}{a}$

2. a. $y - 2 = -\frac{1}{2}(x + 1)$

b. $y - 1 = \frac{6}{5}(x - 3)$

c. $y + 1 = -\frac{2}{3}(x - 2)$

3. a. $5x + 12y - 169 = 0$
b. $4x + 3y - 23 = 0$ **c.** $3x + 4y = 0$
d. $4x + 3y - 45 = 0$
4. a.

		Slope of secant line
P	Q	PQ
$(1, -1)$	$(7, -4)$	-3
$(1, -1)$	$(1.5, -2.25)$	-2.5
$(1, -1)$	$(1.1, -1.21)$	-2.1
$(1, -1)$	$(1.01, -1.0201)$	-2.01

		Slope of secant line
P	Q	PQ
$(1, -1)$	$(0, 0)$	-1
$(1, -1)$	$(0.5, -0.25)$	-1.5
$(1, -1)$	$(0.9, -0.81)$	-1.9
$(1, -1)$	$(0.99, -0.9801)$	-1.99

b. -2 **c.** $-2 - h, h \neq 0$ **d.** -2

5. a.

		Slope of secant line
P	Q	PQ
$(2, 8)$	$(3, 27)$	19.00
$(2, 8)$	$(2.5, 15.625)$	15.25
$(2, 8)$	$(2.1, 9.261)$	12.61
$(2, 8)$	$(2.01, 8.120\ 601)$	12.0601

		Slope of secant line
P	Q	PQ
$(2, 8)$	$(1, 1)$	7
$(2, 8)$	$(1.5, 3.375)$	9.25
$(2, 8)$	$(1.9, 6.859)$	11.41
$(2, 8)$	$(1.99, 7.880\ 599)$	$11.940\ 10$

b. 12 **c.** $h^2 + 6h + 12, h \neq 0$ **d.** 12
6. a. 4 **b.** -8 **c.** 0 **7. a.** 2; $y = 2x$
b. 4; $y = 4x - 13$ **c.** 1; $y = x - 4$ **d.** -3;
$y = -3x$ **e.** -9; $y = -9x + 6$
f. -1; $y = -x - 4$ **g.** 9; $y = 9x - 6$
h. 6; $y = 6x + 7$ **8.** Slope at $x = 3$ is -4
and slope at $x = -1$ is 4.

Problems 1.2
1. $(2, 4)$

Exercises 1.3
1. a. (i) 36 km/h (ii) 30.6 km/h
(iii) 30.06 km/h **b.** 30 km/h
c. $(6\Delta t + 30)$ km/h, $\Delta t \neq 0$ **d.** 30 km/h
2. a. 5 m/s, 15 m/s, 25 m/s, 35 m/s
b. $20 + 5\Delta t, 40 + 5\Delta t, 60 + 5\Delta t$

c. 20 m/s, 40 m/s, 60 m/s **3. a.** $-\dfrac{90}{4(4 + \Delta t)}$,

$-\dfrac{90}{6(6 + \Delta t)}$, $-\dfrac{90}{8(8 + \Delta t)}$ **b.** $-\dfrac{45}{8}$, $-\dfrac{5}{2}$, $-\dfrac{45}{32}$

4. a. $-\dfrac{1}{3}$ mg/h **b.** amount of drug in the

blood stream is decreasing **5 a.** 12 **b.** 2

c. 0 **d.** -4 **6. a.** 6 **b.** -2 **c.** -4
d. -12 **7. a.** -2000 L/min
b. -1000 L/min **8.** $-\dfrac{20}{3}$ °C/km

9. 25π mL/cm

Problems 1.3

2. a. (i) decrease (ii) increase **b.** (i) for
speeds between 80 km/h and 120 km/h
(ii) for speeds between 40 km/h and 80 km/h
c. 80 km/h; 0 **3.** $\dfrac{1}{4}$

Exercises 1.4

1. a. -2 **b.** -10 **c.** 3 **d.** 5 **e.** -4 **f.** 5
2. a. does not exist; discontinuous **b.** does
not exist; discontinuous **c.** 2; continuous
d. does not exist; discontinuous **e.** $\dfrac{1}{2}$;
continuous **f.** does not exist; discontinuous
g. does not exist; discontinuous **h.** 2;
continuous **3.** discontinuous at $x = -1$ and
$x = 1$ **5.** $A = -3$, $B = 1$ **6. a.** 10 **b.** 6, 0
c. $t = 3$, $t = 4$

Problems 1.4

1. b. -1 and 1 **c.** $-3, 0, 0, -3$ **2. b.** 6, 4
c. 2000 **d.** $6\sqrt{2}$ **3. a.** 1, -1, does not
exist **4.** yes; $f(1) = f(-1) = -1$ **5.** $A = 6$,
$B = 4$ **6. b.** at all integer values **7. a.** $\dfrac{1}{20}$

b. $\dfrac{1}{200}$ **c.** 5.0×10^{-7}

Exercises 1.5

1. a. poly **b.** alg. **c.** alg. **d.** rat.
e. poly. **f.** alg. **g.** rat. **h.** alg. **2. a.** 1
b. $\dfrac{9\sqrt{2}}{2}$ **c.** 1 **d.** $\dfrac{25}{4}$ **e.** $5\pi^3$ **f.** 2 **g.** $\sqrt{2}$

h. $\dfrac{1}{2\sqrt{x}}$ **i.** $\sqrt{3}$ **j.** $-\dfrac{7}{5}$ **k.** 64 **1.** 2

3. a. 9 **b.** 3 **c.** $\dfrac{19}{5}$ **d.** 5 **e.** 10 **f.** $\sqrt{5}$

Problems 1.5

1. 2 **2. a.** 0 **b.** 0 **c.** $\dfrac{1}{2}$

Exercises 1.6

1. a. 4 **b.** 4 **c.** 3 **d.** 0 **e.** 27 **f.** 1
g. $-\dfrac{7}{3}$ **h.** $\dfrac{7}{2}$ **2. a.** $\dfrac{1}{2}$ **b.** $\dfrac{1}{4}$ **c.** $\dfrac{1}{4}$
d. $-\dfrac{1}{2}$ **e.** $-\dfrac{1}{2}$ **f.** 6 **g.** -2 **h.** 4
3. a. does not exist **b.** does not exist
c. does not exist **d.** 0 **4.** $\dfrac{1}{2}$ **5. a.** $\dfrac{1}{27}$
b. $\dfrac{1}{6}$ **c.** $\dfrac{1}{12}$ **d.** $\dfrac{1}{2}$ **6. a.** 4, slope of tangent
to $y = x^2$ at $x = 2$ **b.** $-\dfrac{1}{9}$, slope of tangent
to $y = \dfrac{1}{x}$ at $x = 3$ **c.** $\dfrac{1}{4}$, slope of tangent to
$y = \sqrt{x}$ at $x = 4$ **d.** $-\dfrac{1}{54}$, slope of tangent
to $y = \dfrac{1}{\sqrt{x}}$ at $x = 9$ **e.** $\dfrac{1}{12}$, slope of tangent to
$y = x^{\frac{1}{3}}$ at $x = 8$ **f.** $\dfrac{1}{6}$, slope of tangent to
$y = x^{\frac{1}{6}}$ at $x = 1$ **7. a.** $\dfrac{1}{6}$ **b.** 2 **c.** $\dfrac{11}{2}$
d. $\dfrac{1}{3\sqrt{3}}$ **e.** 4 **f.** 0 **g.** does not exist
h. $-\dfrac{1}{2\sqrt{2}}$ **i.** $\dfrac{1}{3}$ **j.** $\dfrac{2}{3}$ **k.** $-\dfrac{1}{2}$ **l.** $-\dfrac{1}{2}$
m. $-\dfrac{1}{9}$ **n.** 0 **o.** $\dfrac{120}{59}$ **p.** 2 **q.** $\dfrac{1}{32}$
r. does not exist

Problems 1.6

1. does not exist **2.** $A = 2$ **3.** $A = 6$, $B = 9$
4. a. 1, -2 **b.** $\dfrac{2}{3}$, does not exist **5.** $3a^2$
6. $\dfrac{1}{3a^{\frac{2}{3}}}$ **7. a.** na^{n-1} **b.** $\dfrac{1}{n}a^{\frac{1}{n}-1}$

Exercises 1.7

1. a. 2 **b.** -4 **c.** -4 **d.** 0 **e.** $\dfrac{1}{2}$ **f.** $\dfrac{1}{4}$

2. a. $8x$ **b.** $2x + 3$ **c.** 5 **d.** $\dfrac{-3}{(x+2)^2}$

e. $-4 + 2x$ **f.** $-6x + 2$ **g.** $\dfrac{3}{2\sqrt{3x+2}}$

h. $-\dfrac{1}{2x^{\frac{3}{2}}}$ **i.** $\dfrac{x}{\sqrt{x^2+1}}$ **j.** $-\dfrac{2}{x^3}$ **3. a** $-6x$

b. $2x + 3$ **c.** -7 **d.** $\dfrac{35}{(3-7x)^2}$ **e.** $\dfrac{-2}{(x-1)^2}$

f. $-\dfrac{11}{2\sqrt{3-11x}}$ **g.** $-\dfrac{8x}{(x^2+3)^2}$ **h.** $1 - \dfrac{1}{x^2}$

4. a. (i) $3x^2$ (ii) $4x^3$ **c.** $39x^{38}$ **d.** nx^{n-1}

5. $-4, 0, 4$ **6.** 4 m/s, 0 m/s, -4 m/s

7. a. $(2, 6)$ **b.** $\left(\dfrac{5}{2}, \dfrac{25}{4}\right)$ **c.** $(3, 6)$ **8.** 5 s

11. a. (i) sales = 500, rate = 250

(ii) sales = 960, rate = 1.6 **12.** -1 and 1

Problems 1.7

1. $(1, 1)$ **2.** -1 **3. b.** $f(\pi) = 0$ and
$f'(\pi) = 3$ **4.** 3 **5. b.** none **c.** at all
$x = \dfrac{1}{2}n$, n an integer **6. b.** 0

Review Exercises

1. a. (i) $\dfrac{3}{2}$ (ii) $\dfrac{21}{20}$ (iii) $\dfrac{201}{200}$ **b.** $1 + \dfrac{h}{2}$

c. 1 **2. a.** 3, 9, 15, 21 m/s **b.** $12 + 3\Delta t$,
$36 + 3\Delta t$, $108 + 3\Delta t$ m/s **c.** 12, 36,
108 m/s **3. a.** 0.0401 g **b.** 4.01 g/min

c. 4 g/min **4. a.** 7 **b.** $6t - 2$ **c.** $\dfrac{3}{(t+1)^2}$

d. $\dfrac{1}{2\sqrt{9+t}}$ **5. a.** $\dfrac{1}{10}$ **b.** $\dfrac{1}{2\sqrt{3}}$ **c.** 2 **d.** 13

6. a. 1 **b.** $\sqrt{5}$ **c.** $-\dfrac{4}{3}$ **d.** $\sqrt[3]{36}$ **e.** $\dfrac{1}{2\sqrt{a}}$

f. does not exist **g.** $\dfrac{1}{3}$ **h.** 1 **i.** -1

j. $\dfrac{1}{6\sqrt{5}}$ **7. a.** discontinuous; $-3, 3$

b. discontinuous; $-3, 2$ **c.** discontinuous;
4, 3 **d.** discontinuous at $x = 0, -1, 1$

8. a. 10, slope of tangent to $y = x^2$ at $x = 5$

b. $\dfrac{1}{2\sqrt{3}}$, slope of tangent to $y = \sqrt{x}$ at $x = 3$

c. -1, slope of tangent to $y = \dfrac{4}{x}$ at $x = 2$

d. $\dfrac{1}{3}$, slope of tangent to $y = x^{\frac{1}{3}}$ at $x = 1$

9. a. $8x - 4$ **b.** $\dfrac{-5}{(x+5)^2}$ **c.** $\dfrac{-5}{2\sqrt{3-5x}}$

d. -5 **e.** $1 - 2x$ **f.** $2\pi x$ **g.** $\dfrac{1}{\pi\left(1 - \dfrac{x}{\pi}\right)^2}$

h. $\dfrac{2x-1}{(x-x^2)^2}$ **10.** No. **11.** 1 **12. a.** 30

b. 30, 0 **c.** $3 \le t < 5$, 5 **d.** 3, 5 **e.** 2, 0

13. a. $1 + \dfrac{t}{5}$ **b.** (i) 10 (ii) 1 (iii) $\dfrac{8}{5}$

(iv) $21\dfrac{9}{10}$ **14. a.** 2 **b.** 2, 3 **c.** 1, 2, 3

15.

x	x_1	x_2	x_3	x_4	x_5	x_6
$f'(x)$	+	NE	−	0	+	−

Chapter 2

Exercises 2.1

1. a. 3 **b.** $4x + 1$ **c.** $-2x + 4$ **d.** $3x^2 - 2x$
e. $12x^2$ **f.** $12x^3$ **2. a.** -8 **b.** -2 **c.** 0

d. -9 **3. a.** (i) $15x^4$ (ii) $\dfrac{3}{\pi}x^2$ (iii) $3t^8$

(iv) $32x$ (v) $\dfrac{x^3}{4}$ (vi) $7bt^6$

b. (i) $15x - y - 12 = 0$
(ii) $3x - \pi y - 2 = 0$ (iii) $9x - 3y - 8 = 0$
(iv) $y = 32x - 16$ (v) $4x - 16y - 3 = 0$

(vi) $y = 7bt - 6b$ **4. a.** $\dfrac{dy}{dx} = 2x - 4$

b. $f'(x) = 6x^2 - 10x + 4$

c. $g'(m) = 18m^2 - 20m^4$ **d.** $\dfrac{dp}{dq} = 8q^3 + 10q$

e. $\dfrac{dy}{dx} = x^4 + x^2 - x$ **f.** $f'(x) = -4x + 11$

g. $\dfrac{dy}{dx} = 24x^7 + 7x^6 - 21x^2 + 24x$

h. $f'(t) = 4t^3$ **i.** $\dfrac{ds}{dt} = 3\pi^3 t^2 - 3\pi$

j. $f'(x) = 4x^3 - 6x^2$ **k.** $g'(x) = -14x + 35$
l. $v'(x) = 50x + 20$ **5. a.** $v = 7 - 4t$
b. $v = 5 - t^2$ **c.** $v = v_0 + at$ **7.** $(-1, 0)$
8. $32x + 16y - 171 = 0$ **11.** $(1, -3)$ and

$(-1, -3)$ **12.** $y = 20x - 47$ and $y = -4x + 1$

13. a. $(3, 24)$ **b.** $(2, -2)$ **c.** $(-6, 9)$

d. $\left(-\dfrac{b}{2a}, \dfrac{4ac - b^2}{4a}\right)$ **14.** $1 + \dfrac{\sqrt{2}}{2}$ and

$1 - \dfrac{\sqrt{2}}{2}$ min   **15. b.** 1 **16. a.** $\dfrac{dN}{dt} = -6t + 300$

b. 120 people/day (indicates an increase);
-120 people/day (indicates a decrease)

c. 50 days   **17.** $(2, -8)$

Problems 2.1

1. $(0, 0)$ **2.** $p = \dfrac{46}{27}$, $q = 7$ **3.** when $r = s$,

$f'(r) = 0$ **5. a.** 3 **b.** $\pm\sqrt{2}$ **c.** $-1, 0, 1$

Exercises 2.2

1. a. $12x - 13$ **b.** $-12x + 38$

c. $16q - 3$ **d.** $15t^2 + 70t$ **e.** $6x^2 - 2x$

f. $24x^2 - 8x - 2$ **g.** $-10t^4 + 9t^2 - 4t$

h. $45x^8 - 80x^7 + 2x - 2$

i. $8n^7 - 49n^6 + 18n^5 - 25n^4$ **j.** $45x^4 - 12x^2$

2. a. 9 **b.** -4 **c.** -9 **d.** 6 **e.** 70 **f.** 8

3. $10x + y - 8 = 0$ **4.** $6(2x - 1)^2$

5. a. $4(2x + 1)^3(2)$ **b.** $6(5 - x)^5(-1)$

c. $3(x^2 - 4)^2(2x)$ **d.** $5(7 - x^3)^4(-3x^2)$

e. $4(2x^2 + 3x - 5)^3(4x + 3)$

f. $5(5x - x^2)^4(5 - 2x)$ **g.** $3(\pi^2 - x^2)^2(-2x)$

h. $4(1 - x + x^2 - x^3)^3(-1 + 2x - 3x^2)$

i. $3[(2 - x)^4 + 16]^2(4(2 - x)^3(-1))$

j. $5[(3x + 1)^3 - x]^4(3(3x + 1)^2(3) - 1)$

6. a. $3(x + 4)^2(x - 3)^5(3x + 5)$

b. $4(2x - 1)^3(2 - 3x)^3(-12x + 7)$

c. $15x^2(3x - 5)(x - 1)$

d. $4x^3(1 - 4x^2)^2(1 - 10x^2)$

e. $6x(x^2 + 3)^2(x^3 + 3)(2x^3 + 3x + 3)$

f. $12(4 - 3x^3)^3(1 - 2x)^5(9x^3 - 3x^2 - 4)$

7. a. $(x + 1)(x + 2) + x(x + 2) + x(x + 1)$

b. $2(x^2 + 1)(x^3 - 3x) +$
$(2x - 3)(2x)(x^3 - 3x) +$
$(2x - 3)(x^2 + 1)(3x^2 - 3)$

c. $3x^2(7 + 2x)^4(1 - x)^2 +$
$x^3(4)(7 + 2x)^3(2)(1 - x)^2 +$
$x^3(7 + 2x)^4(2)(1 - x)(-1)$

d. $2x(1 - x)^3(2x + 1)^4 +$
$x^2(3)(1 - x)^2(-1)(2x + 1)^4 +$
$x^2(1 - x)^3(4)(2x + 1)^3(2)$

e. $5(1 - x^3)^3(2 + 3x)^2 +$
$5x(3)(1 - x^3)^2(-3x^2)(2 + 3x)^2 +$
$5x(1 - x^3)^3(2)(2 + 3x)(3)$

f. $3(-2x)(2x^3 - 3)^2(2x - x^2)^3 +$
$3(1 - x^2)(2)(2x^3 - 3)(6x^2)(2x - x^2)^3 +$
$3(1 - x^2)(2x^3 - 3)^2(3)(2x - x^2)^2(2 - 2x)$

8. $y + 25 = -\dfrac{1}{210}(x + 1)$ **10.** $\dfrac{dA}{dt} = 88$

11. $x = 0$ and $x = 1$; no

Problems 2.2

1. $100\sqrt{2}$ L/day   **2. a.** $p'(x)q(x)r(x)s(x) +$
$p(x)q'(x)r(x)s(x) + p(x)q(x)r'(x)s(x) +$
$p(x)q(x)r(x)q'(x)$ **b.** 10 **4. a.** $x(300 - \dfrac{1}{2}x)^2$

b. $(300 - \dfrac{1}{2}x)^2 - x(300 - \dfrac{1}{2}x)$ **c.** (i) yes

(ii) no   **7.** 72 **8. b.** $\dfrac{n(n + 1)}{2}$

Exercises 2.3

1. a. $-\dfrac{1}{x^2}$ **b.** $-\dfrac{2}{x^3}$ **c.** $\dfrac{1}{(x + 1)^2}$ **d.** $\dfrac{-6}{(3x + 2)^3}$

2. a. $\dfrac{(x + 1)(2x) - x^2(1)}{(x + 1)^2}$ **b.** $\dfrac{(1 - 2x)2x - x^2(-2)}{(1 - 2x)^2}$

c. $\dfrac{(x + 3)(2) - (2x - 1)(1)}{(x + 3)^2}$

d. $\dfrac{(5x + 6)(3) - (3x + 4)(5)}{(5x + 6)^2}$

e. $\dfrac{(q + 2)(2q - 4) - (q^2 - 4q)(1)}{(q + 2)^2}$

f. $\dfrac{(t + 5)(2) - (2t - 3)(1)}{(t + 5)^2}$

g. $\dfrac{(2n^2 - 1)(3n^2) - (n^3)(4n)}{(2n^2 - 1)^2}$

h. $\dfrac{(1 + w^3)(-3w^2) - (1 - w^3)(3w^2)}{(1 + w^3)^2}$

3. a. $\dfrac{-2x}{(x^2 + 5)^2}$

b. $\dfrac{(1 - x^2)(6x + 5) - (3x^2 + 5x)(-2x)}{(1 - x^2)^2}$

c. $\dfrac{(x^2 + 3)(2x - 1) - (x^2 - x + 1)(2x)}{(x^2 + 3)^2}$

d. $\dfrac{(x^3 + 3x + 4)(4x) - (2x^2 - 4)(3x^2 + 3)}{(x^3 + 3x + 4)^2}$

e. $\dfrac{(x^2 + 9)(2x) - (x^2 - 9)(2x)}{(x^2 + 9)^2}$

f. $\dfrac{(8 - x^3)(3x^2) - x^3(-3x^2)}{(8 - x^3)^2}$

g. $\dfrac{(3x^2 + x)(2x) - (x^2 - 1)(6x + 1)}{(3x^2 + x)^2}$

h. $[(x + 1)[2(2x + 3) + (2x - 3)(2)] - (2x - 3)(2x + 3)(1)] \div (x + 1)^2$

4. a. $\dfrac{-(2x - 1)(2x + 5)}{(x - 2)^4}$ **b.** $\dfrac{8x(x^2 - 1)}{(x^2 + 1)^3}$

c. $\dfrac{2x(1 - x)^2(1 - 3x - x^2)}{(1 + x)^4}$

d. $\dfrac{5(5x - 3)^2(-2x + 9)}{(x + 2)^6}$ **5. a.** $-6x^{-3}$ **b.** $6x^{-4}$

c. $-\dfrac{8}{x^3}$ **d.** $\dfrac{15}{x^6}$ **e.** $-3(2x - 1)^{-4}\,(2)$

f. $-3(4 - x^2)^{-2}(-2x)$ **g.** $\dfrac{-(10x + 1)}{(5x^2 + x)^2}$

h. $\dfrac{-6\pi x^2}{(x^3 - \pi)^3}$ **6. a.** $2x - 2x^{-3}$ **b.** $\pi - \dfrac{2\pi^2}{x^3}$

c. $-6x^{-4} + 6x^{-3}$ **d.** $-21x^{-8} + 7x^6$

e. $-\dfrac{4x - 3}{(2x^2 - 3x + 5)^2}$ **f.** $3(x - \tfrac{1}{3}x^{-3})^2(1 + x^{-4})$

g. $\dfrac{2}{(1 - x)^3} - \dfrac{1}{(2 - x)^2}$ **h.** $-\dfrac{6\pi x}{(x^2 + \pi^2)^4}$

7. a. $\dfrac{6}{(x + 2)^2}$ **b.** $\dfrac{-30x}{(4x - 3)^3}$ **8. a.** 10 **b.** -9

c. $-\dfrac{1}{4}$ **d.** $\dfrac{896}{27}$ **9. a.** $x + 52y - 522 = 0$

b. $x - 2y + 7 = 0$ **c.** $x + 3y + 10 = 0$

d. $y + 125 = -\dfrac{1}{800}(x + 1)$

10. $\left(4 + 2\sqrt{5},\ \dfrac{15 + 6\sqrt{5}}{5}\right)$,

$\left(4 - 2\sqrt{5},\ \dfrac{15 - 6\sqrt{5}}{5}\right)$ **11. a.** $(0, 0),\ (8, 32)$

b. $(0, -1)$ **c.** $\left(-2, \dfrac{1}{12}\right)$ **12. a.** 150 cars per

week/week, $\dfrac{750}{169}$ cars per week/week **b.** no

13. $x = \pm\dfrac{1}{\sqrt{3}}$, no **14. a.** yes **b.** no

Problems 2.3

1. a. 20 m **b.** 1.1 m/s **2.** $ad - bc > 0$

3. a. $\left(\dfrac{5}{2}, \dfrac{15}{4}\right)$

Exercises 2.4

1. a. $\dfrac{1}{2\sqrt{x}}$ **b.** $\dfrac{1}{2x^{\frac{3}{2}}}$ **c.** $\dfrac{3}{2\sqrt{3x + 1}}$

d. $\dfrac{-1}{2\sqrt{x}(\sqrt{x} + 1)^2}$ **2. a.** $2x^{-\frac{4}{5}}$ **b.** $-\dfrac{200}{x^{\frac{5}{3}}}$

c. $2x + \dfrac{1}{2x^{\frac{3}{2}}}$ **d.** $\dfrac{1}{2\sqrt{x}} + 9\sqrt{x}$ **e.** $\dfrac{5}{2\sqrt{5x + 7}}$

f. $\dfrac{x}{\sqrt{x^2 - 3}}$ **g.** $\dfrac{-t}{(\sqrt{4 + t^2})^3}$ **h.** $\dfrac{-1}{\sqrt{t}(2\sqrt{t} + 3)^2}$

i. $2(1 + u^{\frac{1}{3}})^5\,u^{-\frac{2}{3}}$ **j.** $\dfrac{1 - u^{-2}}{2\sqrt{u + u^{-1}}}$

k. $\dfrac{1}{2\sqrt{x}}(4 - x)^2 - 2\sqrt{x}(4 - x)$

l. $x^{\frac{2}{3}} - x^{\frac{1}{2}} - x^{-\frac{3}{2}}$ **m.** $5(2x - 5)^{\frac{3}{2}}$

n. $2x\sqrt{1 - x^2} - \dfrac{x(x^2 + 1)}{\sqrt{1 - x^2}}$ **3. a.** $3 + \dfrac{1}{\sqrt{2}}$

b. 0 **c.** $\dfrac{13}{4}$ **d.** $\dfrac{1}{2\sqrt{2}}$ **e.** $\dfrac{91}{36}$ **f.** $\dfrac{13}{6}$ **g.** $-\dfrac{7}{48\pi}$

h. $40\pi^4$ **4. a.** $\dfrac{dy}{dx} = \dfrac{x - 3}{2\sqrt{1 - x}(1 + x)^2}$

b. $\dfrac{dy}{dx} = \dfrac{-x}{2(2x^2 - x)^{\frac{3}{2}}}$ **5. a.** $y - 32 = 12(x - 4)$

b. $y - 2 = -\dfrac{1}{5}(x - 2)$

c. $7x + 108y - 107 = 0$

6. $y - 3 = \dfrac{1}{24}(x - 4)$ **7. a.** 49.92 km

b. 0.125 km/m

Problems 2.4

2. none

Exercises 2.5

1. a. $y = u^4 + 4u^2$ where $u = 3x^3 + x - 2$

b. $y = 2u^3 - 3u + 5$ where $u = \sqrt{x^2 + 1}$

c. $y = \dfrac{u^2}{1 + u^3}$ where $u = 1 - 2x^{\frac{5}{2}}$

d. $y = u^2\sqrt{1 + u^3}$ where $u = 3 - \frac{2}{\sqrt{x}}$

2. a. 18 b. $\frac{1}{12}$ c. $\frac{6}{\sqrt{14}}$ d. $-\frac{1}{8}$

3. a. $\frac{dy}{dx} = \frac{dy}{du}\left(\frac{-x}{\sqrt{5 - x^2}}\right)$

b. $\frac{dy}{dt} = \frac{dy}{dx} \times \frac{5t^2 + 4t}{2\sqrt{t + 1}}$

c. $\frac{du}{dw} = \frac{du}{dv} \times w^{-\frac{2}{3}}(w^{\frac{1}{3}} + 1)^2$ 4. a. $2y\frac{dy}{dx}$

b. $\frac{1}{3}y^{-\frac{2}{3}}\frac{dy}{dx}$ c. $2x + 2y\frac{dy}{dx}$ d. $y^3 + 3xy^2\frac{dy}{dx}$

5. a. $-48\,608$ b. $-\frac{45}{16}$ c. $\frac{1}{64}$

6. $\frac{dA}{dt} = 60\pi$ cm²/s 7. $\frac{dV}{dt} = 1.08\pi$ m³/s

8. a. $\frac{dT}{dx} = -3$ degrees/cm, $\frac{dx}{dt} = 2$ cm/s

b. $\frac{dT}{dt} = -6$ degrees/s 9. a. $\frac{dV}{dt} = 20$ L/min,

$\frac{dh}{dV} = 0.1$ cm/L b. $\frac{dh}{dt} = 2$ cm/min

10. a. $\frac{3}{4}f'(\frac{1}{8})$ b. $3\left[f\left(\frac{1}{2}\right)\right]^2 \times f'\left(\frac{1}{2}\right)$

c. $2\left(1 + f\left(\frac{1}{2}\right)\right) \times f'\left(\frac{1}{2}\right)$ 11. $\frac{dy}{dx} = 10$

12. a. $\frac{dy}{dx} = -\frac{42}{25}$ b. $\frac{dp}{dt} = -\frac{5}{16}$ c. $\frac{dv}{du} = -9$

13. $\frac{dy}{dx} = -\frac{3}{16}$ 14. $\frac{dy}{dx} = \frac{19}{2\sqrt{3}}$

Problems 2.5

1. 2.67 s, 35.6 m 2. (i) -2 (ii) $g'(-\frac{1}{2})$

3. $f'\left(\frac{p(x)}{q(x)}\right)\left[\frac{p'(x)q(x) - p(x)q'(x)}{(q(x))^2}\right]$

4. b. $\frac{1}{2} - \frac{1}{4x}$

Review Exercises

1. a. $10x^4 - 21x^2 + 3$ b. $18x^{-7}$ c. $-\frac{1}{x^6}$

d. $5 - \frac{6}{x^3}$ e. $44t(11t^2 + 1)$ f. $\frac{8x}{(5 - x^2)^3}$

g. $\frac{1}{2\sqrt{t}} + \frac{t}{\sqrt{t^2}}$ h. $\frac{-3}{(3u + 1)^2} + \frac{2}{(2u + 1)^2}$

i. $\frac{9t}{\sqrt{9t^2 + 4}}$ j. $48t^3(3t^4 - \pi)^3$

k. $\frac{35}{9}x^6(x^7 + 1)^{-\frac{4}{9}}$ l. $6x^4(3x^5 - 2)^{-\frac{3}{5}}$

2. a. x^{-2} b. $2(x^3 - 3x)(3x^2 - 3)$

c. $\frac{11}{2}x^{\frac{9}{2}} - \frac{7}{2}x^{\frac{5}{2}}$ d. $\frac{9}{2}x^{\frac{7}{2}} - \frac{5}{2}x^{\frac{3}{2}}$ e. $\frac{3x - 1}{2\sqrt{x - 1}}$

f. $\frac{-6x^2}{(x^3 - 1)^2}$ g. $\frac{3x^4 - 12x^3 + 4}{(3 - x)^2}$ h. $\frac{2x^{\frac{1}{3}}(x - 10)}{3(2x - 5)^2}$

i. $\frac{1 - 2x}{2\sqrt{(x + 1)(2 - x)}}$ j. $\frac{1}{(x + 1)^2}$

3. a. $\frac{-4x}{(1 + x^2)^2}$ b. $\frac{16}{(x + 1)^3}$

4. a. $(x - 2)^2\left(\frac{1}{2}x + 1\right)^3\left(\frac{7}{2}x - 1\right)$

b. $2x^3(3x - 1)^5(15x - 2)$ c. $\frac{2(2x - 5)^3(13 - x)}{(x + 1)^5}$

d. $3(9x - 1)^3(1 - 10x)^{\frac{1}{2}}(17 - 165x)$

e. $\frac{u^3(3u - 8)}{(3u - 2)^4}$ f. $\frac{1}{3}t^{\frac{2}{3}}(3 - t)(15 - 11t)$

g. $15t^2 + 14t - 2$ h. $\frac{12t(t^3 - 1)^2}{(t^2 + 1)^4}$

i. $\frac{3(\sqrt{x} - 1)^2}{\sqrt{x}(\sqrt{x} + 1)^4}$ j. $\frac{4 - 3t}{2t^3\sqrt{t - 1}}$ 5. a. $-\frac{408}{13}$

b. $-\frac{2}{49}$ c. $-\frac{8}{5}$ d. 12 e. 2 6. a. $\frac{y - x\frac{dy}{dx}}{y^2}$

b. $y^2 + 2xy + (2xy + x^2)\frac{dy}{dx}$ c. $\frac{y^2 - x^2 - 2xy\frac{dy}{dx}}{(x^2 + y^2)^2}$

d. $\frac{x + y\frac{dy}{dx}}{\sqrt{x^2 + y^2}}$ 7. $x + y - 3 = 0$ 8. a. -14

b. $a = -3\sqrt{2}, b = 3\sqrt{2}$

9. a. $\frac{10}{3}\left[\left(\frac{5}{2}\right)^{\frac{2}{3}} - \left(\frac{2}{5}\right)^{\frac{1}{3}}\right] \approx 3.68$ b. 1

10. $y = \sqrt{6}x + \frac{7}{2}$ and $y = -\sqrt{6}x + \frac{7}{2}$

12. 8π, increasing; -25π, decreasing

13. -25, decreasing 14. (i) $\left(\frac{1}{\sqrt{2}}, \frac{3}{\sqrt{2}}\right)$,

$\left(-\frac{1}{\sqrt{2}}, -\frac{3}{\sqrt{2}}\right)$ (ii) None 15. (i) (0, 0)

(ii) $\left(1, \frac{1}{4}\right)$ 16. 176π 17. a $\frac{10}{7}\left(\frac{t}{14} - 2\right)$

b. $-\frac{15}{7}, -\frac{10}{7}$ c. $-\frac{15}{7}$ 18. 9 m/s, 9.91 m/s

19. 0.015 20. a. 300, 35; 720, 5.6

b. in the first month **21.** -4, decreasing

22. a. $\frac{1}{5}x\left(30 - \frac{x}{50}\right)^2$

b. $\frac{1}{5}\left(30 - \frac{x}{50}\right)\left(30 - \frac{3x}{50}\right)$ **c.** (i) increase

(ii) decrease **23. a.** $\frac{1}{2}b\frac{dh}{dt} + \frac{1}{2}\frac{db}{dt}h$

b. -5 cm²/min, decreasing

24. a. $2\pi r\frac{dr}{dt}h + \pi r^2\frac{dh}{dt}$ **b.** 640π cm³/min

25. $\frac{1}{\sqrt{5\pi}}$ cm/min

Chapter 3

Exercises 3.1

1. a. $\frac{-4x}{y}$ **b.** $\frac{3}{8y}$ **c.** $-\frac{2x}{2y+5}$ **d.** $-\frac{y}{2x}$

e. $\frac{x+y}{y-x}$ **f.** $\frac{4}{1+3y^2}$ **g.** $\frac{2xy}{4y^3 - x^2 - 3}$ **h.** $\frac{x-1}{1-y}$

i. $\frac{-y^3 - 3x^2y}{3xy^2 + x^3}$ **j.** $-\sqrt{\frac{y}{x}}$ **2. a.** $\frac{x}{4y}$;

$3x + 4y - 5 = 0$ **b.** $-\frac{x}{2\sqrt{x^2 - 5}}$;

$3x + 4y - 5 = 0$ **3. a.** $2x + 3y + 25 = 0$,
tangent; $3x - 2y + 18 = 0$, normal
b. $5x + 6y + 9 = 0$, tangent;
$18x - 15y + 130 = 0$, normal
c. $x + 4y - 32 = 0$, tangent;
$4x - y - 60 = 0$, normal
d. $x + 7y - 23 = 0$, tangent;
$7x - y - 11 = 0$, normal **e.** $2x + y - 1 = 0$,
tangent; $x - 2y - 3 = 0$, normal
f. $24x + 43y - 225 = 0$, tangent;
$43x - 24y - 100 = 0$, normal
g. $17x - 5y - 14 = 0$, tangent;
$5x + 17y - 78 = 0$, normal **4. a.** $y^2 = 4x$,

$\frac{dy}{dx} = \frac{2}{y}$ **b.** $y^2 = 3 - x$, $\frac{dy}{dx} = -\frac{1}{2y}$ **c.** $y^3 = x$,

$\frac{dy}{dx} = \frac{1}{3y^2}$ **d.** $y^2 = 4 - x^2$, $\frac{dy}{dx} = -\frac{x}{y}$

e. $xy^2 = 9$, $\frac{dy}{dx} = -\frac{y}{2x}$ **f.** $y^2 - 10y + 25 = x$,

$\frac{dy}{dx} = \frac{1}{2y - 10}$ **6.** $y^6 = 65 - x^6$,

$x - 32y - 65 = 0$ **7.** $\left(-\frac{4}{3}, 1\right)$ and

$(-2, -1)$ **8.** $\left(-\frac{9}{5}, \frac{16}{5}\right)$ and $\left(\frac{9}{5}, -\frac{16}{5}\right)$

9. a. $-\frac{v}{p}$ **b.** $-\frac{r}{4h}$ **c.** $\frac{3t^2 - 10t^{\frac{3}{2}} + 8t}{2s}$

d. $\frac{u^2}{1 - 2ux}$

Problems 3.1

1. $(2 - 2\sqrt{5}, \pm 2\sqrt{10\sqrt{5} - 22})$

2. $x = 4$ and $2x - 3y + 10 = 0$

4. $y - b = -\left(\frac{b}{a}\right)^{\frac{1}{3}}(x - a)$; distance is 1 unit

Exercises 3.2

1. a. $v = 10t - 2$, $a = 10$ **b.** $v = 16t^3 - t$,
$a = 48t^2 - 1$ **c.** $v = 6t^2 - 30t + 36$,

$a = 12t - 30$ **d.** $v = 1 - \frac{6}{t^2}$, $a = \frac{12}{t^3}$

e. $v = \frac{t}{2(\sqrt{t} + 1)^3}$, $a = \frac{2 - t}{4(\sqrt{t} + 1)^5}$

f. $v = 3t^2 - 12t + 9$, $a = 6t - 12$

g. $v = 1 - \frac{4}{(t + 2)^2}$, $a = \frac{8}{(t + 2)^3}$

h. $v = \frac{160}{(8 + t)^2}$, $a = -\frac{320}{(8 + t)^3}$ **2. a.** 0 m/s

b. -1 m/s **c.** 2 m/s² **d.** 2 m/s²
3. a. 24 m/s **b.** 28.8 m **c.** $t = 48$ s,
$v = -24$ m/s **4. a.** away at $t = 1$, toward at
$t = 4$ **b.** stopped at $t = 1$, away at $t = 4$
c. toward at $t = 1$, toward at $t = 4$ **d.** away at
$t = 1$, toward at $t = 4$ **5.** $v = -35$ m/s
6. a. 55 s **b.** 65 s **c.** 21 127 m
7. a. (i) 64 (ii) 32 **b.** (i) 5625 (ii) 3125
c. (i) 111.8 (ii) 62.4 **d.** (i) 3456

(ii) 1450.24 **8.** 1; away **9.** $v_1 = -\frac{2}{3}$ m/s,

$v_2 = \frac{35}{3}$ m/s **10.** 400 m **11. a.** $\frac{100}{9}$ s

b. yes, 246.9 m **12. a.** $a = 2k$
b. $t = 5 - 3k$, $s = -9k^3 + 30k^2 - 23k$

Problems 3.2

2. a. $v(t) = \begin{cases} 2t \\ 4 \\ 20 - 2t \end{cases}$ $a(t) = \begin{cases} 2 \\ 0 \\ -2 \end{cases}$

d. 4 m/s; 2 m/s²   **3. b.** $v(t) = 1$, $a(t) = 0$

Exercises 3.3

1. $\dfrac{dA}{dt} = 2\pi r \dfrac{dr}{dt}$ **2. a.** $\dfrac{3}{\pi}$ m/s   **b.** $\dfrac{15}{2\sqrt{10\pi}}$ m/s

3. $-\dfrac{1}{16}$ m/s   **4.** $\dfrac{32}{15}$ m/s   **5.** (i) $\dfrac{5}{72\pi}$

(ii) 0.09 m/min   **6.** 0.145π m³/year

7. 2.51 million dollars/hour   **8.** $\dfrac{5}{\pi}$ m/hour

9. $\dfrac{20}{\pi}$ **10.** $-\dfrac{34}{5}$ km/h, approaching

11. $70\sqrt{2}$ km/h   **12.** $\dfrac{1}{2\pi}$ **13.** $-\dfrac{50}{13}$ km/h

14. $\dfrac{\sqrt{3}}{4}$ m/s   **15.** 0.09 m/min

17. -8.75 g/cm²/s   **18. a.** 0.75 m/s
b. 0.75 m/s   **19. a.** 2.25 m/s   **b.** 2.25 m/s

Problems 3.3

1. 120 m/s   **2. a.** $\dfrac{4}{5\pi}$ cm/s   **b.** $\dfrac{8}{25\pi}$ cm/s

3. $x^2 + y^2 = \dfrac{25}{4}$ **4. a.** $\dfrac{5\sqrt{3}h^2}{72}$

b. $\dfrac{10\sqrt{3}}{3}(15 + h)$ **5.** $\dfrac{1}{2\sqrt{2}}$ m/s

Exercises 3.4

1. a. max 3, min -1 **b.** max 4, min 0
c. max 0, min -4 **d.** max 0, min -20

e. max 8, min -3 **f.** max $\dfrac{16}{3}$, min 0

2. a. max $\dfrac{5}{3}$, min 1   **b.** max 4, min 3

c. max 1, min $\dfrac{1}{2}$ **d.** max $\dfrac{52}{5}$, min 4

e. max 2, min -2 **f.** max $\dfrac{8}{5}$, min $\dfrac{16}{17}$

g. max -6, min $6 - 8\sqrt{3}$

h. max $\dfrac{8}{289}$, min $-\dfrac{1}{64}$ **i.** max $5\sqrt{17}$, min 16

3. a. max $\dfrac{4}{3}$ (m/s), min $\dfrac{4}{5}$ (m/s)

b. max $\dfrac{64}{17}$ (m/s), min 2 (m/s)

4. max $2 + 3\sqrt{3}$, min 2   **5.** 20
6. a. 80 km/h   **b.** 50 km/h   **7.** max 0.0083,

min 0.0063   **8.** 250   **9.** $\dfrac{4}{81}$ years

10. 70 km/h   **11.** 245   **12.** 300

Exercises 3.5

1. 160 000 m²   **2.** 12   **3.** $\dfrac{200}{3} \times \dfrac{200}{3} \times \dfrac{50}{3}$ cm

4. a. 324 000 m²   **b.** 320 000 m²   **5.** width
13.9 cm, depth 19.6 cm   **6.** $h = d = 6.83$,
$h : d = 1 : 1$ **7. a.** 0, 10   **b.** 5, 5
8. 60 m × 122.5 m (60 m wall of glass)

9. $\dfrac{10\sqrt{6}}{3} \times \dfrac{5\sqrt{6}}{3} \times \dfrac{20\sqrt{6}}{9}$ **10.** 12, 12, 12 cm

11. a. $\dfrac{30\ 000}{\pi}$ m   **b.** $8000 - 400\pi$ m

12. \$58 per day   **13.** 4 of 15 cm, 2 of 60 cm
14. c. \$4.50   **15.** 5000 m²   **16. a.** $(\sqrt{17}, 1)$
b. (5, 3)   **c.** PQ is a normal

17. a. $\left(\pm\dfrac{4}{9}, \dfrac{8}{9}\right)$ **b.** $\left(\pm\dfrac{2}{3}, \dfrac{1}{3}\right)$ **c.** (0, 0)

18. 0.75 km   **19.** Paddle directly to the pub.

20. $\dfrac{1}{4\sqrt{6}}$ km from point closest to island

Problems 3.5

2. $2ab$, $2 : \pi$ **3.** $0 \le k \le \dfrac{1}{2}$, $k > \dfrac{1}{2}$

4. $(2\ pm, pm^2)$ **5.** $6\sqrt{3}$

6. a. $\dfrac{3600v}{L} \le n \le 1 + \dfrac{3600v}{L}$ **b.** 12 m/s

Exercises 3.6

1. a. $y = \dfrac{1}{20}x + 5$; 10.05, 10.1, 10.15, 10.2

b. too large   **2.** (i) $y = \dfrac{1}{16}x + 4$, 7.875

(ii) $y = \frac{1}{20}x + 5$, 9.85

(iii) $y = \frac{1}{200}x + 50$, 100.84

(iv) $y = \frac{1}{24}x + 6$, 12.125

3. $y = \frac{1}{300}x + \frac{20}{3}$; 9.933, 9.967, 10.033,

10.067   **4.** 1.9953   **5.** 2.006, 1.997, 1.014,

1.15   **6.** 40π cm^3 **7.** 0.28 cm

8. 0.855 cm^2 **9.** near $x = 0$

Problems 3.6

2. $1 + \frac{1}{n}x$

Exercises 3.7
1. b. $x_0 = 2$, $x_1 = 1.75$, $x_2 = 1.732\ 142\ 857$,
$x_3 = 1.732\ 050\ 81$, $x_4 = 1.732\ 050\ 808$
2. b. 2.1855   **c.** -2.3×10^{-8}
3. a. 1.148 698   **b.** $-0.429\ 467\ 7$
c. 0.258 652 022   **4. b.** $x_1 = 1.220\ 744$ and
$x_2 = -0.724\ 492$ **5.** 0.347 30,
$f(x^*) = -9.61 \times 10^{-5}$ **6.** 33, 8.644
7. $x = 0.453\ 397\ 652$ **8. a.** 1.179 433
b. 1.800 684   **9.** 0.509 595 5
10. b. 1.258 925 4

Review Exercises
1. a. $-\frac{2}{3}$ **b.** $\frac{7}{15}$ **c.** -4 **d.** 7   **2. a.** 2
b. $(2\sqrt{3}, \sqrt{3}), (-2\sqrt{3}, -\sqrt{3})$
3. $\left(\frac{\sqrt{6}}{4}, \pm\frac{\sqrt{2}}{4}\right), \left(-\frac{\sqrt{6}}{4}, \pm\frac{\sqrt{2}}{4}\right)$
4. a. $x + 3y - 5 = 0$ **b.** $(6, -3)$
5. a. $-\pi(2hr + r^2)$ cm^3/month
b. -1975π cm^3/month   **c.** $\frac{101}{49}$
6. (2599.74) k   **8.** $5\sqrt{2}$
9. a. $v(t) = 12t^3 - 48t^2 + 48t$,

$a(t) = 36t^2 - 96t + 48$ **b.** 0, 2   **c.** 0   **d.** $\frac{128}{9}$
10. towards   **11. a.** positive: $0 < t < 2$ and
$4 < t < 5$, negative: $2 < t < 4$ **b.** $2 < t < 3$
and $4 < t < 5$ **c.** 2, 4   **12.** decreasing,
$-\frac{15}{4}$ m/s   **13.** (i) $\frac{\sqrt{101}}{20}$ m/s   (ii) $\frac{\sqrt{5}}{4}$ m/s
14. $36\sqrt{3}$ **15.** $1 \times 1 \times 1$ **16.** 32
17. a. 62 m   **b.** yes (by 2 m)   **18.** \$25
19. $\frac{3}{20}$ m/s   **20.** $\frac{200}{7}$ m $\times$ 70 m
21. a. $40\sqrt{5}$ km/h   **b.** 80 km/h   **c.** no
22. no, 78.26 km/h   **23.** 135 items
24. $a = 0.770\ 917$ **25.** farther away, 8 cm/s
26. height $\frac{2\sqrt{3}R}{3}$ and radius $\frac{\sqrt{6}}{3}R$

Chapter 4

Exercises 4.1
1. a. $(2, -7)$ **b.** $\left(\frac{3}{2}, \frac{35}{2}\right)$ **c.** $(-2, 16)$,
$(2, -16)$ **d.** $(-2, -4), (-1, -5)$ **e.** none
f. none   **g.** $(0, 3), (3, 57)$ **h.** none
i. $(0, 4)$ **j.** $(-2, -80), (2, 48), (3, 45)$
k. $(1, -1)$ **l.** $(-4, -128), (0, 0), (1, -3)$
m. none   **n.** $(-2, 28\sqrt{2}), (2, -28\sqrt{2})$
3. $a = -2, b = 2, c = 3$ **4. a.** $M = 45$,
$m = -7$ **b.** local min $\left(\frac{3}{2}, -17\right)$, local max
$\left(-\frac{3}{2}, 37\right)$, $M = 158, m = -138$
c. local min $(0, 0)$, $M = 19, m = 0$
5. (59.83, 27.36)   **6. a.** (i) increasing for
$x < 3$, decreasing for $x > 3$ (ii) local max at
$x = 3$ **b.** (i) increasing for $x < -2$ or $x > 0$,
decreasing for $-2 < x < 0$ (ii) local max at
$x = -2$, local min at $x = 0$ **c.** (i) increasing
for $-1 < x < 2$, decreasing for $x < -1$ or
$x > 2$ (ii) local max at $x = 2$, local min at
$x = -1$ **9. a.** $f(3)$ **b.** not possible
c. $f(-10)$ **d.** not possible   **e.** $f(5)$
f. not possible.

10.

	Increasing	Decreasing
a.	$x > \dfrac{1}{2}$	$x < \dfrac{1}{2}$
b.	$x > 2,\ x < -1$	$-1 < x < 2$
c.	$x \neq \dfrac{5}{2}$	never
d.	$0 < x < 1,\ x > 2$	$x < 0,\ 1 < x < 2$
e.	$x \neq 0$ and $x < 1$ or $x > 2$	$1 < x < 2$
f.	$x \neq 1$ $x \neq -1$	never

11. $a = 3,\ b = 2$ **12.** $a = \dfrac{3}{2},\ b = -\dfrac{9}{2}$, $c = 0,\ d = 2$

Problems 4.1

1. Case 1. $b > \dfrac{a^2}{3}$ Case 2. $b = \dfrac{a^2}{3}$

Case 3. $b < \dfrac{a^2}{3}$ **2.** f and g intersect at most in one point **4. a.** $1.179\ 509\ 025$

Exercises 4.2

1. a. $+\infty$ **b.** $-\infty$ **c.** $+\infty$ **d.** $-\infty$ **e.** $+\infty$
f. $+\infty$ **g.** $-\infty$ **h.** $+\infty$ **i.** $+\infty$ **j.** $-\infty$
k. $-\infty$ **1.** $+\infty$ **2. a.** $\lim\limits_{x \to 0^+} f(x) = +\infty$,

$\lim\limits_{x \to 0^-} f(x) = -\infty$ **b.** $\lim\limits_{x \to 0} f(x) = +\infty$,

c. $\lim\limits_{x \to 0^+} f(x) = -\infty$, $\lim\limits_{x \to 0^-} f(x) = +\infty$

d. $\lim\limits_{x \to 0^+} f(x) = -\infty$, $\lim\limits_{x \to 0^-} f(x) = +\infty$

e. $\lim\limits_{x \to 3^+} f(x) = +\infty$, $\lim\limits_{x \to 3^-} f(x) = -\infty$

f. $\lim\limits_{x \to 3} f(x) = +\infty$, **g.** $\lim\limits_{x \to -3^+} f(x) = -\infty$,

$\lim\limits_{x \to -3^-} f(x) = +\infty$ **h.** $\lim\limits_{x \to 3} f(x) = -\infty$

i. $\lim\limits_{x \to 2^+} f(x) = +\infty$, $\lim\limits_{x \to 2^-} f(x) = -\infty$,

$\lim\limits_{x \to -1^+} f(x) = +\infty$, $\lim\limits_{x \to -1^-} f(x) = -\infty$,

j. $\lim\limits_{x \to \frac{2}{3}^+} f(x) = +\infty$, $\lim\limits_{x \to \frac{2}{3}^-} f(x) = -\infty$,

$\lim\limits_{x \to -\frac{2}{3}^+} f(x) = -\infty$, $\lim\limits_{x \to -\frac{2}{3}^-} f(x) = +\infty$

k. $\lim\limits_{x \to 0^+} f(x) = +\infty$, $\lim\limits_{x \to 0^-} f(x) = -\infty$,

$\lim\limits_{x \to 2^+} f(x) = +\infty$, $\lim\limits_{x \to 2^-} f(x) = -\infty$

l. $\lim\limits_{x \to 0^+} f(x) = -\infty$, $\lim\limits_{x \to 0^-} f(x) = +\infty$,

$\lim\limits_{x \to 1} f(x) = -\infty$

Problems 4.2

3. a. $\lim\limits_{x \to a^+} f(x) = +\infty$, $\lim\limits_{x \to a^-} f(x) = +\infty$

b. $\lim\limits_{x \to a^+} f(x) = -\infty$, $\lim\limits_{x \to a^-} f(x) = -\infty$

c. $\lim\limits_{x \to a^+} f(x) = +\infty$, $\lim\limits_{x \to a^-} f(x) = -\infty$

d. $\lim\limits_{x \to a^+} f(x) = -\infty$, $\lim\limits_{x \to a^-} f(x) = +\infty$

4. Domain $= \{x \in R \mid x < 2 \text{ or } x > 3\}$

Exercises 4.3

1.

	Horizontal asymptote	Direction of approach	
		$x \to +\infty$	$x \to -\infty$
a.	$y = 0$	below	above
b.	$y = 0$	above	above
c.	$y = 0$	above	below
d.	$y = 0$	below	above
e.	$y = 0$	above	above
f.	$y = 2$	above	below
g.	$y = -\dfrac{5}{2}$	below	above
h.	$y = -\dfrac{3}{2}$	above	below

2. a. $x = 1,\ y = 0$ **b.** $x = -2,\ y = 0$

c. $x = 3,\ y = 2$ **d.** $x = \dfrac{3}{4},\ y = 1$

3.

	$\lim\limits_{x\to+\infty} f(x)$	$\lim\limits_{x\to-\infty} f(x)$
a.	$-\infty$	$+\infty$
b.	$+\infty$	$-\infty$
c.	$-\dfrac{3}{4}$	$-\dfrac{3}{4}$
d.	$-\infty$	$-\infty$
e.	3	3
f.	$+\infty$	$-\infty$
g.	0	0
h.	$-\infty$	$-\infty$
i.	$-\infty$	$+\infty$
j.	$\dfrac{7}{8}$	$\dfrac{7}{8}$

4. a. $x = \pm 1,\ y = 0$ **b.** $x = \pm 1,\ y = 0$
c. $x = \pm 1,\ y = 0$ **d.** $x = -1,\ y = 3$
e. $x = -2,\ y = -\dfrac{1}{3}$ **f.** $x = 0,\ y = -3$
g. $x = 0,\ y = \dfrac{1}{2}$ **h.** $x = 1,\ y = -3$
i. $x = \pm 1,\ y = 2$ **j.** $x = 0,\ x = -1,\ y = 1$
5. local min $\left(3 + \sqrt{10},\ \dfrac{4 + 4\sqrt{10}}{9}\right)$, local min
$\left(3 - \sqrt{10},\ \dfrac{4 - 4\sqrt{10}}{9}\right);\ (3, 2)$
6. a. $(-1,\ -3)$ **b.** $\left(\dfrac{1}{2},\ 2\right)$ **7.** $y = \dfrac{a}{c}$

Problems 4.3
1. b. -3 **2. a.** $\lim\limits_{x\to+\infty} f(x) = 1$,
$\lim\limits_{x\to-\infty} f(x) = -1$ **b.** $\lim\limits_{x\to+\infty} f(x) = -\dfrac{2}{3}$,
$\lim\limits_{x\to-\infty} f(x) = \dfrac{2}{3}$ **c.** $\lim\limits_{x\to+\infty} f(x) = \dfrac{3}{2}$,
$\lim\limits_{x\to-\infty} f(x) = -\dfrac{3}{2}$

Exercises 4.4
1.

	Local extrema	Increasing	Decreasing
a.	$\left(\sqrt{3}, \dfrac{2\sqrt{3}}{3}\right),$ $\left(-\sqrt{3}, \dfrac{-2\sqrt{3}}{3}\right)$	$x < -\sqrt{3},$ $x > \sqrt{3}$	$-\sqrt{3} < x < 0,$ $0 < x < \sqrt{3}$
b.		$x \in R,\ x \neq 0$	
c.	$(-1,\ -3)$	$x < -1, x > 0$	$-1 < x < 0$
d.	$\left(\sqrt{3}, \dfrac{2\sqrt{3}}{9}\right),$ $\left(-\sqrt{3}, \dfrac{-2\sqrt{3}}{9}\right)$	$-\sqrt{3} < x < 0,$ $0 < x < \sqrt{3}$	$x < -\sqrt{3},$ $x > \sqrt{3}$
e.	$\left(2, \dfrac{1}{4}\right)$	$0 < x < 2$	$x < 0, x > 2$
f.	$(-1, 1),\ (3, 9)$	$x < -1, x > 3$	$-1 < x < 0,$ $1 < x < 3$
g.	$(4, 1)$	$-4 < x < 4$	$x < -4, x > 4$
h.	$(-3, 27)$	$-3 < x < -2,$ $x > -2$	$x < -3$

2. a. $y = \dfrac{1}{3}x$ **b.** $y = \dfrac{1}{3}x$ **c.** $y = 2x$
d. $y = \dfrac{1}{x}$ **e.** $y = \dfrac{1}{x}$ **f.** $y = x$ **g.** $y = \dfrac{1}{x}$
h. $y = x^2$ **4.** Even: $d,\ l,\ m$; Odd: $c,\ n$
7. a. $y = 2 + \dfrac{1}{x}$ **b.** $y = \dfrac{1}{x - 1}$
c. $y = \dfrac{x^2}{(x + 1)(x - 2)}$ **d.** $y = 2x + \dfrac{1}{x}$

Exercises 4.5
1. a. $5x^3$ **b.** 6 **c.** $60x^3 + 30x$ **d.** 0
e. $\dfrac{3}{4}x^{-\frac{1}{2}} - \dfrac{1}{4}x^{-\frac{3}{2}}$ **f.** $\dfrac{6}{x^3}$ **g.** $-\dfrac{9}{4}(4 - 3x)^{-\frac{3}{2}}$
h. $12(1 - 3x)^{-3}$ **i.** $\dfrac{6x^2 - 8}{(x^2 + 4)^3}$ **j.** $\dfrac{12(x - 5)}{x^6}$
2. a. $6x^4$ **b.** $\dfrac{20}{9}t^{-\frac{1}{3}}$ **c.** $360(2x - 6)^8$
d. $\dfrac{54}{(3t - 2)^4}$ **e.** $8(t^2 + \pi^2)^2(7t^2 + \pi^2)$
f. $3(5 - 2v)^{-\frac{5}{2}}$ **g.** $2 - \dfrac{2}{(10 - t)^3}$ **h.** $\dfrac{-4}{(4 - u^2)^{\frac{3}{2}}}$
3. a. 24, above   **b.** 180, above   **c.** $\dfrac{5}{2}$, above

d. $\frac{20}{27}$, above

4.

	Concave upward	Concave downward	P.O.I.
a.	$x \in R$		
b.		$x \in R$	
c.	$x > 0$	$x < 0$	$(0, 0)$
d.	$x > -\frac{3}{2}$	$x < -\frac{3}{2}$	$\left(-\frac{3}{2}, -\frac{9}{2}\right)$
e.	$x > 0$	$x < 0$	$(0, -4)$
f.	$x > -1$	$x < -1$	$(-1, -1)$
g.	$x < \frac{3}{2}$	$x > \frac{3}{2}$	$\left(\frac{3}{2}, 30\right)$
h.		$x \in R$	
i.	$x < 0, x > \frac{2}{3}$	$0 < x < \frac{2}{3}$	$\left(\frac{2}{3}, -\frac{16}{27}\right)$ $(0, 0)$
j.	$x < 0$	$x > 0$	$(0, 5)$

6.

	Concave upward	Concave downward	P.O.I.
a.	$x < 1$	$x > 1$	$x = 1$
b.	$x < 0, x > 2$	$0 < x < 2$	$x = 0, x = 2$
c.	$x < 0,$ $0 < x < 1$	$x > 1$	$x = 1$
d.	$-2 < x < 0$ $0 < x < 2$ $x > 4$	$x < -2$ $2 < x < 4$	$x = -2$ $x = 2$ $x = 4$

9. $a = 3, b = 1$ **10.** $\frac{27}{64}$ **11. a.** $a > 0$

b. $a < 0$ **12. a.** $x = 0, -3$ **b.** $x = 0, \pm \sqrt{5}$

c. $x = 0, -\frac{2}{3}$ **d.** $x = -3, \pm 2$

13. a. $f'(2)$ **b.** $f'(1)$ **c.** $f'(3)$
d. impossible to determine   **e.** $f'(-7)$
f. impossible to determine

Problems 4.5

1. $a = -\frac{1}{4}, b = 0, c = 3, d = 0$

2. $p''(x)q(x) + 2p'(x)q'(x) + p(x)q''(x)$
3. -10 **6.** $3a^2 \le 8b; 3a^2 > 8b$

Exercises 4.6

2.

	(i)	(ii) positive	(iii) increasing	(iv)
a.	1, 3	$t < 1, t > 3$	$t > 2$	124
b.	1, 3	$t < 1, t > 3$	$t > 2$	62
c.	1	$t \ne 1$	$t > 1$	126
d.	3	$t > 3$	$t > 0$	1134
e.	0, 2	$t > 0, t \ne 2$	$0 < t < \frac{2}{3},$ $t > 2$	1296

3.

	v	a	I/D
a.	$+$	$-$	D
b.	$-$	$-$	I
c.	$+$	$+$	I
d.	$-$	$+$	D

4. a. (i) $t = 6$ (ii) $v > 0$ when $0 < t < 6$, $v < 0$ when $6 < t < 9$ (iii) $t = 3$ (iv) $a > 0$ when $0 < t < 3$, $a < 0$ when $3 < t < 9$ (v) speeding up when $0 < t < 3$, slowing down when $3 < t < 9$ **b.** (i) $t = 0, 4, 8$ (ii) $v > 0$ when $4 < t < 8$, $v < 0$ when $0 < t < 4$ (iii) $t = 2, 6$ (iv) $a > 0$ when $2 < t < 6$, $a < 0$ when $0 < t < 2$ and $6 < t < 8$ (v) speeding up when $a > 0$, slowing down when $a < 0$

6. (ii) $t = \frac{4}{3}\sqrt{6}$ **7.** max when $t = 4$, most

rapidly spreading when $t = 4 - \frac{4}{3}\sqrt{6}$

8. a. 11 000   **b.** $t = \frac{10\sqrt{3}}{3}$ **9. a.** min

$(5, -22)$ **b.** min $(2, -11)$, max $(-2, 21)$
c. min $(0, 2)$ and $(3, -25)$, max $(1, 7)$
d. min $(3, 6)$, max $(-3, -6)$ **e.** min $(2, 8)$,

and $(-2, 8)$ **f.** max $(0, 1)$, min at $x = \pm\frac{1}{2}$

g. max $(-3, 216)$ and $(1, 8)$, min $(-1, -88)$
and $(3, -216)$ **h.** min $(3, 27)$ **10. a.** min

$\left(\frac{3}{2}, -\frac{27}{16}\right)$ **b.** max $\left(k, \frac{1}{2k}\right)$, min $\left(-k, -\frac{1}{2k}\right)$

c. no local extrema **d.** min $(1, -4)$, max

$(-1, 4)$ **e.** min $\left(2, \frac{1}{2}\right)$, max $(-1, 2)$

f. max $(0, 1)$, min at $x = \pm\frac{1}{2}$ **g.** max

$\left(\frac{3\sqrt{2}}{2}, \frac{9}{2}\right)$, min $\left(-\frac{3\sqrt{2}}{2}, -\frac{9}{2}\right)$

Problems 4.6

1. 1.5 **2.** $f'\left(\frac{2\sqrt{2}\,a}{3}\right) = 0$, and

$f''\left(\frac{2\sqrt{2}\,a}{3}\right) = -32a$

Exercises 4.7

1. a. min $(-1, 0)$ cusp, min $(1, 0)$ cusp,
max $(0, 1)$ **b.** min $(0, 0)$ cusp, min

$(1, 0)$ cusp, max $\left(\frac{1}{2}, \frac{1}{4}\right)$ **c.** min $(1, 0)$ cusp

d. $(0, 0)$ cusp **e.** max $(0, 0)$ cusp **f.** max

$(-1, 0)$ cusp, min $\left(-\frac{1}{2}, -\frac{1}{4}\right)$ **2. a.** cusp

$(0,0)$, $f'(0)$ DNE, $f''(0)$ DNE **b.** $f'(0)$ DNE,
$f''(0)$ DNE, P.O.I. $(0, 8)$ **c.** $f'(1)$ DNE,
$f''(1)$ DNE, P.O.I. $(1, 0)$ **d.** $f''(0)$ DNE,
min $(0, -1)$ **e.** $f''(2)$ DNE, P.O.I. $(2, 0)$
f. $f''(2)$ DNE, max $(2, 0)$

Problems 4.7

1. a. $\lim_{x \to +\infty} f(x) = 1$, $\lim_{x \to -\infty} f(x) = -1$

2. a. $y = \frac{3}{2}$, $y = -\frac{3}{2}$ **b.** $x = 1$, $y = 3$,

$y = -3$ **c.** $x = -1$, $y = 1$, $y = -1$
d. $x = 1$, $y = 1$, $y = -1$

Review Exercises

1. a. min $(-2, 11)$, $(1, -16)$, max $(-1, 16)$

2. a. $x = 1$, $y = 2$ **b.** $x = 3$ **c.** $x = 2$
d. $x = 2$, $y = 1$ **e.** $x = -1$ **f.** $x = 2$

g. $x = \pm\frac{3}{2}$, $y = \frac{1}{4}$ **h.** $x = -2$, $x = 1$,

$y = 1$ **3. a.** none **b.** $x = 3 \pm \sqrt{2}$ **c.** none

d. none **e.** $(-2, 8)$ **f.** $\left(-2, -\frac{1}{8}\right)$

g. $\left(0, -\frac{1}{9}\right)$ **h.** $\left(\frac{1}{7}, -\frac{40}{9}\right)$, $(3, 0)$

4. a. $f(x) = \frac{6(x-1)(x-2)}{(x-3)(x-4)}$ **b.** $f(x) = \frac{2}{(x-1)^2}$

5. 4 **6.** $a = 1$, $b = 0$ **7. a.** $N'(t) < 0$,
$N''(t) > 0$ **b.** $C'(t) > 0$, $C''(t) < 0$
c. $P'(t) > 0$, $P''(t) > 0$ **d.** $U'(t) = 0$,
$U''(t) = 0$ **8.** $a = 2$, $b = -6$, $c = 0$, $d = 3$
9. min $(4, 6)$, max $(0, -2)$, no points of
intersection **11. a.** $x_1 < x < x_2$, $x > x_5$
b. $x_2 < x < x_3$ **c.** $x < x_1$, $x_4 < x < x_5$
d. $x_3 < x < x_4$ **12. a.** increasing when
$-3 < x < 2$, $x \neq -1$; decreasing when
$x < -3$, $x > 2$; concave upward when $x < -2$,
$-1 < x < 1$; concave downward when
$-2 < x < -1$, $x > 1$ **b.** local extrema at
$x = -3, 2$; P.O.I at $x = -2, -1, 1$
13. a. $x = -1$, $y = 0$ **b.** $(0, 1)$ **c.** two
14. a. false, $f(x) = (x - 2)^3$ **b.** true
c. false, $f(x) = (x - 1)^4$ **d.** false,

$f(x) = \frac{x^2}{x + 1}$ **15.** $y = x(x + 1)(x - 2)$;

$x = \frac{1 \pm \sqrt{7}}{3}$ **16. a.** $y = \frac{-2x}{x + 1}$

b. $y = \frac{x^2}{2(x - 2)}$ **c.** $y = \frac{2x^2}{x^2 + 1}$

17. a. $(-2, -1)$, $(0, 1)$, $(2, 3)$ **b.** $x < -2$,
$0 < x < 2$ **18. a.** $(-1, 0)$ **b.** $(-1, -1)$
c. $(-2, 0)$, $(-1, 1)$, $(0, 0)$ **19. a.** $(0, 0)$,
$(2, 0)$ **b.** $(0, 0)$

Chapter 5

Exercises 5.1

1. a. $\frac{1}{\sqrt{2}}$ **b.** $\frac{1}{\sqrt{2}}$ **c.** $-\frac{1}{\sqrt{2}}$ **d.** $\frac{1}{2}$ **e.** $\frac{1}{2}$

f. $\frac{1}{\sqrt{2}}$ g. 0 h. $-\frac{\sqrt{3}}{2}$ i. 0 **2. a.** $-\sin\theta$

b. $\sin\theta$ **c.** $-\sin\theta$ **3. a.** $-\cos\theta$ **b.** $\cos\theta$

c. $-\cos\theta$ **4. a.** π **b.** 4π **c.** 2 **d.** 4

e. 2π **f.** π **g.** 2π **h.** 2 **i.** $\frac{\pi}{2}$ **j.** π

k. $\frac{\pi}{2}$ **l.** π **8. a.** $\frac{1}{\sin\theta\cos\theta}$ **b.** $\frac{1-\sin\theta}{\cos\theta}$

c. $\frac{1}{\sin^2\theta\cos^2\theta}$ **d.** $\sin^2\theta - \cos^2\theta$

9. a. $-\frac{12}{13}$, $-\frac{5}{12}$ **b.** $-\frac{2\sqrt{2}}{3}$, $-2\sqrt{2}$

c. $-\frac{1}{\sqrt{5}}$, $-\frac{2}{\sqrt{5}}$ **d.** $-\frac{\sqrt{3}}{2}$, $\sqrt{3}$

e. $\frac{3}{\sqrt{10}}$, $-\frac{1}{\sqrt{10}}$ **f.** $\frac{\sqrt{2}}{\sqrt{3}}$, $-\frac{1}{\sqrt{2}}$

Problems 5.1

1. a. $20\sqrt{13 - 6\sqrt{2}} \approx 42.5$ km

b. $r = 40t\sqrt{13 - 6\sqrt{2}}$ **5. a.** $\frac{\sqrt{3}}{2}a$ **b.** a

6. f is not continuous at the integer values of t

Exercises 5.2

1. a. $\frac{1+\sqrt{3}}{2\sqrt{2}}$ **b.** $\frac{\sqrt{3}-1}{2\sqrt{2}}$ **c.** $\frac{-1-\sqrt{3}}{2\sqrt{2}}$

2. a. $\frac{1+\sqrt{3}}{2\sqrt{2}}$ **b.** $\frac{1-\sqrt{3}}{2\sqrt{2}}$ **c.** $\frac{-1-\sqrt{3}}{2\sqrt{2}}$

4. a. $\frac{\sqrt{3}}{2}\cos x + \frac{1}{2}\sin x$

b. $-\frac{1}{\sqrt{2}}(\cos x + \sin x)$ **c.** $\frac{1}{\sqrt{2}}(\cos x + \sin x)$

d. $-\sin x$ **5. a.** $\sin 3x$ **b.** $\cos x$ **c.** $\sin 2x$

d. $\cos 5x$ **6. a.** $-\frac{\sqrt{15} + 2\sqrt{2}}{12}$ **b.** $\frac{1 - 2\sqrt{30}}{12}$

c. $-\frac{7}{9}$ **d.** $-\frac{\sqrt{15}}{8}$ **e.** $\frac{17}{81}$ **f.** $-\frac{7\sqrt{15}}{32}$

7. a. $\frac{-2 - \sqrt{2}}{\sqrt{15}}$ **b.** $\frac{1 - 2\sqrt{2}}{\sqrt{15}}$ **c.** $\frac{-3 - 4\sqrt{2}}{5\sqrt{3}}$

d. $\frac{1 + 4\sqrt{2}}{3\sqrt{5}}$ **9. a.** $\frac{3}{5}$ **b.** $\frac{4}{5}$; first

10. a. $\frac{\sqrt{3} - 1}{2\sqrt{2}}$ **b.** $\frac{\sqrt{3} - 1}{2\sqrt{2}}$ **11.** $\frac{4}{5}, \frac{3}{5}$

Exercises 5.3

3. a. $-\frac{7\pi}{4}$, $-\frac{\pi}{4}$, $\frac{\pi}{4}$, $\frac{7\pi}{4}$ **b.** $-\frac{\pi}{3}$, $-\frac{\pi}{6}$,

$\frac{5\pi}{6}$, $\frac{11\pi}{6}$ **c.** $\frac{\pi}{2}k$, k any integer **d.** no

solution **e.** $\frac{\pi}{6}$, $\frac{5\pi}{6}$, $\frac{13\pi}{6}$, $\frac{17\pi}{6}$, $\frac{3\pi}{2}$, $\frac{7\pi}{2}$

f. $\frac{\pi}{3}$, $\frac{5\pi}{3}$ **g.** $0.3218 + k\pi$, k any integer

h. πk, k any integer; $\pm\frac{\pi}{3} + 2\pi k$, k any

integer **4. a.** $(0, 0)$, $\left(\frac{\pi}{3}, \frac{\sqrt{3}}{2}\right)$, $(\pi, 0)$,

$\left(\frac{5\pi}{3}, -\frac{\sqrt{3}}{2}\right)$, $(2\pi, 0)$ **b.** $(0, 0)$, $\left(\frac{\pi}{4}, 1\right)$,

$\left(\frac{3\pi}{4}, -1\right)$, $(\pi, 0)$, $\left(\frac{5\pi}{4}, 1\right)$, $\left(\frac{7\pi}{4}, -1\right)$,

$(2\pi, 0)$ **c.** $\left(-\frac{\pi}{2}, -1\right)$, $\left(\frac{\pi}{6}, \frac{1}{2}\right)$, $\left(\frac{5\pi}{6}, \frac{1}{2}\right)$

d. $(0, 0)$, $\left(\frac{2\pi}{3}, \sqrt{3}\right)$ **e.** $(0, 0)$, $\left(\frac{\pi}{4}, \frac{1}{\sqrt{2}}\right)$,

$\left(\frac{3\pi}{4}, \frac{1}{\sqrt{2}}\right)$, $(\pi, 0)$, $\left(\frac{5\pi}{4}, -\frac{1}{\sqrt{2}}\right)$,

$\left(\frac{7\pi}{4}, -\frac{1}{\sqrt{2}}\right)$, $(2\pi, 0)$

Problems 5.3

2. $0 + 2\pi k$, k any integer; $\frac{5\pi}{6} + 2\pi k$, k any

integer **3. a.** $\frac{\tan A - \tan B}{1 + \tan A \tan B}$ **b.** $\frac{\pi}{4}$

Exercises 5.4

1. a. $-12\sin 4x$ **b.** $-3\sin\left(3x + \frac{\pi}{2}\right)$

c. $-6x^2\sin(2x^3)$ **d.** $-6\cos^2(2x)\sin(2x)$

e. $-(2x + 1)\sin(x^2 + x)$

f. $2(x + \cos x)(1 - \sin x)$

g. $-\pi\sin\left(\pi x + \frac{1}{\pi}\right)$

h. $-\pi\sin(\pi x)$ **i.** $2\pi\cos(\pi x) + 2x$

j. $6x\cos(x^2 - 1)$ **k.** $3\sin 2x$

l. $3(\sin 2x + \cos x)^2(2\cos 2x - \sin x)$ **m.** $\sec y$

2. a. $-48\cos(4x)$ **b.** $-9\cos\left(3x + \frac{\pi}{2}\right)$

c. $-36x^4\cos(2x^3) - 12x\sin(2x^3)$

d. $24\cos(2x)\sin^2(2x) - 12\cos^3(2x)$

e. $-(2x + 1)^2 \cos(x^2 + x) - 2 \sin(x^2 + x)$

f. $2(1 - \sin x)^2 - 2 \cos x(x + \cos x)$

g. $-\pi^2 \cos\left(\pi x + \dfrac{1}{\pi}\right)$ **h.** $-\pi^2 \cos(\pi x)$

i. $2 - 2\pi^2 \sin(\pi x)$

j. $6\cos(x^2 - 1) - 12x^2 \sin(x^2 - 1)$ **k.** $6\cos 2x$

l. $6(\sin 2x + \cos x)(2 \cos 2x - \sin x)^2 +$
$3(\sin 2x + \cos x)^2(-4 \sin 2x - \cos x)$

m. $\sec^2 y \tan y$ **3. a.** $\cos x - x \sin x$

b. $3u^2 \sin(2u) + 2u^3 \cos(2u)$

c. $2y \cos(3y^3) - 9y^4 \sin(3y^3)$

d. $-\pi \sin(\pi u) \cos(\cos(\pi u))$ **e.** $\cos 2x$

f. $2 \sec^2(2t)$ **g.** $\dfrac{1}{2\sqrt{t}} \sin(2\sqrt{t})$

h. $\dfrac{1}{2}(1 + \cos t + \sin^2 t)^{-\frac{1}{2}}(2 \sin t \cos t - \sin t)$

i. $2\pi \sin(\pi y) \cos^2(\pi y) - \pi \sin^3(\pi y)$

j. $\cos x \sin 2x \sin 3x + 2 \sin x \cos 2x \sin 3x +$
$3 \sin x \sin 2x \cos 3x$ **k.** $\dfrac{5}{2} \sin(10t)(2 + \sin^2 5t)^{-\frac{1}{2}}$

l. $2(u + \sin(3u))(1 + 3 \cos(3u))$

m. $\dfrac{2x(2 - \cos \pi x) - \pi x^2 \sin \pi x}{(2 - \cos \pi x)^2}$ **n.** $-\dfrac{1}{t^2} \cos\left(\dfrac{1}{t}\right)$

o. $2 \cos(2y)(1 + \sin(2y))^{-2}$

p. $3(x^2 + \cos^2 x)(2x - \sin 2x)$

4. a. $-A \sin(Ax + B)$

b. $-nAB \cos^{n-1}(Bx) \sin(Bx)$

c. $mnx^{n-1} \sin^{m-1}(x^n) \cos(x^n)$

d. $Anx^{n-1} \sin^m Bx + mABx^n \sin^{m-1}(Bx) \cos(Bx)$

5.

	Maximum	Minimum
a.	$\sqrt{3} + \dfrac{\pi}{6}$	$-2 - \pi$
b.	$\sqrt{3} - \dfrac{\pi}{3}$	$-\sqrt{3} - \dfrac{5\pi}{3}$
c.	4π	0
d.	1	-3
e.	2	$-\dfrac{1}{4}$
f.	$\dfrac{\pi}{2}$	-1

6. a. $6x + 8y - 3\pi = 0$ **b.** $x + y - 2 = 0$

7. $\dfrac{\pi}{3}$ **9. a.** $y = x$, below

b. $6\sqrt{3}x - 12y = 2\sqrt{3}\pi - 9$, below

c. $\pi x - \sqrt{2}y - \dfrac{\pi}{2} - 1 = 0$, above

Problems 5.4

1. too large   **2.** $L(x) = \sqrt{2}\, x - 1$,

$L(1.5) = \dfrac{3\sqrt{2}}{2} - 1 \approx 1.121\,32$ **3. a.** $a = 1$,

$b = 0,\ c = -\dfrac{1}{2}$ **4. c.** infinite   **5. a.** $\dfrac{\pi}{180}$

b. 0 **c.** $\dfrac{\pi}{180}\cos x,\ -\dfrac{\pi}{180}\sin x$

Exercises 5.5

1. a. 2   **b.** 2   **2. a.** 3   **b.** π **c.** 1   **d.** 10

e. $\dfrac{1}{2}$ **f.** 2   **g.** $\dfrac{3}{4}$ **h.** $\dfrac{3}{4}$ **i.** 0   **j.** 1

Exercises 5.6

1. a. $2 \sec^2 x - 2 \sec^2(2x)$

b. $12x \sec(2x^2 + 1) \tan(2x^2 + 1)$

c. $15 \sec(5x) \tan(5x)[\tan^2(5x) + 2 \sec^2(5x)]$

d. $\dfrac{x + \sec^2 x \tan x}{\sqrt{x^2 + \sec^2 x}}$ **e.** $\dfrac{2x \tan(\pi x) - \pi x^2 \sec^2(\pi x)}{\tan^2(\pi x)}$

f. $2x \sec^2(x^2) - 2 \tan x \sec^2 x$

g. $\dfrac{1}{2} \sec\sqrt{x}\left(\tan\sqrt{x} + x^{-\frac{1}{2}}\right)$

h. $2x \tan\left(\dfrac{1}{x}\right) - \sec^2\left(\dfrac{1}{x}\right)$ **i.** $\dfrac{y \sec^2(xy)}{1 - x \sec^2(xy)}$

j. $\dfrac{y \sec^2 x - \tan y}{x \sec^2 y - \tan x}$ **k.** $(\sec^2(\sin x))(\cos x)$

l. $(\cos(\tan x))(\sec^2 x)$ **2.** $\sec x \tan x$

4. a. $-2 \csc(2x)[\csc(2x) + \cot(2x)]$

b. $6x^2 \cot x - 2x^3 \csc^2 x$

c. $2(x + \csc x)(1 - \csc x \cot x)$

d. $-\csc^2 x \cot x(\pi^2 + \csc^2 x)^{-\frac{1}{2}}$

e. $-3x(\csc^2\sqrt{x^2 + 1})(x^2 + 1)^{-\frac{1}{2}}$

f. $\dfrac{(1 + \csc^2 x)(-\csc^2 x) + 2 \csc^2 x \cot^2 x}{(1 + \csc^2 x)^2}$

g. $\dfrac{1}{2x} \csc\left(\dfrac{1}{\sqrt{x}}\right)\left[\sqrt{x} + \cot\left(\dfrac{1}{\sqrt{x}}\right)\right]$

h. $-2 \cot(2x) \csc(2x)[2 \csc^2(2x) + \cot^2(2x)]$

i. $\dfrac{-\csc^2(x+y)}{2+\csc^2(x+y)}$ **j.** $\dfrac{-y^2\csc^2(xy^2)}{4+2xy\csc^2(xy^2)}$

k. $\dfrac{2\sec^2 x}{(\tan x+1)^2}$

l. $2(\cot x+\sin x)(-\csc^2 x+\cos x)$

5. $y=\dfrac{1}{1+2\pi}(x-1),\ y=-(1+2\pi)(x-1)$

6. a. min $\left(\dfrac{\pi}{18},\dfrac{1}{\sqrt{3}}-\dfrac{2\pi}{9}\right)$,

max $\left(-\dfrac{\pi}{18},-\dfrac{1}{\sqrt{3}}+\dfrac{2\pi}{9}\right)$ **b.** no local

extrema   **c.** min $(0,0)$ **d.** no local extrema

7. a. $y=4x$ **b.** $\left(-\dfrac{\pi}{6},-\sqrt{3}\right),\left(\dfrac{\pi}{6},\sqrt{3}\right)$

9. no P.O.I.

Problems 5.6

2. 2   **3. a.** (i) $\tan x\approx x$

(ii) $\tan x\approx 2\left(x-\dfrac{\pi}{4}\right)+1$

b. (i) 0.13   (ii) 0.8

4. $\sec x\approx 2+2\sqrt{3}\left(x-\dfrac{\pi}{3}\right),\ 2+\dfrac{2\sqrt{3}\,\pi}{9}$

5. a. 0   **6.** $b\geq a$

Exercises 5.7

1. $80\pi\cos(10\pi t),\ -800\pi^2\sin(10\pi t)$

2. $44\pi\cos(880\pi t),\ -38\ 720\pi^2\sin(880\pi t)$

3. -0.125 rad/s   **4.** 10 m/s   **5.** $\dfrac{\pi}{2}$ **6.** $\dfrac{\pi}{4}$

7. a. local min $-\dfrac{\pi}{6}+2k\pi$, local max

$-\dfrac{5\pi}{6}+2k\pi$, increasing when

$-\dfrac{\pi}{6}+2k\pi<x<\dfrac{7\pi}{6}+2k\pi$, decreasing

when $\dfrac{7\pi}{6}+2k\pi<x<\dfrac{11\pi}{6}+2k\pi$,

P.O.I. $\dfrac{\pi}{2}+k\pi$, concave up when

$-\dfrac{\pi}{2}+2k\pi<x<\dfrac{\pi}{2}+2k\pi$, concave down

when $\dfrac{\pi}{2}+2k\pi<x<\dfrac{3\pi}{2}+2k\pi$ **b.** local

max $\dfrac{2\pi}{3}+2k\pi$, local min $\dfrac{4\pi}{3}+2k\pi$,

increasing $\dfrac{4\pi}{3}+2k\pi<x<\dfrac{8\pi}{3}+2k\pi$,

decreasing $\dfrac{2\pi}{3}+2k\pi<x<\dfrac{4\pi}{3}+2k\pi$, P.O.I.

$k\pi$, concave up $\pi+2k\pi<x<2\pi+2k\pi$,

concave down $2k\pi<x<\pi+2k\pi$ **c.** local

max $-\dfrac{\pi}{6}+2k\pi$, local min $\dfrac{\pi}{6}+2k\pi$,

increasing $\dfrac{\pi}{6}+2k\pi<x<\dfrac{11\pi}{6}+2k\pi$,

decreasing $-\dfrac{\pi}{6}+2k\pi<x<\dfrac{\pi}{6}+2k\pi$,

P.O.I. $k\pi$, concave up $2k\pi<x<\pi+2k\pi$,

concave down $\pi+2k\pi<x<2\pi+2k\pi$

d. local max $\dfrac{\pi}{12}+k\pi$, local min $\dfrac{5\pi}{12}+k\pi$,

increasing $\dfrac{5\pi}{12}+k\pi<x<\dfrac{13\pi}{12}+k\pi$,

decreasing $\dfrac{\pi}{12}+k\pi<x<\dfrac{5\pi}{12}+k\pi$,

P.O.I. $\dfrac{\pi}{4}+k\dfrac{\pi}{2}$, concave up

$\dfrac{\pi}{4}+k\pi<x<\dfrac{3\pi}{4}+k\pi$, concave down

$-\dfrac{\pi}{4}+k\pi<x<\dfrac{\pi}{4}+k\pi$ **8. a.** local max

$\left(\dfrac{\pi}{2},\dfrac{9}{4}\right),\left(\dfrac{3\pi}{2},\dfrac{1}{4}\right)$; local min $\left(\dfrac{7\pi}{6},0\right)$,

$\left(\dfrac{11\pi}{6},0\right)$ **b.** local max $(\pi,3)$, local min

$(0,1)$ **c.** local max $\left(\dfrac{\pi}{2},-1\right)$, local min

$\left(\dfrac{\pi}{4},-\sqrt{2}\right),\left(\dfrac{3\pi}{4},-\sqrt{2}\right)$ **9. a.** local max

$(-2\pi,1),(-\pi,1),(0,1),(\pi,1),(2\pi,1)$;

local min $\left(-\dfrac{3\pi}{2},0\right),\left(-\dfrac{\pi}{2},0\right),\left(\dfrac{\pi}{2},0\right)$,

$\left(\dfrac{3\pi}{2},0\right)$ **b.** local max $\left(-\dfrac{\pi}{4},\sqrt{2}\right)$,

$\left(\dfrac{7\pi}{4},\sqrt{2}\right)$; local min $\left(-\dfrac{5\pi}{4},-\sqrt{2}\right)$,

$\left(\dfrac{3\pi}{4},-\sqrt{2}\right)$ **c.** vertical asymptotes

$x=\pm\dfrac{\pi}{2}$; local max $\left(\dfrac{\pi}{3},3\sqrt{3}\right)$; local min

$\left(-\dfrac{\pi}{3},-3\sqrt{3}\right)$ **d.** local max

$\left(-4.97,\dfrac{9}{8}\right),\left(-1.32,\dfrac{9}{8}\right),\left(1.32,\dfrac{9}{8}\right)$,

$\left(4.97,\dfrac{9}{8}\right)$; local min $(-2\pi,0),(-\pi,-2)$,

(0, 0), $(\pi, -2)$, $(2\pi, 0)$ **e.** local max

$\left(-\frac{3\pi}{2}, 1\right), \left(-\frac{\pi}{2}, 1\right), \left(\frac{\pi}{2}, 1\right), \left(\frac{3\pi}{2}, 1\right)$; local

min $(-2\pi, 0)$, $(-\pi, 0)$, $(0, 0)$, $(\pi, 0)$, $(2\pi, 0)$

f. local max $\left(-\frac{\pi}{2}, 1\right), \left(\frac{\pi}{2}, 1\right)$; local min

$\left(-\frac{3\pi}{2}, -1\right), \left(\frac{3\pi}{2}, -1\right)$ **10.** $75\sqrt{3}$, $-75\sqrt{3}$

11. a. -1, $\frac{3\pi^2}{2}$ **b.** away, slowing down

12. 52π units/s **13.** $\frac{\pi}{18}$ units/s **14.** $\frac{\pi}{6}$

15. $I = k\cos\theta\sin^2\theta$, $\frac{1}{\sqrt{2m}}$ **16. a.** $\frac{13}{5}$, 1

b. 2.55, 0.6058 **c.** $\frac{2}{3\sqrt{3}}$, 0

17. (0.739, 0.739)

Problems 5.7

1. 3π m/s **2.** $\tan\theta = \frac{5}{12}$ **3.** $\frac{\pi + 2\alpha}{4}$

4. a. $m > 1$ **b.** 1.165 561 **5.** $\left(4^{\frac{2}{3}} + 3^{\frac{2}{3}}\right)^{\frac{3}{2}}$

6. $\left(a^{\frac{2}{3}} + b^{\frac{2}{3}}\right)^{\frac{3}{2}}$ **7.** 3.2 m/s **8.** $27\sqrt{3}$

9. $18\sqrt{3}$ **11. a.** $\sin\phi = \frac{1}{4}$ **b.** $\frac{800\pi}{\sqrt{21}}$

d. For $\theta = \frac{\pi}{4}$,

$\frac{dx}{dt} = -200\pi\sqrt{2}\left(1 + \frac{1}{\sqrt{31}}\right)$ m/min; For

$\theta = \frac{3\pi}{4}$, $\frac{dx}{dt} = -200\pi\sqrt{2}\left(1 - \frac{1}{\sqrt{31}}\right)$ m/min

12. Vertical asymptotes: $x = \frac{\pi}{6}$, $x = \frac{5\pi}{6}$, etc.

$\left(\frac{\pi}{2}, -1\right), \left(\frac{3\pi}{2}, \frac{1}{3}\right)$, etc. **13.** -78.71 cm/s

15. $\frac{3\pi}{\sqrt{1 + \pi^2}}$ **16. b.** $x = \frac{1}{k\pi}$, $k \epsilon Z$ **d.** yes, 0

17. $\lim\limits_{x \to 0^+} f(x)$ D.N.E.

Review Exercises

1. $-\frac{\pi}{6}$, $-\frac{5\pi}{6}$

3. a. $6\cos(2x) + 8\sin(2x)$,

$-12\sin(2x) + 16\cos(2x)$

b. $3\sec^2(3x)$, $18\sec^2(3x)\tan(3x)$

c. $-\pi^2 x\sin(\pi x)$, $-\pi^2\sin(\pi x) - \pi^3 x\cos(\pi x)$

d. 0, 0 **e.** $-3\cot^2 x\csc^2 x$,

$6\cot x\csc^4 x + 6\cot^3 x\csc^2 x$

f. $\tan(2x) + 2x\sec^2(2x)$,

$4\sec^2(2x) + 8x\sec^2(2x)\tan(2x)$ **g.** 0, 0

h. $-3\sin(6x)$, $-18\cos(6x)$ **i.** $3x^2\cos(x^3)$,

$6x\cos(x^3) - 9x^4\sin(x^3)$ **j.** $\frac{-\sin x}{(2 - \cos x)^2}$,

$\frac{-2\cos x + \cos^2 x + 2\sin^2 x}{(2 - \cos x)^3}$ **4. a.** $y = x$

b. below **5. a.** $2\pi - 2\pi\sin(2\pi t)$

b. $-4\pi^2\cos(2\pi t)$ **c.** $\frac{1}{4}, \frac{5}{4}, \frac{9}{4}$ **d.** 4π

6. a. $2\pi t\cos(\pi t^2)$

b. $2\pi\cos(\pi t^2) - 4\pi^2 t^2\sin(\pi t^2)$ **c.** $\pm\frac{1}{\sqrt{2}}$, 0

d. $-\frac{1}{\sqrt{2}} < t < 0$, $\frac{1}{\sqrt{2}} < x < 1$ **8. a.** 118, 82

b. 67 **9.** $\frac{\pi}{6}$ **10.** (0, 0), $\left(\frac{2\pi}{3}, \frac{3\sqrt{3}}{4}\right)$,

$\left(\frac{4\pi}{3}, -\frac{3\sqrt{3}}{4}\right)$, $(2\pi, 0)$ **11.** $\frac{1}{50}$ rad/s

12. -0.174 rad/s **13. a.** 0,

$\pi - \cos^{-1}\left(\frac{1}{4}\right)$, π **15. a.** $\frac{1}{2}$ **b.** $\frac{3}{2}$

16. $\frac{2 - \pi}{4}$ **17.** $\pm\frac{\sqrt{3}}{2}$ **18.** $10\sqrt{5}$ **19.** $\frac{\sqrt{3}}{2}$

20. $\left(2^{\frac{2}{3}} + 3^{\frac{2}{3}}\right)^{\frac{3}{2}} \approx 7.02$ **21. b.** -1

22. P.O.I. at $x = -\pi$, 0, π, 2π, 3π

23. $\frac{1}{2}$, $\sqrt{2}$ **24.** $\left(\frac{\pi}{24}, \frac{\sqrt{3}}{2}\right)$

Chapter 6

Exercises 6.1

1. a. $\log_3 27 = 3$ **b.** $\log_4\left(\frac{1}{16}\right) = -2$

c. $\log_6 1 = 0$ **d.** $\log_2 7 = x$ **e.** $\log_a a = 1$

f. $\log_x 3 = 3$ **2. a.** $3^{-1} = \frac{1}{3}$ **b.** $11^2 = 121$

c. $5^x = 7$ **d.** $x^y = 2$ **e.** $125^{\frac{1}{3}} = x$ **f.** $9^{\frac{1}{2}} = 3$

3. a. 3 **b.** 4 **c.** 4 **d.** -4 **e.** 3 **f.** 7

g. $\frac{1}{25}$ h. $\frac{1}{8}$ i. -6 j. 2 k. -1 1. 3

m. 4 n. 2 o. $\frac{1}{2}$ p. 10 4. a. 100

b. 125 c. $\frac{1}{9}$ d. 25 e. 1000 f. 4 g. $\frac{1}{2}$

h. $\frac{3}{5}$ i. 10 j. $\frac{7}{\log_5 10}$ k. $3\sqrt{3}$ l. ± 9

m. $2\sqrt{2}$ n. 2 5. 4 6. $\frac{1}{10}$ 7. a. 2

b. -1 c. $\frac{9}{4}$ d. $\frac{1}{9}$ 8. a. 0 b. -2 c. no

x-int. d. no x-int. 9. a. 4 b. 2 c. $\frac{1}{3}$

d. 5 10. a. 0, 1, 10 b. $10^{140} I_0$

11. a. $I = I_0(10^R)$ 12. a. 7 b. 4.2

c. acidic

Problems 6.1

1. $(2, \log 4)$ 3. $\frac{1}{x} - 1$

Exercises 6.2

1. a. e^3 b. $e^{\frac{1}{5}}$ c. e^3 d. e^8 e. e f. e

2. a. e^2 b. e c. e^3 d. e

Problems 6.2

1. a. 1 b. DNE 2. $Pe^{\frac{r}{100}}$, marginal

Exercises 6.3

1. a. $\frac{1}{x-2}$ b. $\frac{-9}{4-3x}$ c. $\frac{2x}{x^2+5}$ d. $\frac{2}{x}$

e. $\frac{t-1}{2t(t+1)}$ f. $t(2\ln t + 1)$ g. $\frac{4}{x}(\ln x)^3$

h. $\frac{4}{x}$ i. $4(t\ln t)^3(\ln t + 1)$

j. $3(\ln v + v)^2\left(\frac{1}{v} + 1\right)$ k. $\frac{\sin u}{u} + (\cos u)\ln u$

l. $\cot y$ m. $\frac{3}{x(3 + \ln x)^2}$ n. $\frac{\cos t - \sin t}{\sin t + \cos t}$

o. $\frac{-2\cos(\ln x)\sin(\ln x)}{x}$ p. $\frac{\cos(\ln u)}{u}$ q. $\frac{-x}{9 - x^2}$

r. $\frac{2}{(1 + x)(1 - x)}$ 2. a. $x > -1$, $y = x$

b. $x > -\frac{5}{2}$, $y = 2x + 4$ c. $x < 2$,

$y = -x + 1$ d. $x < \frac{1}{3}$, $y = -3x$ 3. a. (i) $\frac{2}{x}$

(ii) $2\cot 2x$ (iii) $\frac{1}{\sin x \cos x}$ 5. $\frac{dy}{dx} = \tan x$

6. a. e b. $-\frac{1}{4}$ c. $-\frac{\sqrt{e}}{2}$ 8. a. $x > 1$

b. $\frac{1}{e}$ 9. $(1, 0)$, $\left(\frac{1}{e}, \frac{1}{e^2}\right)$ 10. a. $-2 < x < 2$

b. $(0, [\ln 4]^2)$, $(\pm\sqrt{3}, 0)$ 11. a. -2

b. $\frac{1}{2}\ln\left(\frac{2}{3}\right)$ c. $\frac{8}{9}$ d. e e. $3 - e\ln 3$

f. $\frac{1}{2}\ln\pi - 1$ 12. a. e^{-3} b. $e^{\frac{5}{2}}$ c. e^2, e^{-2}

d. e^{-2}, e e. 5 13. $\frac{1}{3}$

Problems 6.3

1. 3.46, 8.46 2. 0 3. 0 5. 0 7. b. 0.97

Exercises 6.4

2. a. $15e^{3x}$ b. $(4x - 2)e^{x^2-x}$ c. $6\cos te^{2\sin t}$

d. $6\cos 2te^{\sin 2t}$ e. $(3x^2 - 5)e^{-5x}$

f. $e^{3x}(\pi\cos(\pi x) + 3\sin(\pi x))$ g. $4(e^{4u} - e^{-4u})$

h. $\frac{1}{2\sqrt{v}}e^{\sqrt{v}}(1 + \sqrt{v})$ i. $\frac{2e^{2v}}{\pi + e^{2v}}$ j. $\frac{3e^{3u}}{(1 + e^{3u})^2}$

k. $\frac{e^{\sqrt{x}}}{4x}(\sqrt{x}\ln x + 2)$ l. $\frac{xe^x - 1}{(e^x + 1)(x + 1)}$

m. $\frac{e^x - e^{-x}}{e^x + e^{-x}}$ n. $\sqrt{1 + e^{\pi x}} + \frac{\pi xe^{\pi x}}{2\sqrt{1 + e^{\pi x}}}$

o. $\frac{e^x(x\ln x - 1)}{x(\ln x)^2}$ p. $\frac{3e^{\sqrt{3x+2}}}{2\sqrt{3x + 2}}$

3. a. 0, $\ln 4$ b. $\ln 3$ 5. $\left(\pm\frac{1}{\sqrt{2}}, e^{-\frac{1}{2}}\right)$

6. a. $15x - 2y + 9 - 15\ln 2 = 0$, above

b. $y = ex$, below c. $x + 2y - \ln 4 = 0$, above

7. $x + 2y - 1 - \ln 2 = 0$ 8. a. 1 b. 2

c. e^2 9. a. max: $\frac{2}{e}$, min: $\frac{1}{\sqrt{e}}$

b. max: $8\ln 2 + \frac{1}{4}$, min: $-4\ln 4 + 4$

c. max: $\ln\left(\frac{17}{2}\right)$, min: $\ln 4$

d. max: 10, min: 4 e. max: $e^{\sqrt{2}}$, min: $\frac{1}{e}$

10. a. $-\frac{2 + \ln 2}{2}$ b. 1 c. -1 d. 1

Problems 6.4

1. b. $f(x) = 2e^x$, $f(x) = ke^x$ **3.** -3, -2

6. b. $\frac{2}{3}$, $\frac{3}{2}$ **7.** 0

Exercises 6.5

2. local max at $x = \frac{\pi}{4}$, $f\left(\frac{\pi}{4}\right) = 0.3224$; local

min at $x = \frac{5\pi}{4}$, $f\left(\frac{5\pi}{4}\right) = -0.0139$

3. a. max: $\frac{1}{e}$, min: 0 **b.** max: $\ln(7)$,

min: $\ln\left(\frac{3}{4}\right)$ **c.** max: $\frac{27}{e}$, min: 8 **d.** max: 2,

min: $\frac{16}{17}$ **4.** $-\frac{4}{\sqrt{e}}$ m/s **5.** $\frac{e(e-1)}{2}$

6. $\frac{1}{2}(1 + a)^2 e^{-a}$ **8.** 74 715 at $t = 20$

9. $v = -14.2$ cm/s, $a = 2.8$ cm/s²

10. $\frac{2}{e}$, $\frac{1}{2}$ **11.** $\sqrt{\frac{2}{e}}$

12. a. $v = 40\left(1 - e^{-\frac{t}{4}}\right)$ **c.** 40

d. 11.98 s, 327.2 m **13.** 5 **14. a.** 1001
b. 500 **15. a.** 2nd **b.** 2nd slower for
$0 \le t < 0.38$ h and $2.62 < t \le 6$ h, 1st slower
for $0.38 < t < 2.62$ h
16. a. 70% **b.** 52.7%
c. $P(t) = 10^7 \times (0.7)^2 \times (1 - e^{-0.2t}) -$
$5000t - 30\ 000$; $P(28) = 4\ 711\ 880.47$
d. 26 days, 4 712 968

Problems 6.5

4. a. 0 **b.** 0 **6.** $\frac{1}{\sqrt{e}}$ **7. b.** 1.557 146

9. $\frac{R}{3.591\ 121}$

Exercises 6.6

1. a. $2^x \ln 2$ **b.** $\pi^x \ln \pi$ **c.** $\sqrt{2} x^{\sqrt{2} - 1}$
d. $e^x - exe^{-1}$ **e.** $\pi^2 x^{\pi^2 - 1}$ **f.** $2x\ 10^{x^2} \ln 10$
g. $\cos x\ 2^{\sin x} \ln 2$ **h.** $(2x + 3)3^{x^2 + 3x} \ln 3$
2. 10 ln 5 **3. a.** -20 **b.** -12

c. $\frac{\sqrt{2}\pi^3}{32}\left(\frac{12}{\pi} + 7\right)$ **d.** $-\frac{11}{36b^4}$

Problems 6.6

1. a. $x^x(\ln x + 1)$ **b.** $x^{\frac{1}{x} - 2}(1 - \ln x)$

c. $x^{\sin x}\left(\cos(\ln x) + \frac{\sin x}{x}\right)$ **2.** $-\frac{1}{\pi^2}$

3. a. $v(t) = t^{\frac{1}{t} - 2}(1 - \ln t)$,

$a(t) = t^{\frac{1}{t} - 4}[(1 - \ln t)^2 - 3t + 2t \ln t]$

b. at $t = e$, $-e^{\left(\frac{1}{e} - 3\right)}$

4. $e^\pi > \pi^e$

Exercises 6.7

2. a. $\frac{2x}{x^2 - 1}$ **b.** $\frac{3x^2 - 7}{x^3 - 7x + 1}$

c. $-\sin x(\ln|\cos x| + 1)$ **d.** $\frac{3}{t}(\ln|t|)^2$

e. $\frac{2\ln|u|}{u^3}(1 - \ln|u|)$ **f.** $\frac{\sec^2 t}{\tan t}$ **g.** $\frac{6\ln|3y - 1|}{3y - 1}$

h. $\frac{\cos(\ln|y|)}{y}$ **3. a.** tangent
$3x + 2y - 3 - 2\ln 2 = 0$; normal
$2x - 3y + 3\ln 2 - 2 = 0$ **b.** tangent
$3x - y + e^2 = 0$; normal $x + 3y + 7e^2 = 0$
c. tangent $2x - y - 2\pi = 0$; normal
$x + 2y - \pi = 0$ **d.** tangent
$\pi e^2 x - ey + 1 = 0$; normal $ex + \pi e^2 y + 1 = 0$

Problems 6.7

1. a. $|x| > 1$ **b.** $\frac{1}{x \ln|x|}$ **2. a.** $x \neq 0$

b. $\frac{1}{x \ln|x|}$

Review Exercises

2. a. $-\ln 2$ **b.** $\frac{1}{e - 1}$ **c.** $\ln 2$ **d.** 0, e

3. a. $\frac{2}{2x - 3}$ **b.** $(\ln x)^2 + 2\ln x$

c. $(-6x + 2)e^{-3x^2 + 2x}$ **d.** $-2\pi \sin(\pi x)e^{2\cos \pi x}$

e. $\dfrac{\pi e^{\pi x} + \pi e^{-\pi x}}{e^{\pi x} - e^{-\pi x}}$ **f.** $\left(\dfrac{1}{2\sqrt{x}} + \dfrac{1}{x^2}\right) e^{\sqrt{x} - \frac{1}{x}}$

g. $\dfrac{e^{x^3}(3x^3 - 1)}{x^2}$ **h.** $\dfrac{x^2 e^x + x e^x + e^x + 5}{(x + 1)^2}$

i. $\dfrac{1}{x + y - 1}$ **j.** $\dfrac{y e^{xy} - 1}{1 - x e^{xy}}$ **4. a.** $\dfrac{\ln 2}{37}$ **b.** $\dfrac{5 \ln 2}{37}$

c. 2024 **6.** -3 **7.** $x = 1$ **9. c.** 0

10. a. $\dfrac{1}{2}$, local max **11. a.** 3 **b.** $\dfrac{1}{2}$

12. $\dfrac{\ln 3}{2}$ s **13. a.** 2 **14.** max: $200\left(e + \dfrac{1}{e}\right)$;

min: 400 **15.** $y = \dfrac{1}{2}(e^x + e^{-x})$;

$\dfrac{dy}{dx} = \dfrac{1}{2}(e^x - e^{-x})$ **16. a.** $5 \ln\left(\dfrac{9}{4}\right)$ years

b. $5 \ln(9)$ years **17. b.** 0.5671

20. $\dfrac{dy}{dt} = e^4$, increasing

Chapter 7

Exercises 7.1

1. a. $\dfrac{2}{3}x^3 - 4x^2 + C$ **b.** $\dfrac{1}{2}x^6 + x^4 - 7x + C$

c. $\dfrac{1}{2}(x^{10} + x^8 + x^6) + C$ **d.** $\dfrac{1}{5}x^5 - \dfrac{1}{3x^3} + C$

e. $-\dfrac{3}{4x^4} + C$ **f.** $10 \ln|x| + C$

g. $\dfrac{3}{5}x^5 - \dfrac{1}{4}x^4 + C$ **h.** $\dfrac{5}{2}x^{\frac{4}{5}} + \dfrac{5}{7}x^{\frac{7}{5}} + C$

i. $2 \sin x - 3x + C$ **j.** $\dfrac{1}{2}\sin(2x) + x^2 + C$

k. $2x^{\frac{3}{2}} - 2x^{\frac{1}{2}} + C$

l. $-\dfrac{2}{\pi}\cos(\pi x) - \dfrac{1}{\pi}\sin(\pi x) + C$

m. $2e^{5x} + \dfrac{2}{3}e^{-3x} + C$

n. $3 \ln|x| + \dfrac{4}{x} + 2\pi x + C$

o. $\dfrac{3}{5}x^5 - x + \dfrac{1}{\pi}e^{\pi x} + C$

p. $-\sqrt{3}\cos(\sqrt{3}x) - \dfrac{1}{\sqrt{3}}e^{\sqrt{3}x} + C$

2. a. $-\dfrac{7}{2}e^{-2x} + C$ **b.** $t^3 + \dfrac{5}{2}t^2 - 2t + C$

c. $-\cos t - \dfrac{1}{2}\cos 2t - \dfrac{1}{3}\cos 3t + C$

d. $-e^{-t} - e^{-2t} - e^{-3t} + C$ **e.** $\ln\left|\dfrac{u}{u - 1}\right| + C$

f. $\dfrac{1}{5}v^5 + \dfrac{1}{5}(1 - v)^5 + C$

g. $\dfrac{1}{5}\sin\left(5x - \dfrac{\pi}{5}\right) + C$

h. $e^x + \dfrac{1}{e + 1}x^{e+1} + C$

i. $-\dfrac{1}{3\pi}\cos(\pi v + 3) + C$ **j.** $\dfrac{5}{3}\tan 3x + C$

3. a. $\dfrac{2}{7}x^{\frac{7}{2}} + x^3 + C$ **b.** $\dfrac{1}{2}e^{2x} - \pi e^{-x} + C$

c. $\dfrac{1}{4}(e^{4x} - e^{-4x}) + 2x + C$

d. $\dfrac{1}{2}x^2 - 2x + \ln|x| + C$

e. $\dfrac{7}{3}x^3 + 3 \ln|x| + C$

f. $\dfrac{2}{5}x^{\frac{5}{2}} + \dfrac{8}{3}x^{\frac{3}{2}} + 8x^{\frac{1}{2}} + C$ **g.** $-\dfrac{1}{4}\cos 2x + C$

h. $\sin x + C$ **i.** $x + \sin x + C$

j. $x - \dfrac{1}{2}\cos 2x + C$ **k.** $2 \tan x - x + C$

l. $\dfrac{1}{2}x^2 + x + \ln|x + 1| + C$

4. a. $\dfrac{a}{n + 1}x^{n+1} + C$ **b.** $\dfrac{1}{k}\ln|kx + b| + C$

c. $-\dfrac{A}{k}\cos(kx + b) + C$

d. $-\dfrac{1}{2a}(ax + b)^{-2} + C$ **e.** $-\dfrac{B}{k}e^{-kx} + C$

f. $\dfrac{2}{3c}(cx + d)^{\frac{3}{2}} + C$ **5. a.** $\dfrac{1}{2}x - \dfrac{1}{4}\sin 2x + C$

b. $\dfrac{1}{2}x + \dfrac{1}{4}\sin 2x + C$

6. $y = \dfrac{1}{3}x^3 - x^2 + 8x - \dfrac{19}{3}$; max: $\dfrac{151}{3}$

min: $-\dfrac{145}{3}$ **7.** 180 cm **8.** 200 min

9. a. $r(t) = 10e^{-0.002t} - 9$ **b.** $r(5) = 0.9$ cm
c. 52.7 years **10.** 16.87 m

Problems 7.1

1. a. $x \ln x - x + C$ **b.** $x e^x - e^x + C$
c. $x \sin x + \cos x + C$ **2.** $f(x) = x^2$

3. $f(x) = kx^4$ **4.** $\dfrac{4}{9}(x + 5)^{\frac{3}{2}} - x - 6$

5. a. $-\dfrac{1}{2}e^{-x^2}$ **b.** $\dfrac{1}{3}(x^2 + 1)^{\frac{3}{2}}$

c. $\frac{1}{2}\ln(x^2 + 1)$ **d.** $-\frac{1}{3}\cos^3 x$

e. $-\ln(1 + \cos x)$ **f.** $\ln(1 + e^x)$

Exercises 7.2

1. a. $\frac{3}{2}t^2 - \frac{1}{3}t^3 + 5$ **b.** $-\frac{4}{\pi}(\cos \pi t - 1)$

c. $\frac{2}{9}\left[(1 + 3t)^{\frac{3}{2}} - 1\right]$ **d.** $10\left[t + \frac{1}{1+t} - 1\right]$

e. $5t + \frac{1}{2}e^{-2t} + 1$ **2.** 502 s

3. a. $\frac{5}{2}t^2 + 10t + 20$ **b.** $\frac{1}{6}t^3 - \frac{1}{2}t^2 + t$

c. $\frac{1}{12}t^4 + \frac{1}{6}t^3$ **d.** $-\cos 2t - 3t + 1$

e. $\frac{4}{375}\left[(4 + 5t)^{\frac{5}{2}} - 100t - 32\right]$

f. $9e^{-\frac{t}{3}} + 3t - 2$ **g.** $-\ln(1 + 2t) + 2t + 5$
4. a. $-t^2 + 10t - 12\ln t$ **b.** 9
5. 255.187 km   **6.** second pebble

7. a. 20 m   **b.** 20 m/s   **8. a.** $\frac{1}{8}gT^2$ m

b. $\frac{gT}{2}$ m/s   **9. a.** 128 m   **b.** 25.6 s

10. 15.36 m   **11.** 350 m   **12.** 385 m

Problems 7.2
1. 8.53 s   **2.** 26.6 m/s², 16.9 m/s²

Exercises 7.3
2. a. $y = 3x + C$, $y = 3x - 5$
b. $y = -x^2 + C$, $y = -x^2$
c. $y = 2x^2 - x + C$, $y = 2x^2 - x + 1$
d. $y = 2x^3 + C$, $y = 2x^3 - 4$
e. $y = -2e^{-2x} + C$, $y = -2e^{-2x} + 2$
f. $y = -\frac{3}{2}\cos 2x + C$, $y = -\frac{3}{2}\cos 2x - \frac{3}{2}$
g. $y = x^3 - 3x + C$, $y = x^3 - 3x + 3$
h. $y = \ln|x - 3| + C$, $y = \ln|x - 3| + 1$
i. $y = -2\ln|1 - 2x| + C$,
$y = -2\ln|1 - 2x| + 3$

3. a. $y = 2x^{\frac{3}{2}} - \ln|x| + C$,
$y = 2x^{\frac{3}{2}} - \ln|x| + 1 - 2e^3$

b. $y = -3\cos t - \frac{1}{3}\cos 3t + C$,

$y = -3\cos t - \frac{1}{3}\cos 3t + 4$

c. $x = -\frac{1}{12}(3 - 2t)^6 + C$,

$x = -\frac{1}{12}(3 - 2t)^6 + \frac{13}{12}$ **d.** $y = \frac{2}{(2 - 3x)^2} + C$,

$y = \frac{2}{(2 - 3x)^2} - 2$ **e.** $v = \frac{1}{4}e^{2t} - \frac{8}{3}e^{-3t} + C$,

$v = \frac{1}{4}e^{2t} - \frac{8}{3}e^{-3t} + \frac{1}{3}$

f. $s = \frac{1}{2}e^{2t} - \frac{1}{2}e^{-2t} - 2t + C$,

$y = \frac{1}{2}e^{2t} - \frac{1}{2}e^{-2t} - 2t + 5$ **4.** $f(x) = \frac{3}{5}x^{\frac{5}{3}}$

5. $3\ln 2 - \frac{3}{2}$ **6.** $\frac{3}{4\pi}$ **7. a.** $y = -\frac{1}{3}x + k$

b. $y = \frac{1}{3x} + k$ **c.** $y = e^{-x} + k$

d. $y = -\frac{1}{2}x^2 + x + k$ **8.** -4 **9.** 2

10. $v = \pi e^{-\pi x}$

Problems 7.3
1. $y = x^2$ **2. a.** $y = \frac{k}{x}$ **3.** 9:09 a.m.

Exercises 7.4
1. a. 500 g   **b.** 13.7 days   **c.** 0.08 for all
three   **d.** $W'(t) = 0.08\, W(t)$ **2. a.** 50 W
b. 173.3 days   **c.** 402.4 days
d. $P'(t) = -0.004P(t)$ **3. a.** 1893
b. 49 min   **c.** 11.4 h   **4.** 1.95 billion
5. a. $\frac{\ln 2}{3}$ **b.** 0.98 g   **6.** 20.1 years
7. 458.4 days   **8.** 22 193.5 years
9. a. $N = 40e^{0.15t}$ **b.** 803   **c.** 4.6 years
10. a. 311.8 million   **b.** 69.3 years
11. 0.4 amps   **12.** 0.20%   **13.** 9.5 min
14. $28\frac{1}{3}°C$ **15.** 8 min

Problems 7.4

1. 1:55 p.m.　**4.** \$2718.28, \$2593.74

5. 6.18%

Exercises 7.5

1. a. $x^2 - 4y^2 = k$, $x^2 - 4y^2 = 5$

b. $y = ke^{-\frac{1}{2}x^2}$, $y = 3e^{-\frac{1}{2}x^2}$　**c.** $xy = k$, $xy = 2$

d. $9x^2 - y^2 + 6y = k$, $9x^2 - y^2 + 6y = 17$

2. a. $y^2(2\cos t - 1) = 1$　**b.** $v^2 = \frac{2}{r} + 2$

c. $s = \frac{e^t}{1 + e^t}$　**d.** $N = \frac{1}{2}(15e^{2t} + 5)$

e. $e^{-y} = 3 - 4e^x$　**f.** $y^{\frac{1}{2}} = \frac{1}{2}(\sin t - \cos t + 1)$

3. $y = e^{2-x^2}$　**4.** $y = \frac{1}{2}\ln(4 - 2\cos x)$

5. a. $y = \frac{1}{C}e^{-x} + k$　**b.** $y = ke^{-2Cx}$

7. a. $\sqrt{12}$　**b.** $-\sqrt{13 - e^2}$

Problems 7.5

1. 30 s　**2. a.** $v = \frac{g(1 - e^{-kt})}{k}$　**c.** 9.2 s

3. 16.6 years　**4. b.** $\sqrt{2gR}$　**7. a.** $\frac{\ln(1.5)}{5}$

b. 27.095 h

Review Exercises

1. a. $\frac{5}{3}x^3 - \frac{7}{2}x^2 + 3x + C$

b. $\frac{2}{7}x^{\frac{7}{2}} - 6x + C$

c. $-\frac{1}{\pi}(\cos(\pi x) - \sin(\pi x)) + C$

d. $-\frac{1}{\pi}e^{-\pi x} - 10\cos x + C$

e. $\frac{1}{6}e^{6x} - \frac{2}{3}e^{3x} + C$　**f.** $\ln|x| - \frac{1}{x} - \frac{1}{2x^2} + C$

g. $-\frac{3}{2}\cos\left(2x + \frac{\pi}{4}\right) + C$

h. $\frac{1}{5}(x + 5)^5 + C$　**i.** $\frac{1}{3}(2x - 1)^{\frac{3}{2}} + C$

j. $\frac{1}{60}(6x - 1)^{10} + C$

k. $-\frac{1}{6}\cos(6x) - \frac{1}{2}e^{-2x} + \pi x + C$

l. $e^x + \frac{1}{e + 1}x^{e+1} + C$　**m.** $\frac{1}{5}\ln|5x + 1| + C$

n. $\frac{3}{2}\tan 2x + C$　**2. a.** $y = -3x + C$,

$y = -3x + 2$　**b.** $y = x - x^3 + C$,

$y = x - x^3 + 1$　**c.** $y = \frac{3}{\pi}\sin \pi x + C$,

$y = \frac{3}{\pi}(\sin \pi x - 1)$　**d.** $y = -6e^{-\frac{1}{2}x} + C$,

$y = -6e^{-\frac{1}{2}x} + 5$　**3. a.** $y = x^2 + x + 3$

b. $3x + y + 1 = 0$　**4. a.** $y = x^2 + x^{\frac{3}{2}}$

b. $y = x^2 + x^{\frac{3}{2}} - 4 - \sqrt{8}$　**5.** 1.62 m/s^2

6. $y = \frac{1}{2}x^2 + \frac{1}{\pi}\cos(\pi x) + \frac{1}{\pi}$　**7.** $\frac{35}{24}$

8. $6 - 4\sqrt{3}$　**9.** max: 164.04; min: 0.5

10. 833.3 m　**11.** 7330 years

12. 10.65 years　**13.** \$150.60　**14.** 113

15. a. 2693.7 m　**b.** 6.5 m/s, 2.5 m/s

16. 10°C　**17. a.** 253.1 m　**b.** 4.8 s

18. a. $r = 10e^{0.01t} - 9$ cm　**b.** 2.97 years

19. a. $A = \frac{1}{2}$　**b.** $B = -\frac{1}{2}$　**c.** -0.8

Chapter 8

Exercises 8.1

1. a. $\frac{43}{4}$　**b.** $\frac{7}{4}$　**c.** $\frac{29}{4}$　**d.** $\frac{15}{2}$　**2. a.** $\frac{27}{4}$

b. $\frac{9}{4}$　**c.** $\frac{45}{4}$　**d.** $\frac{7}{2}$　**3. a.** $\frac{69}{8}$　**b.** 2　**c.** $\frac{75}{8}$

d. $\frac{21}{4}$　**4. a.** $\frac{26}{3}$　**b.** 2　**c.** $\frac{28}{3}$　**d.** $\frac{16}{3}$

5. b. $S_n = \frac{1}{3} - \frac{1}{12n^2}$

c. $S_{100} - S_{10} = 0.000\ 825$　**6.** 4

7. c. $A = 0.69$, $n > 50$

Problems 8.1

1. $\frac{1}{4}$　**2. a.** 1　**b.** 2　**3. a.** 1　**c.** $e - 1$

Exercises 8.2

1. $\frac{289}{16}$ **2. a.** $\frac{43\pi}{64}$ **3. a.** 150 g

Exercises 8.3

1. a. $x^2 + 6x + 8$ **b.** $10 + 8x - x^2$ **2. a.** 24

b. 18   **4. a.** $x + \frac{1}{2}e^{2x} - \frac{1}{2}$

b. $x^2 - \cos x + 1$ **c.** $\frac{1}{9}(3x + 1)^3 - \frac{1}{9}$

d. $2\sin x + \frac{1}{2}\sin 2x$ **e.** $\frac{2}{3}(x + 4)^{\frac{3}{2}} - \frac{16}{3}$

f. $\ln\left(\frac{x + 2}{2}\right)$ **5. a.** $\frac{x^3}{3} + x + \frac{4}{3}$

b. $\frac{x^4}{2} + x^3 + \frac{1}{2}$ **c.** $-2e^{-\frac{x}{2}} + 2$ **d.** $2\sqrt{x} - 2$

e. $\frac{x^2}{2} + \ln x - \frac{1}{2}$ **f.** $\ln(x + 2) - \ln(2)$

g. $2x - \frac{1}{2}\cos 2x + \pi - \frac{1}{2}$

h. $\frac{2}{3}(x + 4)^{\frac{3}{2}} - \frac{2}{3}$ **6.** $\frac{32}{3}$ **7. a.** 6   **b.** 2

c. 1   **d.** 2   **e.** $\frac{15}{2} + \ln 4$ **f.** $\ln 3$ **g.** 2π

h. $\frac{2}{3}(7^{\frac{3}{2}} - 1)$

Problems 8.3

1. b. $A_2 \to 1$ **2.** less, $\frac{\pi}{2}$

Exercises 8.4

1. a. $\frac{1}{2}$ **b.** $\ln 9$ **c.** $\frac{38}{3}$ **d.** 3   **e.** $\frac{28}{3}$

f. $\frac{15}{2} + \ln 4$ **g.** $\frac{1}{\pi}$ **h.** 3   **2.** $2\sqrt{3} - \frac{2\pi}{3}$

3. $\frac{4}{3}$ **4.** $\frac{16}{3}$ **5.** $\ln 4 - \frac{3}{2}$ **6.** $\frac{7}{4}$ **7.** $\frac{11}{4}$

Problems 8.4

1. $\ln 2$ **2.** $1 - \frac{\pi}{4}$ **3.** $A_2 = \frac{1}{2}A_1$

Exercises 8.5

1. a. $\frac{21}{2}$ **b.** 10   **c.** $\frac{20}{3}$ **d.** $\ln 2$ **e.** $\frac{5}{2}$

f. $1 - \frac{\sqrt{2}}{2}$ **g.** $\frac{63}{4}$ **h.** $\frac{16}{3}$ **i.** 4   **j.** $\frac{2}{3}$ **k.** 4

l. $\frac{1}{3}(e^3 - e^{-3}) + 4$ **m.** $-\frac{1}{2\pi}$ **n.** $\ln(2 + e^{-2})$

o. 1   **p.** $4 - 2^{-\frac{2}{3}}$ **q.** $\frac{1}{\pi}$ **r.** $\frac{\sqrt{2} - 1}{3}$

2. a. 18   **b.** $\frac{9}{2}$ **c.** 4   **d.** 6   **e.** $4\ln 2 - \frac{3}{2}$

f. $\ln 4$ **g.** $\frac{1}{2}$ **h.** $\frac{e^4}{2} + \frac{3}{2}$ **i.** $18\ln 3 - \frac{40}{9}$

j. $\frac{9}{2}$ **3.** e **4. a.** $\int_0^1 x^3\, dx = \frac{1}{4}$

b. $\int_{-1}^2 x^2\, dx = 3$ **c.** $\int_1^3 x^4\, dx = \frac{242}{5}$

d. $\int_1^2 \frac{1}{x}\, dx = \ln 2$ **e.** $\int_{-\frac{\pi}{2}}^{\frac{\pi}{4}} \cos x\, dx = 1 + \frac{\sqrt{2}}{2}$

f. $\int_0^{\ln 2} e^x\, dx = 1$ **5. a.** $1 - \frac{\pi}{4}$ **b.** $\frac{1}{4}$

c. $\frac{1}{2}$

Problems 8.5

3. $\ln 2$ **4.** $\ln 2$ **5.** n is the smallest integer greater than $e^{20} - 1$ **6. a.** $\frac{2}{3}$ **b.** $\frac{2}{3}$ **c.** 1

Exercises 8.6

1. a. $\frac{64}{3}$ **b.** $1 - \frac{\pi}{4}$ **c.** $2\ln 2 - 1$ **d.** $e - \frac{3}{2}$

e. $\sqrt{2} - 1$ **f.** $\frac{4}{3}$ **g.** $6 + 4\ln 4$ **2.** $\frac{9}{2}$ **3.** 9

4. $\frac{1}{12}$ **5.** $\frac{37}{12}$ **6.** $\frac{37}{12}$ **7.** $3\ln 3$ **9.** $2\ln 2 - \frac{1}{2}$

10. $4\ln 4 - 3$ **11.** $\frac{9}{2}$ **12.** $\frac{40}{3}$ **13. a.** $\frac{7}{3}$

b. 0   **c.** $\ln 4 - \frac{3}{2}$

Problems 8.6

1. 3   **2.** $-\frac{2}{3}$ **3.** $\frac{e}{2} - 1$ **4.** 2   **5.** 8π

6. $\sqrt{2}$ **7. a.** $\frac{1}{4}$ **b.** $\frac{2\sqrt{3}}{\pi} + \frac{1}{3}$

c. $1 + \frac{1}{e} - \ln 2$

Exercises 8.7

1. 18 m   **2.** $\frac{2\pi}{3}$ **3.** $\frac{\pi r^2 h}{3}$ **4.** 150 g   **5. a.** $\frac{\pi}{2}$

b. $\sqrt{\dfrac{6}{\pi}}$ **6.** 5000   **7.** 5300

Problems 8.7

1. $\frac{39\pi}{2}$ **2.** 1400   **3.** 7600 g   **4.** $\frac{a^2 h}{3}$

Review Exercises

1. a. $\frac{31}{5}$ **b.** 35   **c.** $6\pi^4$ **d.** 2   **e.** $\frac{83}{8}$

f. $\frac{242}{5}$ **g.** $\frac{26}{3}$ **h.** 3   **i.** 2   **j.** $\frac{1}{2}$ **k.** 0

l. $\ln 3$ **2. a.** $\frac{27}{2}$ **b.** $\frac{2}{3}$ **c.** $\frac{38}{3}$

d. $\frac{\pi}{3} + 2\sqrt{3} - 4$ **e.** $4\ln 2 - \frac{3}{2}$

f. $6 - 3\ln 2$ **g.** $\ln 11$ **h.** 2   **3. a.** $\frac{125}{6}$

b. $\frac{\pi^4}{12}$ **c.** $6 - 8\ln 2$ **d.** $\pi - \ln\pi - 1$ **e.** 3

4. 6   **5.** 6   **6.** 400 m³   **7.** 1   **8. b.** $\frac{27}{4}$

9. $\frac{9}{2}$ **10.** $\pm\sqrt[3]{24}$ **11.** $\frac{1}{4}$ **12.** $\frac{4}{3}$ **13.** $\frac{4}{15}$

14. a. $\int_0^1 4x^2\,dx = \frac{4}{3}$ **b.** $\int_{-\frac{\pi}{2}}^{\frac{\pi}{2}} \cos x\,dx = 2$

c. $\int_0^1 \frac{1}{(1+x)^2}\,dx = \frac{1}{2}$ **15. b.** 1   **16.** 1

17. $2\sqrt{2}$ **18. a.** 1   **19.** $A(b) = 1 - \frac{1}{b}$, 1

20. e^{100}

Index